Introduction to Signal Transmission

McGRAW-HILL ELECTRICAL AND ELECTRONIC ENGINEERING SERIES

FREDERICK EMMONS TERMAN, *Consulting Editor*
W. W. HARMAN, J. G. TRUXAL, AND R. A. ROHRER,
Associate Consulting Editors

Introduction to Signal Transmission

William R. Bennett

Charles Batchelor Professor of Electrical Engineering,
Columbia University

McGraw-Hill Book Company
NEW YORK   ST. LOUIS   SAN FRANCISCO   DÜSSELDORF
LONDON   MEXICO   PANAMA   SYDNEY   TORONTO

Introduction to Signal Transmission

This book was set in Modern by The Maple Press
Company, and printed on permanent paper and
bound by The Maple Press Company. The designer
was Edward Zytko; the drawings were done by
Harry Lazarus. The editors were B. G. Dandison, Jr.
and Peter R. Karsten. Sally R. Ellyson supervised
the production.

TO BOB

Preface

Although many excellent books on communication engineering have become available in recent years, there still appears to be an unfilled need for an appropriately simple introductory text which will prepare and motivate the student for more advanced and sophisticated treatments. It is understandable that most authors wish to cover every topic which is thought to be interesting and important in the field. However, the extensive developments in the various branches of communication theory have reached the point where separate texts and courses giving in-depth coverage of such subjects as information theory, random processes, detection, and decision theory are preferable to a single book or course with brief glimpses of everything. The author's experience is that the student can comprehend the advanced disciplines more readily if substantial preliminary effort is expended on the basic physical facts often concealed in a specialized approach.

The basis of the present offering is that communication theory is essentially a study of sine waves and that the student should learn how this comes about before getting embroiled in more complicated matters. Accordingly, the first chapter deals with representing signals by sine waves and with solving problems in terms of the response to single-frequency components. The basic ideas are applied to develop useful auxiliary techniques for early inclusion in the student's repertoire. The level of exposition is meant to be suitable for seniors and first-year graduate students in electrical engineering. A first course in linear networks or systems should provide excellent preparation.

The second chapter extends the idea of sine waves as building blocks to the representation of noise waves and introduces some elementary notions of probability. The material can be absorbed without a preliminary course in probability theory and should provide motivation for parallel or future statistical studies. More topics are included than are actually necessary in the remainder of the text, and individual instructors may select material at this stage in accordance with their tastes.

Chapter 3 shows how the fundamental principles can be applied to the important everyday problem of reproducing sound waves at a distance from the source. The concepts of sinusoidal composition and transmission bandwidth are not difficult to relate to acoustical experience and are used here to introduce many of the techniques important in telephony and related engineering aspects of sound.

In Chapter 4, which deals with the more venerable art of telegraphy, the sine-wave approach is less obvious, and it may be anticipated that some students will encounter trouble. Extra effort on this material will be rewarding, for its mastery is necessary in order to bridge the gap between primitive key-and-battery circuits and modern high-speed digital transmission.

Chapter 5 discusses the television signal, which differs from the waves used for telephony and telegraphy in that a two-dimensional source is reduced to one-dimensional form for transmission. The theory of the scanning process by which the reduction is accomplished has important applications in other aspects of signal transmission.

With the nature of the original signal sources established, the student should be ready for Chapter 6, in which translation of the frequency range by modulation processes is explored. The emphasis is on the simple but powerful principle of interpreting what happens in the various carrier systems by examining the response to a single-frequency signal component. Trigonometry is the chief mathematical ingredient and serves the purpose very well. To those who may feel insulted because of the elementary nature of the exposition, the author can only say that these matters really are very simple and that it would be dishonest to present them as more profound. After the basic facts have been adequately described, a more comprehensive and sophisticated development is given in Chapter 7 for linear modulation systems and in Chapter 8 for nonlinear modulation. The detailed analyses of these two chapters are to be regarded in the main as shorthand techniques by means of which the sometimes long-winded and tedious applications of basic knowledge can be expedited.

Multiplexing is the subject of Chapter 9. The characteristic features of frequency-division and time-division methods are explained in terms of the sine-wave models previously formulated. This chapter leads naturally into the tenth and final chapter, which exhibits the fascinating advantages promised by the digitalizing of analog signals.

The notes from which this book was prepared have been used as the text for a two-semester course offered to seniors and first-year graduate students in electrical engineering at Columbia University. Although the book may seem short for two full semesters, the instructor should not equate brevity to hasty coverage. Even simple ideas require exposure time with repetition and problem drill for successful implantation. An endeavor has been made to furnish illuminative problems worthy of substantial study.

The author is very happy to acknowledge the invaluable assistance of his wife, Viola M. Bennett, throughout the preparation of the manuscript.

William R. Bennett

Contents

List of Abbreviations and Symbols

Approximately equal to	$\approx$
Asymptotically equal to	$\sim$
Average	av
Bessel functions of order n	$J_n(x), I_n(x) = j^{-n}J_n(jx)$
Complementary error function	erfc
Complex conjugate of Z	Z^*
Continuous wave	CW
Convolution of S_1 and S_2	$S_1 * S_2$
Decibel	db
Decibels above one milliwatt	dbm
Decibels above reference noise	dbrn
Degrees centigrade	$°C$
Degrees Kelvin	$°K$
Error function	erf
Farad	F
Fourier transform of $z(t)$	$Z(f)$
Fourier transform of $z^*(t)$	$Z\dagger(f)$
Gigahertz (10^9 Hz)	GHz
Henry	H
Hertz (cycle per second)	Hz
Hilbert transform of x	$\hat{x}$
Imaginary part of Z	Im Z
Imaginary unit ($\sqrt{-1}$)	j
Intermediate frequency	i-f
Kilohertz (10^3 Hz)	kHz
Mathematical expectation of x	$\mathbf{E}x$
Megahertz (10^6 Hz)	MHz
Micro (10^{-6})	μ
Micromicro (10^{-12})	$\mu\mu$
Milli (10^{-3})	m
Natural logarithm	ln
Phase angle of Z	ph Z
Radian	rad
Radio frequency	r-f
Real part of Z	Re Z

Second	sec
Signum function	sgn
Terahertz (10^{12} Hz)	THz
Volt	V
Volume unit	vu
Watt	W

Introduction to Signal Transmission

1
Representation of Signals

The word "signal" comes from the Latin word *signum* meaning "sign."
In the present text, a signal is any information-bearing entity, as, for
example, a sequence of symbols or a function of a variable. The object
in signal transmission is to reproduce the signal accurately at some
location other than at the source. We shall be concerned chiefly with
electrical means of transmission but will use principles which are also
applicable in acoustical, mechanical, optical, and various other systems.

1-1 DIGITAL AND ANALOG SIGNALS

Two general classes of signal sources will be distinguished. In the
first class, called *discrete* or *digital*, the signals are defined in terms of
specified symbols, which can, for example, be numbers or letters. Discrete signals form a countable set and can be listed as entries in a
table. The performance of a system transmitting discrete signals can
be characterized very definitely in terms of the errors in the received
message.

In the second class of sources, called *continuous* or *analog*, the signals are defined by waves which can assume a continuous range of values. The waves representing distinct signals can differ by arbitrarily small nonzero amounts. Continuous signals are not denumerable, and it is not possible to define performance of a transmitting system in terms of errors. Instead, a measure of deviation between the received and transmitted signals must be established. The mean-square value of the difference is sometimes used. More often, the significant difference can be expressed in terms of certain distortion components, interference from other signals, and noise originating in the channel. In these cases, the ratios of signal to distortion, signal to interference, and signal to noise are used as measures of channel performance.

It is possible both conceptually and practically to replace continuous signals by a satisfactory approximate representation in terms of discrete signals. The reason for this is that the ultimate receiver of continuous signals is not in fact capable of distinguishing signals arbitrarily close together. An example of a source of continuous signals is the human vocal apparatus. Infinitesimal changes in the parameters of the vocal tract can produce correspondingly infinitesimal differences in the sound waves emitted. The ultimate destination of the information contained in these sound waves is a human ear, which has definite limitations on the smallness of differences which it can detect. Speech waves can, therefore, be *quantized* or *digitalized* without loss of observable quality. The process of quantization is conveniently done in two steps: (1) a sampling in time and (2) a replacement of each sample by the nearest member of a set of discrete values. By subjective testing it is possible to determine how close together the samples must be taken in time and how small the quantizing steps must be in order to make the quantized substitute for speech waves as acceptable to the human ear as the original unquantized form. By universal application of such an approximating procedure, we could regard all signals as discrete.

It is to be noted, however, that when analog signals are transmitted by digital representation, the receiver must perform a conversion back to analog form. Digital errors are thereby converted to analog noise, and the signal-to-noise ratio rather than the error rate becomes the ultimate measured performance. It is also to be remarked that digital signals are actually transmitted over analog channels, that is, channels which permit a continuum of response waveforms. In analysis the analog nature of the channel is often concealed by assumption of a discrete decision process at the receiver. The quality of the decisions can be expressed in terms of discrete error probabilities, but these probabilities are themselves determined from the properties of analog waveforms.

1-2 SINUSOIDAL RESOLUTION OF SIGNALS

In the case of both analog and digital signals, an analysis of transmission requires a method of representing waveforms. In theory there are many possible approaches to the problem of signal representation, but in practice resolution of the signal wave into sinusoidal components overshadows all other methods in usefulness. The reason for this is that the ultimate goal is a linear time-invariant relationship between the received signal and the original signal. Nonlinear and time-varying operations may be performed in the transmission path either by deliberate intent or because of unavoidable defects, but the signal as finally recovered should not be appreciably contaminated by these processes. The important virtue possessed by the sine wave as an excitation function applied to a real linear time-invariant system is that the corresponding response must also be a sine wave of the same frequency. To show this, we first state the definitions of linearity and time invariance as follows:

1. *Linearity.* Suppose that the excitation $s_1(t)$ produces the response $r_1(t)$ and that $s_2(t)$ produces the response $r_2(t)$. The system is said to be linear if and only if the excitation $a_1s_1(t) + a_2s_2(t)$ produces the response $a_1r_1(t) + a_2r_2(t)$ for all $s_1(t)$, $s_2(t)$, a_1, and a_2. The definition includes (1) the *principle of superposition*, which says that the response to the sum of excitations is the sum of the responses to the excitations applied separately, and (2) the *principle of proportionality*, which says that multiplication of the excitation by a factor multiplies the response by the same factor.
2. *Time Invariance.* Suppose the excitation $s(t)$ produces the response $r(t)$. The system is said to be time-invariant if and only if the excitation $s(t + \tau)$ produces the response $r(t + \tau)$ for all $s(t)$ and τ. The meaning of this definition is that if we shift the excitation along the time scale, the response function is shifted in time by the same amount.

The definitions apply to a general system described by mathematical relations in which the values of the time t are restricted to real numbers, but in which the multiplying constants and the functions of time can be complex numbers. This generalization leads to important computational advantages because it enables sines and cosines to be replaced by the more easily manipulated exponential equivalents obtained from Euler's identities, which, with $j = \sqrt{-1}$, furnish the basic relations $e^{j\omega t} = \cos \omega t + j \sin \omega t$, $2 \cos \omega t = e^{j\omega t} + e^{-j\omega t}$, and $2j \sin \omega t = e^{j\omega t} - e^{-j\omega t}$.

With the definitions in mind, assume that $r(t)$ is the response of a linear time-invariant system to the exponential excitation function

$$s(t) = Ae^{j\omega t} \tag{1-1}$$

where $j = \sqrt{-1}$, and A and ω are constants.   Then the response to

$$\frac{1}{\Delta t}\, s(t + \Delta t) - \frac{1}{\Delta t}\, s(t)$$

must be

$$\frac{1}{\Delta t}\, r(t + \Delta t) - \frac{1}{\Delta t}\, r(t)$$

If we take the limit as Δt approaches zero, the response to $ds(t)/dt$ is found to be $dr(t)/dt$.   But

$$\frac{ds(t)}{dt} = j\omega A e^{j\omega t} = j\omega s(t) \tag{1-2}$$

Since the response to $j\omega s(t)$ is $j\omega r(t)$,

$$\frac{dr(t)}{dt} = j\omega r(t) \tag{1-3}$$

The solution of the linear first-order differential equation is

$$r(t) = B e^{j\omega t} \tag{1-4}$$

where B is an arbitrary constant.   From the property of proportionality of response with excitation, B must be proportional to A.   The ratio can, however, change with ω, and we show this by defining

$$Y(\omega) = \frac{B}{A} \tag{1-5}$$

$Y(\omega)$ is called the *transmittance function, transfer ratio,* or *system function.* It is a characteristic property of the system and, in general, can have complex values.   In the language of the theory of operators, $e^{j\omega t}$ is an eigenfunction of the operator defining the response of a linear time-invariant system.   The result of an operator applied to one of its eigenfunctions is proportional to the eigenfunction.

We define a *real* system as one in which the response to a real excitation is real.   If the excitation of a real system is a general sinusoidal function

$$s(t) = A \cos (\omega t + \theta) = \left(\frac{A}{2}\, e^{j\theta}\right) e^{j\omega t} + \left(\frac{A}{2}\, e^{-j\theta}\right) e^{-j\omega t} \tag{1-6}$$

with A, ω, and θ real, the response $r(t)$ of a real linear time-invariant system is, from the results (1-1) to (1-5),

$$r(t) = \frac{A}{2}\, e^{j\theta} Y(\omega) e^{j\omega t} + \frac{A}{2}\, e^{-j\theta} Y(-\omega) e^{-j\omega t} \tag{1-7}$$

For $r(t)$ to be real, we must have

$$Y(-\omega) = Y^*(\omega) \tag{1-8}$$

where the notation Y^* designates the conjugate of Y. It follows that

$$r(t) = A \operatorname{Re}\left[Y(\omega)e^{j(\omega t+\theta)}\right] = A \operatorname{Re}\left[|Y(\omega)|e^{j \text{ ph } Y(\omega)}e^{j(\omega t+\theta)}\right]$$
$$= A|Y(\omega)| \cos\left[\omega t + \theta + \text{ph } Y(\omega)\right] \tag{1-9}$$

The abbreviation "ph" will be used throughout for the phase angle of a complex quantity. Our claim that the response is sinusoidal with the same frequency as the excitation is thus demonstrated. We have also demonstrated the existence of $Y(\omega)$, a complex-valued function of frequency, whose absolute value is the constant of proportionality relating amplitude of output to amplitude of input and whose phase angle is the phase shift between the output and input sine waves.

Representation of a signal in terms of sine-wave components thus leads to a simple solution for the response of a linear time-invariant system to the signal. In the case of a series representation

$$s(t) = \sum_n A_n e^{j\omega_n t} \tag{1-10}$$

the response is given by

$$r(t) = \sum_n Y(\omega_n)A_n e^{j\omega_n t} \tag{1-11}$$

Since an integral is the limit of a summation, we also deduce that if

$$s(t) = \int_{-\infty}^{\infty} S(f)e^{j2\pi ft}\, df \tag{1-12}$$

then

$$r(t) = \int_{-\infty}^{\infty} H(f)S(f)e^{j2\pi ft}\, df \tag{1-13}$$

where

$$H(f) = Y(2\pi f) \tag{1-14}$$

The relations of (1-10) and (1-11) are useful if $s(t)$ can be expanded in a Fourier series, while (1-12) and (1-13) apply when a Fourier-integral representation is possible. In practical cases either formulation can be used. The function represented by the Fourier series

$$s(t) = \sum_{n=-\infty}^{\infty} s_n e^{j2n\pi t/T} \qquad -\frac{T}{2} < t < \frac{T}{2} \tag{1-15}$$

with

$$s_n = \frac{1}{T}\int_{-T/2}^{T/2} s(t)e^{-j2n\pi t/T}\, dt$$

would repeat its values periodically with period T if the series were used outside the defining interval from $-T/2$ to $T/2$. However, if we use the expansion in the defining interval only, the periodic behavior outside this interval is of no consequence. By taking T sufficiently large, we can represent $s(t)$ by sinusoidal components throughout as much time as we wish.

Similarly, the Fourier-integral relationships

$$s(t) = \int_{-\infty}^{\infty} S(f)e^{j2\pi ft}\, df \qquad S(f) = \int_{-\infty}^{\infty} s(t)e^{-j2\pi ft}\, dt \qquad (1\text{-}16)$$

can be made applicable to practical cases in which the values of $s(t)$ in the remote past or future are immaterial by merely assuming that $s(t) = 0$ outside the time interval of interest. We call attention to the notational scheme of (1-16) in which the time function and frequency function are represented by corresponding small and capital letters, respectively, in the Fourier-integral relationships. We shall use this convention throughout the text. The frequency function $S(f)$ will be called the *Fourier transform* of the time function $s(t)$, and $s(t)$ will be called the *inverse Fourier transform* of $S(f)$. We assume that the reader has had at least a first exposure to Fourier analysis. Details of the proofs of Eqs. (1-15) and (1-16) are given in numerous texts and need not be repeated here.

Physical phenomena are usually considered to be describable in terms of continuous functions, but we shall often find it convenient to introduce idealized signal waves which have discontinuities. For example, if $s(t)$ is generated by operating a switch, an exact description of the continuous transition between the open and closed conditions may be immaterial as far as the measured response is concerned. An advantageous simplification can then be made by assuming that $s(t)$ changes instantaneously from s_1 to s_2. The Fourier series and integral formulas remain applicable except at the point of discontinuity, where the series or integral converges to the *average* of s_1 and s_2. This result is sometimes indicated by replacing $s(t)$ in Eqs. (1-15) and (1-16) by $\frac{1}{2}[s(t + 0) + s(t - 0)]$, where $s(t + 0)$ and $s(t - 0)$ represent the limits of $s(t + \epsilon)$ and $s(t - \epsilon)$, respectively, as the positive quantity ϵ approaches zero. Similarly, $S(f)$ is replaced by $\frac{1}{2}[S(f + 0) + S(f - 0)]$ to allow for a discontinuity in the Fourier transform.

The primary utility of Fourier series and integrals in signal-transmission theory rests on their ability to express general waveforms in terms of sinusoidal components. The principle of superposition can then be invoked to express the response of linear systems to an arbitrary stimulus straightforwardly in terms of the response to a sine wave. The essential features of a signal-transmission system are therefore contained in the solution for a single-frequency input. A corollary is that trigonometry is the principal mathematical ingredient in the treatment of problems in signal transmission. However, we would subject ourselves to unnecessarily long and dreary analysis at times if we failed to make appropriate use of the powerful theorems and methods available from the theory of Fourier series and integrals. The remainder of this chapter will be devoted to an exposition of such matters and will include applications to representation of typical signal waveforms.

1-3 CONVOLUTION AND RELATED TOPICS

We are frequently faced with the problem of finding the Fourier transform of the product of two functions when the Fourier transforms of the individual functions are known. Suppose we are given $S_1(f)$ and $S_2(f)$ as the Fourier transforms of $s_1(t)$ and $s_2(t)$, respectively. We wish to find $S_{12}(f)$ such that

$$s_1(t)s_2(t) = \int_{-\infty}^{\infty} S_{12}(f)e^{j2\pi ft}\, df \tag{1-17}$$

Inversion of (1-17) gives

$$S_{12}(f) = \int_{-\infty}^{\infty} s_1(t)s_2(t)e^{-j2\pi ft}\, dt \tag{1-18}$$

For $s_2(t)$, substitute

$$s_2(t) = \int_{-\infty}^{\infty} S_2(g)e^{j2\pi gt}\, dg \tag{1-19}$$

in (1-18). Note the essential step of introducing an integration variable g which is different from the variable f already present in (1-18). We obtain the double integral

$$S_{12}(f) = \iint_{-\infty}^{\infty} s_1(t)S_2(g)e^{j2\pi(g-f)t}\, dt\, dg \tag{1-20}$$

Next substitute for g a new integration variable $\lambda = f - g$, leaving the other variable t unchanged. If we assume the order of integration is immaterial, the result can be written in the form

$$S_{12}(f) = \int_{-\infty}^{\infty} S_2(f - \lambda)\, d\lambda \int_{-\infty}^{\infty} s_1(t)e^{-j2\pi\lambda t}\, dt \tag{1-21}$$

We recognize the inner integral as $S_1(\lambda)$ and thus obtain a formal demonstration of the *convolution theorem:*

$$S_{12}(f) = \int_{-\infty}^{\infty} S_1(\lambda)S_2(f - \lambda)\, d\lambda \tag{1-22}$$

A function $S_{12}(f)$ defined in terms of $S_1(f)$ and $S_2(f)$ by Eq. (1-22) is called the *convolution* of $S_1(f)$ and $S_2(f)$, and is abbreviated by

$$S_{12}(f) = S_1(f) * S_2(f) \tag{1-23}$$

Note that the operation of convolution is commutative, i.e.,

$$S_1(f) * S_2(f) = S_2(f) * S_1(f) \tag{1-24}$$

Convolution in the time domain has corresponding application with respect to the inverse transform of the product of two functions of frequency. If we write

$$S_1(f)S_2(f) = \int_{-\infty}^{\infty} s_{12}(t)e^{-j2\pi ft}\, dt \tag{1-25}$$

we deduce that

$$s_{12}(t) = \int_{-\infty}^{\infty} s_1(\lambda)s_2(t - \lambda)\, d\lambda = s_1(t) * s_2(t) \tag{1-26}$$

Equating Eqs. (1-18) and (1-22) gives

$$\int_{-\infty}^{\infty} s_1(t)s_2(t)e^{-j2\pi ft}\, dt = \int_{-\infty}^{\infty} S_1(\lambda)S_2(f - \lambda)\, d\lambda \tag{1-27}$$

Setting $f = 0$, and then replacing λ by f, we obtain the general Parseval formula

$$\int_{-\infty}^{\infty} s_1(t)s_2(t)\, dt = \int_{-\infty}^{\infty} S_1(f)S_2(-f)\, df \tag{1-28}$$

If $s_2(t)$ is replaced by its conjugate, the formula becomes

$$\int_{-\infty}^{\infty} s_1(t)s_2^*(t)\, dt = \int_{-\infty}^{\infty} S_1(f)S_2^*(f)\, df \tag{1-29}$$

In the special case in which $s_1(t)$ and $s_2(t)$ are real,

$$\int_{-\infty}^{\infty} s_1(t)s_2(t)\, dt = \int_{-\infty}^{\infty} S_1(f)S_2^*(f)\, df \tag{1-30}$$

Finally, if $s_1(t) = s_2(t) = s(t)$ with $s(t)$ real, we obtain the more usual statement of Parseval's formula:

$$\int_{-\infty}^{\infty} s^2(t)\, dt = \int_{-\infty}^{\infty} |S(f)|^2\, df \tag{1-31}$$

When the signal $s(t)$ is specified as a voltage or current wave, the left-hand member of (1-31) is proportional to the total energy of the signal. The equation thus provides a useful method of calculating the energy of signals specified in the frequency domain.

The concept of correlation of two signals is closely related to convolution. The *cross-correlation function* $R_{xy}(\tau)$ of two complex-valued signals $x(t)$ and $y(t)$ with relative time shift τ is defined by

$$R_{xy}(\tau) = \int_{-\infty}^{\infty} x(t + \tau)y^*(t)\ dt \tag{1-32}$$

The justification for the name is that if $x(t)$ and $y(t)$ tend to have nearly the same nonzero values when the time scale of y lags that of x by τ, a large value of the defining integral can be attained. By a change of sign in the variable of integration, we have also

$$\begin{aligned} R_{xy}(\tau) &= \int_{-\infty}^{\infty} y^*(-t)x(\tau - t)\ dt \\ &= y^*(-\tau) * x(\tau) \end{aligned} \tag{1-33}$$

Interchange of x and y gives

$$R_{yx}(\tau) = x^*(-\tau) * y(\tau) = R_{xy}^*(-\tau) \tag{1-34}$$

The *autocorrelation function* of a signal $x(t)$ is defined as $R_{xx}(\tau)$, which is the cross-correlation function of $x(t)$ with itself. $R_{xx}(0)$ is proportional to the total energy of the signal.

We readily verify that the Fourier transform of $x(t + \tau)$ is $X(f)e^{j2\pi f\tau}$. Letting $s_1(t) = x(t + \tau)$ and $s_2(t) = y(t)$ in Parseval's formula (1-29), we can transform Eq. (1-32) to

$$R_{xy}(\tau) = \int_{-\infty}^{\infty} X(f)Y^*(f)e^{j2\pi f\tau}\ df \tag{1-35}$$

This result shows that $X(f)Y^*(f)$ is the Fourier transform of the cross-correlation function $R_{xy}(\tau)$. It follows that the Fourier transform of the autocorrelation function $R_{xx}(\tau)$ is $|X(f)|^2$.

1-4 REPRESENTATION OF USEFUL AUXILIARY TIME FUNCTIONS

One important elementary form of signal is the rectangular pulse, Fig. 1-1. Following the notation of Woodward,[1]‡ we define

$$\text{rect } t = \begin{cases} 1 & |t| < \frac{1}{2} \\ 0 & |t| > \frac{1}{2} \end{cases} \tag{1-36}$$

for a pulse of unit height and unit duration centered at the origin. A rectangular pulse of height A and duration T centered at the origin is then represented by

$$A \text{ rect } \frac{t}{T} = \begin{cases} A & |t| < \dfrac{T}{2} \\ 0 & |t| > \dfrac{T}{2} \end{cases} \tag{1-37}$$

‡ The superior numbers refer to the references appearing at the end of each chapter.

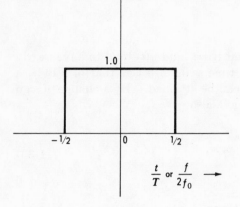

Fig. 1-1 Graph of rect (t/T) or rect $[f/(2f_0)]$.

By (1-16), we can write

$$\text{rect } t = \int_{-\infty}^{\infty} S(f)e^{j2\pi ft}\, df \tag{1-38}$$

where

$$S(f) = \int_{-\frac{1}{2}}^{\frac{1}{2}} e^{-j2\pi ft}\, dt = \frac{\sin \pi f}{\pi f} \tag{1-39}$$

Again using Woodward's notation, we define

$$\text{sinc } f = \frac{\sin \pi f}{\pi f} \tag{1-40}$$

Then

$$\text{rect } t = \int_{-\infty}^{\infty} \text{sinc } f \, e^{j2\pi ft}\, df \tag{1-41}$$

and

$$A \text{ rect } \frac{t}{T} = \int_{-\infty}^{\infty} AT \text{ sinc } fT \, e^{j2\pi ft}\, df \tag{1-42}$$

A graph of the function sinc fT is shown in Fig. 1-2. The range over which the values of sinc fT are appreciable indicates the bandwidth required to transmit a rectangular pulse accurately. As $|f|$ becomes large, the peaks vary as $1/|f|$, which is not a rapid rate of decay. The reason for the slow decrease is that the time function is discontinuous at its beginning and end, thus requiring components of very high frequency to reproduce the sharp changes. Suppression of these high frequencies would round off the waveform.

The response $r(t)$ of a linear time-invariant network with transmittance function $H(f)$ to the rectangular pulse $A \operatorname{rect} t/T$ is given by

$$r(t) = \int_{-\infty}^{\infty} A T \operatorname{sinc} fT \, H(f)e^{j2\pi ft} \, df \tag{1-43}$$

A case of particular interest is that of a very short rectangular pulse of unit area. For this case, $AT = 1$, and we can calculate

$$\lim_{T \to 0} r(t) = \int_{-\infty}^{\infty} H(f)e^{j2\pi ft} \, df = h(t) \tag{1-44}$$

The function $h(t)$ is defined as the *impulse response* of the system. It is often represented symbolically as the response of the network to the *delta function* or *unit impulse*

$$\delta(t) = \lim_{T \to 0} \frac{1}{T} \operatorname{rect} \frac{t}{T} = \int_{-\infty}^{\infty} e^{j2\pi ft} \, df \tag{1-45}$$

In this equation, neither the limit nor the integral actually exists, and the use of the δ function is a shorthand notation for obtaining the meaningful result (1-44).

The impulse response has important usefulness in calculating the response of the system to a general input wave $g(t)$. Let

$$g(t) = \int_{-\infty}^{\infty} G(f)e^{j2\pi ft} \, df \tag{1-46}$$

Then the response of the system to $g(t)$ is

$$r_g(t) = \int_{-\infty}^{\infty} G(f)H(f)e^{j2\pi ft} \, df \tag{1-47}$$

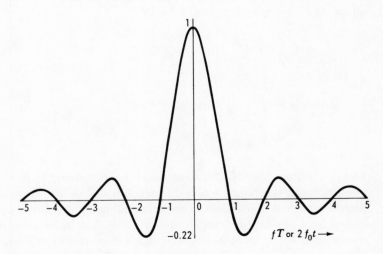

Fig. 1-2 Graph of sinc fT or sinc $2f_0t$.

By the convolution theorem of Sec. 1-3,

$$r_g(t) = \int_{-\infty}^{\infty} g(\lambda)h(t - \lambda)\,d\lambda \qquad (1\text{-}48)$$

We note formally that if $H(f) = 1$, we obtain $h(t) = \delta(t)$, $r_g(t) = g(t)$, and hence

$$g(t) = \int_{-\infty}^{\infty} g(\lambda)\,\delta(t - \lambda)\,d\lambda \qquad (1\text{-}49)$$

This equation is sometimes used as the definition of the δ function. By change of variable, the definition can also be written

$$g(t) = \int_{-\infty}^{\infty} g(t - \lambda)\,\delta(\lambda)\,d\lambda \qquad (1\text{-}50)$$

The physical interpretation of (1-49) is that $\delta(t - \lambda)$ is a pulse of unit area sharply concentrated at $\lambda = t$ on the λ scale. If we multiply such a pulse by $g(\lambda)$, the area is multiplied by $g(t)$. Continuing with this definition we can derive (1-48) heuristically without using the convolution theorem. The argument is that (1-49) expresses $g(t)$ as the limit of the sum of infinitesimal components of form $[g(\lambda)\,d\lambda]\,\delta(t - \lambda)$. Since the response of the system to $\delta(t)$ is $h(t)$, the response to $g(\lambda)\,d\lambda\,\delta(t - \lambda)$ is, by the properties of linearity and time invariance, $g(\lambda)\,d\lambda\,h(t - \lambda)$. Taking the limit of the sum of such responses reproduces (1-48).

The reciprocal properties of the Fourier-integral relationships enable another set of useful formulas to be derived by interchanging the frequency and time variables. Corresponding to (1-42), we obtain by replacing t by f, f by $-t$, and T by $2f_0$

$$\frac{1}{2f_0}\operatorname{rect}\frac{f}{2f_0} = \int_{-\infty}^{\infty} \operatorname{sinc} 2f_0 t e^{-j2\pi ft}\,dt \qquad (1\text{-}51)$$

and

$$\operatorname{sinc} 2f_0 t = \int_{-\infty}^{\infty} \frac{1}{2f_0}\operatorname{rect}\frac{f}{2f_0}\,e^{j2\pi ft}\,df$$

$$= \int_{-f_0}^{f_0} \frac{1}{2f_0}\,e^{j2\pi ft}\,df \qquad (1\text{-}52)$$

The resolution of sinc $2f_0 t$ into sinusoidal components thus contains only frequencies in the range $-f_0$ to f_0. Such a function of time is said to be *band-limited*. A band-limited function cannot have finite duration. It is seen from (1-40) that sinc $2f_0 t$ decays as $1/|t|$ as $|t|$ becomes large. The slow rate of decay is a consequence of the discontinuities in the frequency function at $f = \pm f_0$. The regularly spaced axis crossings except for the peak at $t = 0$ furnish an important method of transmitting independent signals at a rate $2f_0/\text{sec}$ without using frequencies greater than f_0.

As the bandwidth is made infinitesimally small, we obtain the formal expression

$$\lim_{f_0 \to 0} \left(\frac{1}{2f_0} \operatorname{rect} \frac{f}{2f_0} \right) = \delta(f) = \int_{-\infty}^{\infty} e^{-j2\pi ft} \, dt \qquad (1\text{-}53)$$

As in the corresponding case of a narrow pulse in the time domain, neither the limit nor the integral exists, and the equations are only useful as shorthand notations in operations for which convergence is finally obtained. In a similar fashion we write

$$\delta(f - f_0) = \int_{-\infty}^{\infty} e^{j2\pi f_0 t} e^{-j2\pi ft} \, dt \qquad (1\text{-}54)$$

and

$$e^{j2\pi f_0 t} = \int_{-\infty}^{\infty} \delta(f - f_0) \, e^{j2\pi ft} \, df \qquad (1\text{-}55)$$

These equations state formally that the exponential time function $e^{j2\pi f_0 t}$ has a Fourier transform equal to a unit impulse in frequency at $f = f_0$. This is a plausible physical interpretation based on the concept that a single-frequency wave in the time domain should be represented in the frequency domain by only one frequency. A real sinusoidal component in time requires impulses at positive and negative values of the frequency, viz.,

$$\cos \left(2\pi f_0 t + \theta \right) = \frac{1}{2} e^{j(2\pi f_0 t + \theta)} + \frac{1}{2} e^{-j(2\pi f_0 t + \theta)}$$

$$= \int_{-\infty}^{\infty} \left[\frac{1}{2} e^{j\theta} \, \delta(f - f_0) + \frac{1}{2} e^{-j\theta} \, \delta(f + f_0) \right] e^{j2\pi ft} \, df \qquad (1\text{-}56)$$

The use of the δ function or its equivalent has a long history in electrical engineering beginning with the original work of Heaviside in the latter part of the nineteenth century. A concise treatment was given in 1928 by Campbell and Foster,[2] who used the term *singularity function*. In more recent times pure mathematicians have become interested and have established a formalism meeting standards of rigor satisfactory to them. A lucid review of their methods has been given by Lighthill.[3] The manipulative rules thereby validated provide machinery for deriving mathematical results which are much harder to obtain by more conventional analysis.

As an example of operations performed in the δ symbolism, consider the so-called *Dirac comb*, which consists of a train of regularly spaced δ

functions.   The periodicity suggests a Fourier-series expansion.   If we write

$$\delta_T(t) = \sum_{n=-\infty}^{\infty} \delta(t - nT) = \sum_{m=-\infty}^{\infty} c_m e^{j2m\pi t/T} \tag{1-57}$$

and proceed formally, we obtain

$$\begin{aligned}
c_m &= \frac{1}{T} \int_{-T/2}^{T/2} \delta_T(t) e^{-j2m\pi t/T} \, dt \\
&= \frac{1}{T} \int_{-T/2}^{T/2} \sum_{n=-\infty}^{\infty} \delta(t - nT) e^{-j2m\pi t/T} \, dt \\
&= \frac{1}{T} \sum_{n=-\infty}^{\infty} \int_{-T/2}^{T/2} \delta(t - nT) e^{-j2m\pi t/T} \, dt \\
&= \frac{1}{T} \sum_{n=-\infty}^{\infty} \int_{-nT-T/2}^{-nT+T/2} \delta(t') e^{-j2m\pi t'/T} \, dt' \\
&= \frac{1}{T} \int_{-\infty}^{\infty} \delta(t) e^{-j2m\pi t/T} \, dt = \frac{1}{T}
\end{aligned} \tag{1-58}$$

Hence,

$$\delta_T(t) = \frac{1}{T} \sum_{m=-\infty}^{\infty} e^{j2m\pi t/T} = \frac{1}{T} \sum_{m=-\infty}^{\infty} e^{-j2m\pi t/T} \tag{1-59}$$

The Dirac comb has a sampling property expressed by

$$\begin{aligned}
\int_{-\infty}^{\infty} s(t) \, \delta_T(t) \, dt &= \sum_{n=-\infty}^{\infty} \int_{-\infty}^{\infty} s(t) \, \delta(t - nT) \, dt \\
&= \sum_{n=-\infty}^{\infty} s(nT)
\end{aligned} \tag{1-60}$$

But from (1-59), we have also

$$\begin{aligned}
\int_{-\infty}^{\infty} s(t) \, \delta_T(t) \, dt &= \frac{1}{T} \sum_{m=-\infty}^{\infty} \int_{-\infty}^{\infty} s(t) e^{-j2m\pi t/T} \, dt \\
&= \frac{1}{T} \sum_{m=-\infty}^{\infty} S\left(\frac{m}{T}\right)
\end{aligned} \tag{1-61}$$

Equating the two results, (1-60) and (1-61), gives Poisson's summation formula

$$\sum_{n=-\infty}^{\infty} s(nT) = \frac{1}{T} \sum_{m=-\infty}^{\infty} S\left(\frac{m}{T}\right) \tag{1-62}$$

This relation between the sum of samples of a function and the sum of samples of its Fourier transform can be valuable from the computational standpoint if one series converges more rapidly than the other.

1-5 CONVERGENCE OF FOURIER SERIES AND INTEGRALS

We have tacitly implied that the infinite series of Eq. (1-15) and the infinite integrals of Eqs. (1-16) actually converge to define physically interesting signals and their transforms.   An apparent exception in the case of the δ function, Eq. (1-45), is interpreted as shorthand notation for a convergent integral in which the nonconvergent behavior of the contributions of the integrand at $\pm \infty$ has no effect in the intended applications.

Conditions for convergence of Fourier series and integrals are demonstrated in standard texts, for example, Refs. 4 to 6.   The most general conditions are more intricate than ever needed in physical applications.   It is sufficient for our purposes to note that a convergent Fourier series representing $s(t)$ in a finite interval exists if $s(t)$ is bounded and integrable throughout the interval and has only a finite number of discontinuities and of maxima and minima.   Unbounded functions which do not approach infinity too fast to have a finite integral can also be represented by Fourier series but are not realistic for signaling purposes.

The conditions for convergence of the Fourier integral are similar to those for the Fourier series except that behavior of the integrand at $\pm \infty$ must be examined.   It is sometimes stated that $s(t)$ must approach zero at $t = \pm \infty$, but such a condition is too stringent.   The contributions to the integral can approach zero by an accelerating rate of oscillation without decay in amplitude as in the example $s(t) = e^{jk^2t^2}$, which has the Fourier transform $S(f) = \pi^{1/2}k^{-1}e^{-j(\pi f/k)^2+j(\pi/4)}$.   In such cases, positive and negative contributions at the endpoints cancel each other before the accumulated area becomes more than infinitesimal.

However, in most signaling problems, the functions of time are vanishingly small in the remote past and the distant future, and the Fourier transform approaches zero at large values of $|f|$.   We have previously observed that high-frequency components are needed to reproduce a steep wavefront.   It seems reasonable, therefore, to expect that a discontinuity in $s(t)$ would force $|S(f)|$ to decrease slowly as $|f|$ becomes large.   To examine the relations quantitatively, consider the case in which (1) the signal $s(t)$ and all its derivatives approach zero when $|t|$ is large, (2) all derivatives of $s(t)$ exist except at $t = t_0$, and (3) $s(t)$ is discontinuous at $t = t_0$ with $s(t + 0) = s_+$ and $s(t - 0) = s_-$.   Then

$$S(f) = \int_{-\infty}^{t_0} s(t)e^{-j2\pi ft}\,dt + \int_{t_0}^{\infty} s(t)e^{-j2\pi ft}\,dt \qquad (1\text{-}63)$$

Let us perform an integration by parts on each integral, setting $u = s(t)$ and $dv = e^{-j2\pi ft} dt$. The result is

$$S(f) = \frac{s_- - s_+}{j2\pi f} e^{-j2\pi ft_0} + \frac{1}{j2\pi f} \int_{-\infty}^{t_0} s'(t)e^{-j2\pi ft} dt$$
$$+ \frac{1}{j2\pi f} \int_{t_0}^{\infty} s'(t)e^{-j2\pi ft} dt \quad (1\text{-}64)$$

where $s'(t) = ds(t)/dt$. The absolute value of the first term on the right goes to zero as $1/|f|$ when $|f|$ is large. The second and third terms are Fourier transforms of functions which satisfy the same conditions as $s(t)$. Therefore, a similar integration by parts can be performed on them, giving a first term in each case which goes to zero as $1/|f|^2$ because of the preliminary multiplying factor containing $1/f$. Since successive integrations by parts produce terms containing still higher inverse powers of $|f|$, we conclude that $|S(f)|$ itself goes to zero as $1/|f|$ when $|f|$ is large. The same conclusion holds if $s(t)$ contains a plurality of distinct discontinuities.

The same analysis applied to the case in which $s(t)$ is continuous and $s'(t)$ is discontinuous leads to the conclusion that $|S(f)|$ eventually goes to zero as $1/f^2$. In general, if $s(t)$ and its first $(m - 1)$ derivatives are continuous and the mth derivative is discontinuous, $|S(f)|$ decays as $1/|f|^{m+1}$ for large $|f|$. A similar argument applied to Fourier-series representation shows that the amplitude of the nth harmonic approaches zero as $1/n^{m+1}$. For this result the conditions on $s(t)$ are specified only in the interval of expansion, but continuity requires the value of the function to be the same at the end of the interval as at the beginning.

If the least upper bound of the absolute value of the integrand of an infinite integral approaches zero no faster than the inverse first power of the variable as the variable becomes infinite, the convergence depends on cancellation of positive and negative contributions as well as on the approach to zero. (Note that $\int_a^{\infty} dx/|x|$ does not exist.) Such convergence is called *conditional*, and is characteristic of the Fourier integral representing a discontinuous signal. If the signal is continuous throughout all time, the convergence becomes *absolute* because the decay of the integrand is at least as fast as the inverse square and the sign does not matter. Analogous statements hold for Fourier series.

In the case of a *band-limited* function, we have

$$s(t) = \int_{-f_0}^{f_0} S(f)e^{j2\pi ft} df \quad (1\text{-}65)$$

Since the limits of integration are finite and all derivatives of the exponential function exist, there is no difficulty in proving the validity of the general formula

$$\frac{d^n s(t)}{dt^n} = \int_{-f_0}^{f_0} (j2\pi f)^n S(f) e^{j2\pi ft} \, df \tag{1-66}$$

It follows that $s(t)$ and all of its derivatives are continuous for all values of t.

From the symmetrical roles played by time and frequency in the Fourier-integral formulas, we can interchange t and f in the relations demonstrated in this section. We thereby obtain analogous results on the behavior of $s(t)$ as $|t|$ approaches infinity in terms of continuity of $S(f)$ and its derivatives. We can also show for a time-limited function $s(t)$ that $S(f)$ and all its derivatives are continuous.

The rate of decrease of the Fourier transform for large $|f|$, or the Fourier-series coefficients for large $|n|$, has important bearing on the legitimacy of evaluating derivatives of a function by differentiating after the integral or summation sign. For example, if we calculate the time derivative of a signal by writing

$$\begin{aligned} s'(t) &= \frac{d}{dt} \int_{-\infty}^{\infty} S(f) e^{j2\pi ft} \, df \\ &= \int_{-\infty}^{\infty} j2\pi f S(f) e^{j2\pi ft} \, df \end{aligned} \tag{1-67}$$

we note that if $|S(f)|$ goes to zero as $|f|^{-m}$ for large $|f|$, the indicated Fourier transform $j2\pi f S(f)$ for the derivative can only decay as $|f|^{-(m-1)}$. In particular if $m = 1$, the Fourier transform of $s'(t)$ does not exist unless we adopt the δ-function symbolism.

Calculation of the integral of $s(t)$ by an analogous procedure leads to no difficulty at $|f| = \infty$, but may introduce trouble in the finite part of the path of integration. Integrating both sides of the Fourier-transform relationship from an arbitrary instant $t = -T$ gives

$$\begin{aligned} \int_{-T}^{t} s(t) \, dt &= \int_{-T}^{t} dt \int_{-\infty}^{\infty} S(f) e^{j2\pi ft} \, df \\ &= \int_{-\infty}^{\infty} \frac{e^{j2\pi ft} - e^{-j2\pi fT}}{j2\pi f} S(f) \, df \end{aligned} \tag{1-68}$$

The denominator of the last integrand vanishes when $f = 0$, but there is no singularity because the numerator vanishes to the same order. We should like to take the limit as T goes to infinity, but it is not obvious that such a limit exists. We observe that a function $s_{-1}(t)$ can be defined by

$$s_{-1}(t) = \int_{-\infty}^{\infty} \frac{S(f)}{j2\pi f} e^{j2\pi ft} \, df \tag{1-69}$$

if $S(0)$ vanishes to at least the first power of f and $|S(f)/f|$ is sufficiently small as $|f|$ approaches infinity. Let us further require that $|S(f)|$ vanish at least as fast as $1/|f|$ as $|f|$ becomes infinite, thereby forcing $s_{-1}(t)$ to be continuous for all t. Then

$$\int_{-T}^{t} s(t)\, dt = s_{-1}(t) - s_{-1}(-T) \tag{1-70}$$

and since $s_{-1}(-\infty)$ must be zero,

$$\int_{-\infty}^{t} s(t)\, dt = s_{-1}(t) = \int_{-\infty}^{\infty} \frac{S(f)}{j2\pi f}\, e^{j2\pi ft}\, df \tag{1-71}$$

This is the formula usually given for the Fourier transform of the integral of a signal. Note that there are restrictions on the validity.

Let us explore the effect of removing the restriction on $S(0)$. If $S(0)$ does not vanish, Eq. (1-71) is meaningless as it stands, because an infinite contribution to the integral occurs at $f = 0$. The remedy for this is to introduce the Cauchy principal value

$$P \int_{-\infty}^{\infty} \frac{S(f)}{j2\pi f}\, e^{j2\pi ft}\, df = \lim_{\epsilon \to 0} \left(\int_{-\infty}^{-\epsilon} + \int_{\epsilon}^{\infty} \right) \frac{S(f)}{j2\pi f}\, e^{j2\pi ft}\, df \tag{1-72}$$

Substitution of $S(f) = |S(f)| e^{j\,\text{ph}\,S(f)}$ gives

$$\begin{aligned}
P \int_{-\infty}^{\infty} \frac{S(f)}{j2\pi f}\, & e^{j2\pi ft}\, df \\
&= \lim_{\epsilon \to 0} \left(\int_{-\infty}^{-\epsilon} + \int_{\epsilon}^{\infty} \right) \frac{|S(f)| \cos\,[2\pi ft + \text{ph}\,S(f)]}{j2\pi f}\, df \\
&\quad + j \lim_{\epsilon \to 0} \left(\int_{-\infty}^{-\epsilon} + \int_{\epsilon}^{\infty} \right) \frac{|S(f)| \sin\,[2\pi ft + \text{ph}\,S(f)]}{j2\pi f}\, df
\end{aligned} \tag{1-73}$$

For real signals, we deduce from Eq. (1-8) that $|S(f)|$ is an even function of f and that $\text{ph}\,S(f)$ is an odd function of f. It follows that the first integrand on the right-hand side of Eq. (1-73) is an odd function of f and hence that the integrals over negative and positive values of f cancel each other. The second integrand is an even function of f and is finite at $f = 0$. Therefore, the indicated limiting process can be performed to give

$$\begin{aligned}
\int_{-\infty}^{t} s(t)\, dt &= P \int_{-\infty}^{\infty} \frac{S(f)}{j2\pi f}\, e^{j2\pi ft}\, df \\
&= \int_{-\infty}^{\infty} \frac{|S(f)| \sin\,[2\pi ft + \text{ph}\,S(f)]}{2\pi f}\, df
\end{aligned} \tag{1-74}$$

A useful interpretation can thus be made for a Fourier transform which varies as $1/f$ in the neighborhood of $f = 0$.

If we relax the requirement on continuity of $s_{-1}(t)$, Eq. (1-70) is no longer true, and the subsequent results are likewise invalid. Since a discontinuity in $s_{-1}(t)$ implies that $s(t)$ contains a δ function, it is of interest to examine the special case in which $s(t) = \delta(t)$ and $S(f) = 1$. Then

$$\int_{-\infty}^{t} s(t)\, dt = \int_{-\infty}^{t} \delta(t)\, dt = \begin{cases} 0 & t < 0 \\ 1 & t > 0 \end{cases} \tag{1-75}$$

$$s_{-1}(t) = P\int_{-\infty}^{\infty} \frac{e^{j2\pi ft}}{j2\pi f}\, df = \int_{-\infty}^{\infty} \frac{\sin 2\pi ft}{2\pi f}\, df = \frac{1}{2}\begin{cases} -1 & t < 0 \\ 1 & t > 0 \end{cases} \tag{1-76}$$

In this case, Eq. (1-70) is replaced by

$$\int_{-\infty}^{t} s(t)\, dt = s_{-1}(t) + \frac{1}{2} \tag{1-77}$$

These relations are useful in the solution of Prob. 1-4.

1-6 LINEAR CIRCUIT THEORY

We have seen that a linear time-invariant system can be characterized either by its impulse response $h(t)$ or by its transmittance function $H(f)$. The response $r_g(t)$ to an arbitrary excitation $g(t)$ can be found either from (1-47) by means of the product $R_g(f) = G(f)H(f)$ or from (1-48) by means of the convolution $r_g(t) = g(t) * h(t)$. Design of systems with desired impulse responses or transmittance functions belongs to the domain of linear circuit theory. Although it would be out of place here to attempt any extensive coverage of the methods employed, some basic observations may be helpful toward a further understanding of the relations between the time-domain and frequency-domain descriptions.

Real systems are *causal;* i.e., the response does not begin before the stimulus. In a causal linear time-invariant system, $h(t) = 0$ when $t < 0$. The causal condition implies restrictions on $H(f)$. We shall not discuss this fascinating subject in all its generality here, but will make a few observations bearing on what can and cannot be done to the frequency content of signals by causal networks. The intent will be to show basic facts rather than the most sophisticated and general results.

Our first remark is that since the derivative of zero is zero, the condition $h(t) = 0$ for $t < 0$ implies $d^n h(t)/dt^n = 0$ for $t < 0$, $n = 1, 2, \ldots$. This means that if in a causal system $h(t)$ and all of its derivatives are continuous for all t, $h(t)$ and all of its derivatives must vanish not only for negative t but for all values of t. Therefore, except in the trivial case in which $h(t) = 0$ identically, there must be a discontinuity at some $t \geq 0$ in either $h(t)$ or a derivative of $h(t)$.

In the previous section we showed that a band-limited function and all of its derivatives are free from discontinuities. It follows that, with the trivial exception of the no-pass system in which $H(f) = 0$ identically, a band-limited system is not causal.

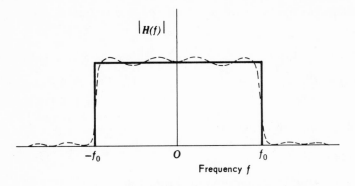

Fig. 1-3   Physical approximation to an ideal low-pass filter.

The graph of sinc $2f_0t$ shown in Fig. 1-2 is an example of the impulse response of a band-limited system. The impulse is applied at $t = 0$, but the response begins at $t = -\infty$. It is difficult to answer the question once asked of the author by a veteran telegraph engineer: "What would happen if the man at the switch changed his mind and did not apply the impulse?" Does the obvious logical contradiction make band-limited frequency responses a useless concept? The answer may be yes for strictly band-limited systems, but the possibility of a realizable approximation to a knife-edge cutoff changes the prospects drastically.

The full-line characteristic in Fig. 1-3 shows the absolute value of the transmittance function of an ideal low-pass filter plotted as a rectangle centered around the zero-frequency axis. Even without the causality argument, we would know that it would be impossible to realize this curve exactly, because the response is undefined at $f = \pm f_0$. We could, however, design and build a filter with $|H(f)|$ following the dashed approximation, which passes continuously, although steeply, through the transition from full response to very small response and reaches negligibly small values at very high frequencies without completely vanishing. Design of a close approximation would require many reactive elements and would inherently introduce a great amount of phase lag between a sine-wave response and a sine-wave input. We cannot describe the approximation fully without considering this phase shift, which we have ignored in plotting $|H(f)|$.

In general, the phase angle of $H(f)$ can be a very complicated function of frequency and can have a profound effect on $h(t)$. There is one simple phase function, however, which has no other effect than to shift the time scale of $h(t)$. This is the linear phase-vs.-frequency function. If

$$H(f) = H_0(f)e^{-j2\pi f\tau} \tag{1-78}$$

we readily calculate

$$h(t) = \int_{-\infty}^{\infty} H_0(f)e^{-j2\pi f\tau}e^{j2\pi ft}\, df = \int_{-\infty}^{\infty} H_0(f)e^{j2\pi f(t-\tau)}\, df = h_0(t-\tau)$$

$$(1\text{-}79)$$

The impulse response associated with $H_0(f)$ is delayed by τ, the slope of the phase curve plotted against $\omega = 2\pi f$. This relationship gives the clue to approximating the ideal low-pass filter. We should design for constant amplitude and linear phase within the band and make the response as small as possible outside the band. The resulting impulse response is an approximation to sinc $2f_0(t - \tau)$ instead of sinc $2f_0 t$. Since improving the approximation requires more reactive elements and a more rapid increase of phase shift with frequency, the value of τ becomes larger as the match is made better. In terms of Fig. 1-2, the central peak of the impulse response is no longer at $t = 0$ but is moved to $t = \tau$. As τ is increased, more and more of the anticipatory ripples in approximated form appear after $t = 0$ in the causal domain. In the limit as τ approaches infinity, all but the weakest lobes of the sinc function can be approximated and shifted to follow the applied impulse in time as they should in real life. Since the actual filter must be causal, there can be no lobes for negative values of t, and for any finite delay a leftmost segment of the sinc function must be flattened to coincide with the time axis.

In many practical cases, the amount of delay needed to secure a satisfactory approximation of the significant parts of a noncausal response need not be inordinately great. We shall often introduce band-limited response functions as design ideals for signal-transmission systems. When we do this, we tacitly imply that the actual approximate realization must allow for a time delay and a corresponding linear-phase transmittance factor. The formulas are simplified by not including these easily inserted modifications.

A corollary to our demonstration that in a band-limited system the impulse response and all of its derivatives must be continuous is that a discontinuity in the impulse response or any of its derivatives implies an unlimited band of transmitted frequencies. The rate of decay of $H(f)$ at high frequencies is controlled by the highest order of the continuous derivatives of $h(t)$, as described in the previous section.

A useful example of a linear time-invariant system is the tuned circuit shown in series and parallel form in Fig. 1-4. In the series case, the stimulus is the applied voltage $s(t)$ and the response is the current $i(t)$. Equating $s(t)$ to the sum of the voltage drops across the inductance L, resistance R, and capacitance C gives

$$L\frac{di(t)}{dt} + Ri(t) + \frac{1}{C}\int_{-\infty}^{t} i(t)\, dt = s(t)$$

$$(1\text{-}80)$$

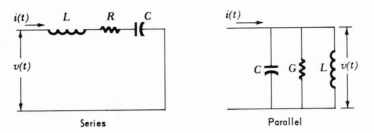

Fig. 1-4 Series- and parallel-tuned circuits.

If $i(t)$ and $s(t)$ are replaced by their Fourier-integral representations, the equation transforms to

$$\int_{-\infty}^{\infty} \left(j2\pi fL + R + \frac{1}{j2\pi fC} \right) I(f)e^{j2\pi ft}\, df = \int_{-\infty}^{\infty} S(f)e^{j2\pi ft}\, df \qquad (1\text{-}81)$$

It follows that

$$I(f) = \frac{j2\pi fCS(f)}{1 + j2\pi fCR - 4\pi^2 f^2 LC} \qquad (1\text{-}82)$$

It is convenient to substitute the parameters

$$f_0 = \frac{1}{2\pi \sqrt{LC}} \qquad Q = \frac{2\pi f_0 L}{R} \qquad (1\text{-}83)$$

Then,

$$H(f) = \frac{I(f)}{S(f)} = \frac{jf/f_0}{RQ[1 - f^2/f_0^2 + (j/Q)f/f_0]} \qquad (1\text{-}84)$$

The larger the quality factor Q, the more sharply selective the tuned circuit becomes with respect to frequency. We can establish a method of determining $|S(f)|^2$ at $f = f_0$ by measuring the total energy W absorbed in the resistance R. Applying Parseval's formula to the definition of W, we obtain

$$\begin{aligned} W &= R \int_{-\infty}^{\infty} i^2(t)\, dt = R \int_{-\infty}^{\infty} |I(f)|^2\, df = 2R \int_{0}^{\infty} |I(f)|^2\, df \\ &= 2R \int_{0}^{\infty} |H(f)|^2 |S(f)|^2\, df \\ &= \frac{2}{R} \int_{0}^{\infty} \frac{(f/f_0)^2 |S(f)|^2\, df}{Q^2(1 - f^2/f_0^2)^2 + f^2/f_0^2} \qquad (1\text{-}85) \end{aligned}$$

If we substitute $f = f_0(1 + y/Q)$, we find

$$W = \frac{2f_0}{RQ} \int_{-Q}^{\infty} \frac{(1 + y/Q)^2 |S[f_0(1 + y/Q)]|^2\, dy}{y^2(2 + y/Q)^2 + (1 + y/Q)^2} \qquad (1\text{-}86)$$

We can now evaluate the limit as $Q \to \infty$. The result is

$$\lim_{Q \to \infty} (QW) = \frac{2f_0}{R} \int_{-\infty}^{\infty} \frac{|S(f_0)|^2 \, dy}{4y^2 + 1}$$

$$= \frac{f_0 |S(f_0)|^2}{R} [\arctan 2y]_{-\infty}^{\infty}$$

$$= \frac{\pi f_0}{R} |S(f_0)|^2 \qquad\qquad (1\text{-}87)$$

Hence

$$|S(f_0)|^2 = \frac{R}{\pi f_0} \lim_{Q \to \infty} (QW) \qquad\qquad (1\text{-}88)$$

which is the relation sought.

PROBLEMS

1-1. Derive convolution theorems for Fourier series as defined by Eq. (1-15). Consider the following cases:

    (a) Given $s(t)$, $q(t)$, and $r(t)$ with $s_n = q_n r_n$, find $s(t)$ in terms of $q(t)$ and $r(t)$.

    (b) Given $s(t) = q(t)r(t)$, find s_n in terms of q_n and r_n.

1-2. Suppose a signal $s(t)$ is zero outside the interval $|t| < T/2$ and is expanded in a Fourier series valid for $|t| < T/2$. Express the coefficient s_n in terms of the Fourier transform $S(f)$.

1-3. Apply Poisson's summation formula to the result of Prob. 1-2 to obtain a formula for the sum of the Fourier-series coefficients of a time-limited signal in terms of the value of the signal at one instant. Verify that your result is valid for $s(t) = t \operatorname{rect}(t/T)$.

1-4. The unit step function $u(t)$ is defined by

$$u(t) = \begin{cases} 0 & t < 0 \\ 1 & t > 0 \end{cases}$$

    (a) Express $u(t)$ in terms of the δ function.

    (b) Express the response $r_u(t)$ of a linear time-invariant network to $u(t)$ in terms of $h(t)$.

1-5. (a) Express the function "signum of t," abbreviated as sgn t, and defined by

$$\operatorname{sgn} t = \begin{cases} -1 & t < 0 \\ 1 & t > 0 \end{cases}$$

in terms of the δ function.

    (b) Show that $d \operatorname{sgn} t/dt = 2\delta(t)$.

1-6. Using Eq. (1-49) or (1-50) as the definition of the δ function, show that the following representations are valid:

    (a) $\delta(t) = \lim_{k \to \infty} \dfrac{\sin kt}{\pi t}$

    (b) $\delta(t) = \lim_{k \to \infty} \dfrac{k}{\sqrt{\pi}} e^{-k^2 t^2}$

1-7. (a) Show that the Fourier transform of the unit step function $u(t)$ is given by

$$U(f) = \frac{1}{j2\pi f} + \frac{\delta(f)}{2}$$

(b) What is the Fourier transform of sgn t?

1-8. By expressing $g(t)$ as the sum of even and odd functions, i.e.,

$$g(t) = g_e(t) + g_o(t)$$

where

$$g_e(t) = \tfrac{1}{2}[g(t) + g(-t)]$$
$$g_o(t) = \tfrac{1}{2}[g(t) - g(-t)]$$

show that $\delta(\lambda)$ as defined by (1-49) or (1-50) must be an even function.

Hint: Note that $g_o(0) = 0$.

1-9. Consider the signal

$$s(t) = \begin{cases} e^{bt} - e^{at} & t < 0 \\ e^{-at} - e^{-bt} & t > 0 \end{cases}$$

with $a > 0$, $b > 0$, and $a \neq b$. Find the highest order of derivative of $s(t)$ continuous for all t and thereby deduce the rate of decay of $S(f)$ as $|f| \to \infty$. Verify your conclusion by calculating $S(f)$.

1-10. A channel is said to be distortionless if the response $r_o(t)$ to stimulus $g(t)$ is equal to $kg(t - \tau)$, where k and t are constants. Show that if the transmittance function of the channel is $A(f)e^{-jB(f)}$ with $A(f)$ and $B(f)$ real, the necessary and sufficient conditions for distortionless transmission are

$$A(f) = k$$
$$B(f) = 2\pi\tau f \pm n\pi \qquad n = 0, 1, 2, \ldots$$

1-11. An ideal bandpass filter centered at $f = \pm f_0$ with width f_d has a transmittance function defined by

$$H(f) = \begin{cases} 0 & |f| < f_0 - \dfrac{f_d}{2} \\[2mm] 1 & f_0 - \dfrac{f_d}{2} < |f| < f_0 + \dfrac{f_d}{2} \\[2mm] 0 & |f| > f_0 + \dfrac{f_d}{2} \end{cases}$$

(a) Find an expression for $|S(f_0)|^2$ in terms of the total energy in the output of the filter when $s(t)$ is the voltage applied as input and the output is a voltage $v(t)$ across a resistance R.

(b) By comparing the answer to part (a) with Eq. (1-88), define an equivalent bandwidth of a high-Q tuned circuit.

1-12. Give the analysis corresponding to Eqs. (1-80) to (1-88) for the parallel-tuned circuit of Fig. 1-4.

REFERENCES

1. Woodward, P. M.: "Probability and Information Theory, with Applications to Radar," Pergamon Press, Macmillan, New York, 1953.

2. Campbell, G. A., and R. M. Foster: The Practical Application of the Fourier Integral, *Bell System Tech. J.*, vol. 7, pp. 639–707, October, 1928.
3. Lighthill, M. J.: "An Introduction to Fourier Analysis and Generalized Functions," Cambridge University Press, Cambridge, England, 1958.
4. Carslaw, H. S.: "Introduction to the Theory of Fourier's Series and Integrals," Macmillan, London, 1930, and Dover, New York, 1950.
5. Hobson, E. W.: "Theory of Functions of a Real Variable and the Theory of Fourier's Series," Cambridge University Press, Cambridge, England, 1927, and Dover, New York, 1957.
6. Titchmarsh, E. C.: "Introduction to the Theory of Fourier Integrals," Oxford University Press, London, 1937.

2
Representation of Noise

In physical systems, the transmission of signals is disturbed by the presence of unwanted waves over which we have incomplete control. It is customary to designate such disturbing waveforms as *noise* by extending the familiar acoustic usage of the word. Noise waves resemble signal waves in many respects but have an important difference in that there is insufficient knowledge about them to enable a determinate description. Any particular specimen of noise could be represented over a specified finite interval of observation time by a Fourier series or integral, but such a representation would not hold for earlier or later segments of the same noise wave.

2-1 SOME BASIC STATISTICAL CONCEPTS[1,2]

Since we cannot make precise statements predicting the instantaneous values of the noise in a system, we fall back on a statistical description. It is convenient to regard the actual noise wave as a member of a large ensemble of possible noise waves which could occur in a similarly prepared

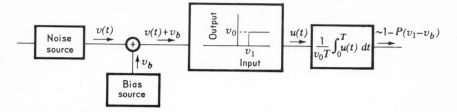

Fig. 2-1 Method of measuring probability distribution function of a noise source.

system. Statistics concerning the noise can be evaluated from observations made on a single member of the ensemble at different times or on different members of the ensemble at the same time. In an important class of noise sources called *stationary*, the statistics do not vary with time. In a subclass of stationary noise sources called *ergodic*, the statistics over the ensemble are the same as those of a single member of the ensemble. Unless a contrary statement is made, we shall assume ergodic noise sources in our treatment.

One elementary statistical property of noise is the relative likelihood of occurrence of different numerical values for the ordinates of the noise wave. This property is defined by either the probability distribution function $P(v)$ equal to the probability that a noise sample has a value not greater than v, or the probability density function $p(v)$, which when multiplied by dv gives the probability that the noise sample has a value in an interval of infinitesimal width dv centered at v. We shall use the abbreviations PDF and pdf for the probability distribution function and probability density function, respectively.

An experimental method for finding the probability distribution function $P(v)$ is shown in Fig. 2-1. The noise source drives a threshold device which delivers zero output when the input is less than v_1 and a fixed nonzero output when the input is greater than v_1. The fraction of time throughout which zero output is obtained furnishes an estimate of $P(v_1)$ when the observation time is made sufficiently long. Appropriate biasing of the threshold device enables different values of v_1 to be tested. The resulting data can be plotted as an approximation of $P(v)$, and a smoothed estimate drawn as shown in Fig. 2-2. The probability density function $p(v)$ can be estimated by measuring $[P(v_2) - P(v_1)]/(v_2 - v_1)$ when v_2 and v_1 are close together. In the limit as v_2 and v_1 are taken very close together, we obtain $p(v)$ as the slope of the smoothed $P(v)$ curve as shown in Fig. 2-2.

It may be helpful to think of probability as a quantity analogous to mass with $P(v)$ corresponding to the total mass in a specified region and

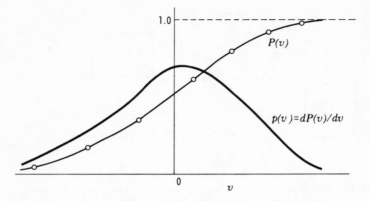

Fig. 2-2 Estimation of probability distribution function $P(v)$ and probability density function $p(v)$ from measurement of Fig. 2-1.

$p(v)$ to the density. $P(v)$ can be calculated from $p(v)$ by integration as follows:

$$P(v) = \int_{-\infty}^{v} p(v)\, dv \tag{2-1}$$

Inversely, we can write

$$p(v) = \frac{dP(v)}{dv} \tag{2-2}$$

if the derivative exists. As v increases from $-\infty$ to ∞, $P(v)$ increases monotonically from zero to unity. $P(v)$ satisfies the mathematical relations $P(-\infty) = 0$, $P(\infty) = 1$, and $P(v_2) \geq P(v_1)$ if $v_2 > v_1$. It follows from these relations that the value of $p(v)$ cannot be negative and that the total area of the $p(v)$ curve is unity.

The probability density function can be used to calculate averages of various quantities related to the noise wave. If $\mathbf{E}x$ represents the *mathematical expectation* of x, that is, the limit approached by the mean or average of a very large number of samples of x, we deduce from the definitions of probability and average that

$$\mathbf{E}F(v) = \int_{-\infty}^{\infty} F(v)p(v)\, dv \tag{2-3}$$

where $F(v)$ is any function of v for which the integral exists. In particular, the average value of the noise wave itself is given by

$$\mathbf{E}v = \int_{-\infty}^{\infty} vp(v)\, dv \tag{2-4}$$

This is the value which would be read by a d-c meter. The mean-square value is given by

$$\mathbf{E}v^2 = \int_{-\infty}^{\infty} v^2 p(v)\, dv \tag{2-5}$$

If v represents the noise voltage applied to a resistance R, the average power is equal to $\mathbf{E}v^2/R$. The quantity $\mathbf{E}v^2$ is thus the average power in a 1-ohm circuit. The a-c component of the noise is $v - \mathbf{E}v$, and the average square of the a-c component is given by

$$\sigma^2 = \mathbf{E}(v - \mathbf{E}v)^2 = \mathbf{E}v^2 - \mathbf{E}^2 v \tag{2-6}$$

on noting that, in general,

$$\mathbf{E}(x + y) = \mathbf{E}x + \mathbf{E}y \tag{2-7}$$

In statistical language, σ^2 is the *variance* and σ is the *standard deviation* of v. Translated to the nomenclature of electrical engineering, the variance is the a-c power in a 1-ohm circuit, and the standard deviation is the root-mean-square, or rms, value of the a-c noise component.

2-2 ADDITION OF INDEPENDENT NOISE SOURCES

In statistical calculations, the need often arises to calculate the probability density function of the sum of two independent quantities when the individual probability density functions are given. Assume $p_1(x)$ and $p_2(y)$ are the pdf's of the independent quantities x and y, respectively, and let $p_{12}(z)$ be the pdf of $z = x + y$. The probability that the sum of x and y falls in an infinitesimal interval dz centered at z can be calculated by first observing that if x is known, the value of z will be in dz at z if and only if the value of y is in dz at $z - x$. The probability of the latter event is $p_2(z - x)\, dz$. We average this probability over all x to obtain

$$p_{12}(z)\, dz = dz \int_{-\infty}^{\infty} p_1(x) p_2(z - x)\, dx \tag{2-8}$$

Equation (2-8) shows that the pdf of the sum of independent quantities is the convolution of the individual pdf's. In the notation of Chap. 1, we can write

$$p_{12}(z) = p_1(z) * p_2(z) \tag{2-9}$$

or, in general, for the sum of n independent variables,

$$q_n(z) = p_{12\ldots n}(z) = p_1(z) * p_2(z) * \cdots * p_n(z) \tag{2-10}$$

No confusion arises in the representation of multiple convolutions, because the operation is associative; that is,

$$[p_1(z) * p_2(z)] * p_3(z) = p_1(z) * [p_2(z) * p_3(z)] \tag{2-11}$$

In the analogous situation of convolutions in the time domain, we observed in Chap. 1 that simplification could be obtained by introducing Fourier transforms. In statistical theory, the Fourier transform of the pdf is called the *characteristic function*. To conform with statistical usage, we depart from the previous symbolism by expressing the characteristic function in terms of a variable ξ analogous to $\omega = 2\pi f$. We also abandon the use of uppercase and lowercase letters for the function and its transform. The appropriate formulas are

$$C(\xi) = \int_{-\infty}^{\infty} p(v)e^{j\xi v}\,dv$$
$$p(v) = \frac{1}{2\pi} \int_{-\infty}^{\infty} C(\xi)e^{-jv\xi}\,d\xi \tag{2-12}$$

where $C(\xi)$ is the characteristic function of the noise source which has the probability density function $p(v)$. Since, as shown in Sec. 1-3, a convolving of functions multiplies the Fourier transforms, we can express the characteristic function of the sum of n independent noise sources in terms of the individual characteristic functions $C_m(\xi)$, $m = 1, 2, \ldots, n$, by

$$C_{12\ldots n}(\xi) = \prod_{m=1}^{n} C_m(\xi) \tag{2-13}$$

We thereby obtain the following equivalent form for Eq. (2-10):

$$q_n(z) = \frac{1}{2\pi} \int_{-\infty}^{\infty} e^{-jz\xi}\,d\xi \prod_{m=1}^{n} C_m(\xi) \tag{2-14}$$

In many cases this results in a simpler procedure than required to perform the convolutions.

Comparison of (2-12) with (2-3) shows that

$$C(\xi) = \mathbf{E}e^{j\xi v} \tag{2-15}$$

By expanding both sides of (2-15) in powers of ξ, we obtain

$$\sum_{r=0}^{\infty} \frac{C^{(r)}(0)}{r!}\,\xi^r = \sum_{r=0}^{\infty} \frac{\mathbf{E}(v^r)}{r!}\,(j\xi)^r \tag{2-16}$$

where $C^{(r)}(0)$ represents the rth derivative of $C(\xi)$ evaluated at $\xi = 0$. The average value of the rth power of the noise values is called the rth *moment* of the noise source. Designating the rth moment by m_r, we equate coefficients of like powers of ξ in (2-16) and find

$$m_r = \mathbf{E}v^r = j^{-r}C^{(r)}(0) \tag{2-17}$$

From either (2-12), (2-15), or (2-17), we deduce that $C(0) = 1$.

The a-c component of the noise source is given by $v - m_1$. The moments of $v - m_1$ are called the *central moments* of v and will be represented by μ_r. Then $\mu_r = \mathbf{E}(v - m_1)^r$, and straightforward calculation yields the results

$$
\begin{aligned}
\mu_0 &= 1 \\
\mu_1 &= 0 \\
\mu_2 &= m_2 - m_1{}^2 \\
\mu_3 &= m_3 - 3m_1 m_2 + 2m_1{}^3 \\
\mu_4 &= m_4 - 4m_1 m_3 + 6m_1{}^2 m_2 - 3m_1{}^4
\end{aligned}
\tag{2-18}
$$

The variance, which we shall represent as *var v*, is equal to the second central moment μ_2.

Another useful set of parameters of the noise source consists of the semi-invariants s_r defined from the coefficients of ξ^r in the power-series representation of $\log C(\xi)$ by the equation

$$
\log C(\xi) = \sum_{r=0}^{\infty} \frac{(j\xi)^r s_r}{r!}
\tag{2-19}
$$

From Taylor's series expansion

$$
j^r s_r = \frac{d^r \log C(\xi)}{d\xi^r} \bigg|_{\xi=0}
\tag{2-20}
$$

We calculate

$$
\begin{aligned}
s_0 &= 0 \\
s_1 &= m_1 \\
s_2 &= m_2 - m_1{}^2 = \text{var } v = \mu_2 \\
s_3 &= m_3 - 3m_1 m_2 + 2m_1{}^3 = \mu_3 \\
s_4 &= m_4 - 4m_1 m_3 - 3m_2{}^2 + 12m_1{}^2 m_2 - 6m_1{}^4 = \mu_4 - 3\mu_2{}^2
\end{aligned}
\tag{2-21}
$$

The usefulness of the semi-invariants can be demonstrated by taking logarithms of both sides of Eq. (2-13) to obtain

$$
\log C_{12\ldots n}(\xi) = \sum_{m=1}^{n} \log C_m(\xi)
\tag{2-22}
$$

Representing the rth semi-invariant of $C_m(\xi)$ by s_{mr}, we substitute (2-19) in the right-hand side to obtain

$$
\begin{aligned}
\log C_{12\ldots n}(\xi) &= \sum_{m=1}^{n} \sum_{r=1}^{\infty} \frac{(j\xi)^r s_{mr}}{r!} \\
&= \sum_{r=1}^{\infty} (j\xi)^r \sum_{m=1}^{n} \frac{s_{mr}}{r!}
\end{aligned}
\tag{2-23}
$$

It follows that t_{nr}, the rth semi-invariant of the sum of n sources, is given by

$$t_{nr} = \sum_{m=1}^{n} s_{mr} \tag{2-24}$$

In other words the semi-invariants are additive parameters of independent noise sources. The moments are not additive but can be calculated from the semi-invariants by inverting the equations of (2-21). The resulting equations are

$$\begin{aligned}
m_1 &= s_1 \\
m_2 &= s_1{}^2 + s_2 \\
m_3 &= s_1{}^3 + 3s_1 s_2 + s_3 \\
m_4 &= s_1{}^4 + 4s_1 s_3 + 6s_1{}^2 s_2 + 3s_2{}^2 + s_4
\end{aligned} \tag{2-25}$$

The central moments are given by

$$\begin{aligned}
\mu_2 &= s_2 \\
\mu_3 &= s_3 \\
\mu_4 &= 3s_2{}^2 + s_4
\end{aligned} \tag{2-26}$$

The mathematical machinery based on the characteristic function now enables us to give a heuristic demonstration of the *central limit theorem* for the probability density function of the sum of a large number of independent sources. From Eq. (2-15), we see that if ξ and v are real,

$$|C(\xi)| \leq 1 \tag{2-27}$$

In the integrand of Eq. (2-14), we thus have the product of n factors, no one of which can exceed unity in absolute value. If most of the factors have absolute values less than unity, the product is very small when n is large. The principal contributions to the integral must occur when most of the C_m's have absolute values nearly equal to unity. We have previously observed that $C_m(0) = 1$ for all characteristic functions. Furthermore, examination of the defining integral (2-12) shows that if $\xi = 0$, all contributions of the integrand add in phase, while if $\xi \neq 0$, the phase of $e^{j\xi v}$ assumes all possible values. Since the multiplying factor $p(v)$ is real and nonnegative, the integral for $\xi \neq 0$ must be less than when $\xi = 0$ because of the reduction produced by out-of-phase contributions. We conclude that $C_m(\xi) < 1$ when $\xi \neq 0$ and that as n approaches infinity, the product of n characteristic functions in the integral of (2-14) becomes very small except when ξ is near zero.

We can now make an estimate of $q_n(z)$, the pdf of the sum of n independent noise sources for large n, by placing the product of characteristic functions of Eq. (2-14) in the argument of the exponential and applying Eqs. (2-22) to (2-24) to obtain the equivalent form:

$$q_n(z) = \frac{1}{2\pi} \int_{-\infty}^{\infty} \exp\left[-jz\xi + \sum_{m=1}^{n} \log C_m(\xi) \right] d\xi$$

$$= \frac{1}{2\pi} \int_{-\infty}^{\infty} \exp\left[-jz\xi + \sum_{r=1}^{\infty} \frac{(j\xi)^r t_{nr}}{r!} \right] d\xi$$

$$= \frac{1}{2\pi} \int_{-\infty}^{\infty} \exp\left[-j\xi(z - t_{n1}) - \frac{t_{n2}\xi^2}{2} + \sum_{r=3}^{\infty} \frac{t_{nr}(j\xi)^r}{r!} \right] d\xi$$

$$(2\text{-}28)$$

If the principal contribution to the integral occurs for values of ξ near zero, a good estimate can be made by retaining only the terms in ξ and ξ^2 in the argument of the exponential. This gives the asymptotic form of the pdf for large n as

$$q_n(z) \sim \frac{1}{2\pi} \int_{-\infty}^{\infty} \exp\left[-j(z - t_{n1})\xi - \frac{t_{n2}\xi^2}{2} \right] d\xi$$

$$= \frac{1}{\pi} \int_{0}^{\infty} e^{-t_{n2}\xi^2/2} \cos\,(z - t_{n1})\xi\, d\xi$$

$$= (2\pi\tau_n)^{-\frac{1}{2}} e^{-(z-z_n)^2/2\tau_n^2}$$

$$(2\text{-}29)$$

where

$$z_n = t_{n1} = \sum_{m=1}^{n} \mathbf{E} v_m$$

and $$(2\text{-}30)$$

$$\tau_n^2 = t_{n2} = \sum_{m=1}^{n} \mathrm{var}\, v_m$$

The accuracy of the approximation (2-29) is best for values of z near the mean z_n, where the pdf reaches its maximum value. As the name "central limit theorem" implies, the validity is limited to the central part of the distribution. When the value calculated from (2-29) is small, the influence of the neglected terms in (2-28) can be relatively significant. As n is increased, however, the central range of validity widens. We should stress that we have not given a rigorous mathematical proof of the central limit theorem here. For such a proof see, for example, pages 213–218 of Ref. 3.

Since many processes in nature can be described as the sum of a large number of independent subsidiary effects, the pdf of (2-29) is of special importance. The distribution thereby defined is said to be first-order gaussian, and the pdf is commonly written

$$p(x) = \frac{1}{\sigma\sqrt{2\pi}}\, e^{-(x-x_0)^2/2\sigma^2}$$

$$(2\text{-}31)$$

where x_0 is the mean and σ is the standard deviation. The corresponding PDF can be represented in terms of the error function erf x or the complementary error function erfc x by

$$
\begin{aligned}
P(x) &= \frac{1}{\sigma\sqrt{2\pi}} \int_{-\infty}^{x} e^{-(x-x_0)^2/2\sigma^2}\,dx \\
&= \frac{1}{2}\left(1 + \operatorname{erf}\frac{x-x_0}{\sigma\sqrt{2}}\right) \\
&= 1 - \frac{1}{2}\operatorname{erfc}\frac{x-x_0}{\sigma\sqrt{2}}
\end{aligned}
\tag{2-32}
$$

where

$$
\operatorname{erf} x = \frac{2}{\sqrt{\pi}}\int_0^x e^{-x^2}\,dx
\tag{2-33}
$$

and

$$
\operatorname{erfc} x = \frac{2}{\sqrt{\pi}}\int_x^{\infty} e^{-x^2}\,dx = 1 - \operatorname{erf} x
\tag{2-34}
$$

Graphs of $p(x)$ and $P(x)$ for gaussian noise are shown in Figs. 2-3 and 2-4, respectively. It can be readily verified that the sum of independent gaussian processes is also gaussian with mean and variance equal, respectively, to the sums of the individual means and variances. In fact, the result of any linear operation on gaussian noises leads to another gaussian noise. The characteristic function of gaussian noise conveniently turns out to be a gaussian function of the transform variable; that is,

$$
C(\xi) = e^{j\xi x_0 - \sigma^2\xi^2/2}
\tag{2-35}
$$

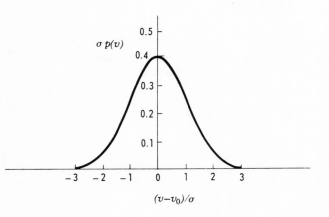

Fig. 2-3 Graph of Eq. (2-31), $p(v) = (1/\sigma\sqrt{2\pi})\,e^{-(v-v_0)^2/2\sigma^2}$; probability density function of gaussian noise.

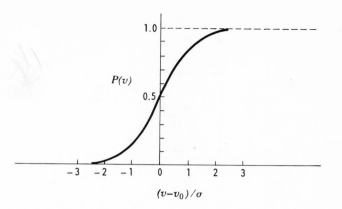

Fig. 2-4 Graph of Eq. (2-32), $P(v) = \frac{1}{2} + \frac{1}{2} \operatorname{erf} [(v - v_0)/\sigma]/\sqrt{2}$; probability distribution function of gaussian noise.

An important example of a gaussian process is the *thermal noise* originating from random motions of the electrons in a resistor. The number of components contributing to this noise is so inconceivably large that the validity of the central limit theorem is unquestionable for even the most refined measurements which could be performed.

2-3 STATISTICAL REPRESENTATION IN THE FREQUENCY DOMAIN

The functions $P(v)$ and $p(v)$ are first-order probabilities which describe the range of noise values observed but do not indicate how fast changes occur with time. We can proceed to a more comprehensive description either on a strictly time-domain basis or by a shift to the frequency domain. From the practical point of view, the latter approach is more straightforward because of the convenient availability of frequency-selective measuring techniques. Rapidity of change in the values of a wave is associated with the frequency range of the components present in the wave. As previously remarked, there is no way of describing a noise wave as a combination of precisely defined sine waves. We can, however, define an average composition of the noise wave in terms of component frequencies by measuring the mean-square responses of sharply tuned circuits.

Figure 2-5 shows how a statistical resolution in the frequency domain can be performed on a noise source. The noise voltage $v(t)$ is applied to a parallel array of resonant circuits with the nth circuit tuned for maximum response at $f = f_n$. All circuits are adjusted to have the same selectivity in terms of response versus frequency displacement from

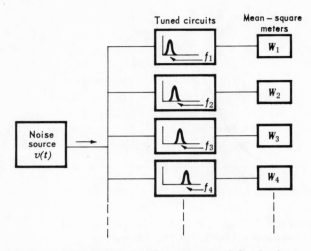

Fig. 2-5 Method of measuring the spectral density function of a noise source.

f_n. In mathematical language, if $H_n(f)$ is the transmittance function of the nth tuned circuit, we adjust $|H_n(f - f_n)|$ to be the same for all n when f and f_n are both positive. Each resonant circuit is followed by an a-c meter giving a reading proportional to the mean-square value of the output. A suitable meter could be realized by a thermocouple and d-c ammeter with large time constants. If the output of the tuned circuit is a voltage or current, the mean-square value is the average power in a 1-ohm circuit. Plotting the meter readings with f_n as abscissa, as indicated in Fig. 2-6, thus gives a curve which with sufficiently sharp

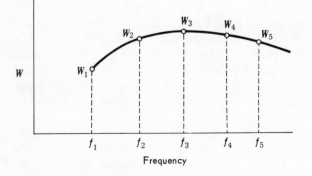

Fig. 2-6 Relative values of spectral density measured as in Fig. 2-5.

selectivity of the tuned circuits and a suitable calibration factor expresses the average power per unit of bandwidth in the neighborhood of individual frequencies. The unit of bandwidth adopted here will be the hertz, abbreviated as Hz, equal to 1 cycle/sec. It is customary to express the average power in watts in a 1-ohm circuit, but it is somewhat less awkward to deal with the mean-square value of voltage or current per Hz of bandwidth. This quantity, which is sometimes called the intensity spectrum, will be defined here as the *spectral density function* $w_v(f)$ of the noise source $v(t)$. If $v(t)$ is expressed in volts, $w_v(f)$ is expressed in (volts)^2/Hz.

A simple quantitative and operational definition of the spectral density function is obtained by postulating that the resonant circuits are rectangular bandpass filters satisfying

$$|H_n(f)| = |H_n(-f)| = \begin{cases} 0 & 0 < f < f_n - \dfrac{\Delta f}{2} \\ 1 & f_n - \dfrac{\Delta f}{2} < f < f_n + \dfrac{\Delta f}{2} \\ 0 & f_n + \dfrac{\Delta f}{2} < f \end{cases} \tag{2-36}$$

Then if $v_n(t)$ is the response of the nth circuit when the noise voltage $v(t)$ is applied as input, the value of $w_v(f)$ is defined for *positive frequencies* by

$$w_v(f) = \lim_{\Delta f \to 0} \frac{\mathbf{E} v_n{}^2}{\Delta f} \tag{2-37}$$

Actual tuned circuits cannot realize rectangular bandpass characteristics, but the definition (2-37) can be extended to approximate realizations by introducing an equivalent bandwidth

$$\Delta f = \int_0^\infty \frac{|H_n(f)|^2}{|H_n(f_n)|^2} \, df \tag{2-38}$$

This value of Δf can be used in (2-37) if $|H_n(f)|$ is sharply peaked at $f = f_n$. As shown in Fig. 2-7, Δf is the width of a rectangular response function giving the same area of squared ordinates as the actual response function. Note that the normalization furnished by the denominator of the integrand in (2-38) removes the requirement of uniform shape for the different response functions.

A better understanding of the spectral density function can be obtained by a statistical Fourier analysis of the noise. In general, we cannot calculate a Fourier transform for even a completely specified noise wave, because the behavior at $t = \pm \infty$ does not lead to a convergent Fourier integral. We can approach the problem by considering the

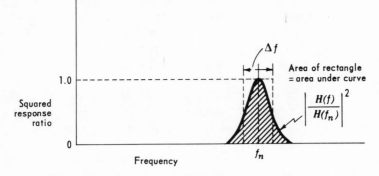

Fig. 2-7   Equivalent ideal bandpass filter for tuned circuit.

Fourier transform $V_T(f)$ of the truncated noise wave $v_T(t)$ defined by

$$v_T(t) = \begin{cases} 0 & |t| > \dfrac{T}{2} \\ v(t) & |t| < \dfrac{T}{2} \end{cases} \tag{2-39}$$

From Eq. (1-16),

$$V_T(f) = \int_{-T/2}^{T/2} v(t)e^{-j2\pi ft}\, dt \tag{2-40}$$

If the resonant circuits are rectangular bandpass filters as defined by (2-36), the response $v_{nT}(t)$ of the nth filter is given by

$$v_{nT}(t) = \left[\int_{-f_n-\Delta f/2}^{-f_n+\Delta f/2} + \int_{f_n-\Delta f/2}^{f_n+\Delta f/2} \right] V_T(f)e^{j2\pi ft - j\,\mathrm{ph}\,H_n(f)}\, df \tag{2-41}$$

Applying Parseval's theorem, Eq. (1-31), we deduce that

$$\int_{-\infty}^{\infty} v_{nT}{}^2(t)\, dt = 2 \int_{f_n-\Delta f/2}^{f_n+\Delta f/2} |V_T(f)|^2\, df \tag{2-42}$$

For a 1-ohm circuit, the left-hand member of Eq. (2-42) represents the total energy received by the nth filter from the truncated noise wave. The energy is delivered by the source in a time interval T, and hence as T is increased, the average power supplied by the source to the filter output must approach the quotient of the energy and T. Therefore, in terms of mean-square values,

$$\begin{aligned} \mathbf{E}v_n{}^2 &= \lim_{T\to\infty} \frac{1}{T} \int_{-\infty}^{\infty} v_{nT}{}^2(t)\, dt \\ &= \lim_{T\to\infty} \frac{2}{T} \int_{f_n-\Delta f/2}^{f_n+\Delta f/2} |V_T(f)|^2\, df \end{aligned} \tag{2-43}$$

and finally,

$$w_v(f) = \lim_{\Delta f \to 0} \left[\frac{1}{\Delta f} \lim_{T \to \infty} \frac{2}{T} \int_{f_n - \Delta f/2}^{f_n + \Delta f/2} |V_T(f)|^2 \, df \right] \tag{2-44}$$

A complete correspondence is thus established between a statistical Fourier analysis and experimental measurement of the spectral density function. Note that the computation of Eq. (2-44) proceeds in the same order as the measurement. In general, an interchange in the order of the analytical steps could lead to error. However, if an ensemble average is taken, the difficulties disappear and we can reduce (2-44) in the case of an ergodic process to

$$w_v(f) = \mathbf{E} w_v(f) = \lim_{T \to \infty} \frac{2}{T} \mathbf{E} |V_T(f)|^2 \tag{2-45}$$

The result we have obtained is sometimes called a one-sided spectral density because it is defined for only positive frequencies. In analytical work it is often convenient to use a two-sided spectral density with $w_v(f)$ divided equally between f and $-f$, as shown in Fig. 2-8.

As in the analogous case of the probability density function, we can define a *spectral distribution function*. In terms of the one-sided spectral density,

$$W_v(f) = \int_0^f w_v(f) \, df \tag{2-46}$$

It follows that

$$\mathbf{E} v^2 = W_v(\infty) = \int_0^\infty w_v(f) \, df \tag{2-47}$$

If $w_v(f)$ is a constant, the noise is said to be *white*. This term is borrowed from the concept of white light meaning uniform composition of all colors. It is evident from (2-46) that noise of finite average total power cannot be white over an unlimited band of frequencies.

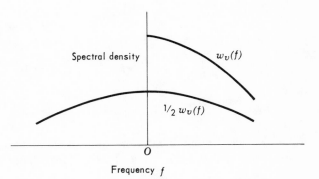

Fig. 2-8 One- and two-sided spectral density functions.

2-4 A SINE-WAVE MODEL FOR A GAUSSIAN NOISE SOURCE

We stated in Chap. 1 that the essential features of a signal-transmission system could be described in terms of sinusoidal components. The first part of the present chapter has departed from the simplest concepts in order to introduce the methods of mathematical statistics needed to deal with noise, but even here we found that Fourier analysis played a dominant role. We shall now show how sinusoidal components can be employed to construct a useful model of a gaussian noise source with a prescribed spectral density function.

Consider a sum of N sine waves with f_n representing the frequency of the nth component and with $f_{n+1} - f_n = \Delta f$. The amplitude a_n is assumed to be specified for each of the components, but the phase ϕ_n is defined only by the rectangular probability density function

$$p_\phi(\phi_n) = \frac{1}{2\pi} \qquad 0 \leq \phi_n \leq 2\pi \tag{2-48}$$

which means that the phase angle of each component is equally likely to have any value in the range 0 to 2π. The phase angles of the different components are assumed to be independent.

We write as an initial approximation for a noise wave

$$v(t) = \sum_{n=1}^{N} a_n \cos (2\pi f_n t + \phi_n) \tag{2-49}$$

Since $v(t)$ is the sum of N components with independent distributions, the central limit theorem can be applied to show that as N approaches infinity, the pdf of $v(t)$ approaches a gaussian distribution with mean and variance equal to the sums, respectively, of the means and variances of the N components.

Let

$$v_n = a_n \cos (2\pi f_n t + \phi_n) \tag{2-50}$$

Then

$$\mathbf{E}v_n = \int_0^{2\pi} v_n p_\phi(\phi_n) \, d\phi_n$$

$$= \frac{1}{2\pi} \int_0^{2\pi} a_n \cos (2\pi f_n t + \phi_n) \, d\phi_n = 0 \tag{2-51}$$

and

$$\mathbf{E}v_n{}^2 = \frac{1}{2\pi} \int_0^{2\pi} a_n{}^2 \cos^2 (2\pi f_n t + \phi_n) \, d\phi_n = \frac{a_n{}^2}{2} \tag{2-52}$$

Since adjacent components are separated in frequency by Δf, a stepped approximation to the spectral density function of $v(t)$ is given

$$w_v(f_n) = \frac{\mathbf{E}v_n{}^2}{\Delta f} = \frac{a_n{}^2}{2\Delta f} \tag{2-53}$$

If $w_v(f_n)$ is given, we make

$$a_n = [2\Delta f w_v(f_n)]^{\frac{1}{2}} \tag{2-54}$$

As N goes to infinity, we approach gaussian noise with mean equal to zero, variance equal to $\sum_{n=1}^{N} a_n^2/2$, and spectral density $w_v(f_n)$. To apply the model practically, we first solve the problem for a finite value of N. We then evaluate the limits of the solution as N goes to infinity and Δf to zero.

As a very elementary illustration, consider the case of a gaussian noise source $v(t)$ of spectral density $w_v(f)$ applied to a linear time-invariant system with transmittance function $H(f)$. The response of the network to a component of form (2-50) is

$$u_n = |H(f_n)|a_n \cos [2\pi f_n t + \phi_n + \text{ph } H(f_n)] \tag{2-55}$$

Since

$$\mathbf{E}u_n^2 = |H(f_n)|^2 \frac{a_n^2}{2} \tag{2-56}$$

we deduce that the spectral density of the output must be

$$w_u(f) = |H(f)|^2 w_v(f) \tag{2-57}$$

As a second example, consider the problem of representing a narrow band of gaussian noise as a rapidly oscillating function with a slowly varying envelope. By a narrow band we mean that the midband frequency is large compared to the bandwidth. The noise wave of (2-49) would have a narrow band if the midband frequency $f_c = (f_N + f_1)/2$ is large compared with $f_N - f_1$. It is then convenient to transform Eq. (2-49) as follows:

$$
\begin{aligned}
v(t) &= \sum_{n=1}^{N} a_n \cos [2\pi(f_n - f_c)t + \phi_n + 2\pi f_c t] \\
&= x(t) \cos 2\pi f_c t - y(t) \sin 2\pi f_c t
\end{aligned} \tag{2-58}
$$

where

$$x(t) = \sum_{n=1}^{N} a_n \cos [2\pi(f_n - f_c)t + \phi_n] \tag{2-59}$$

and

$$y(t) = \sum_{n=1}^{N} a_n \sin [2\pi(f_n - f_c)t + \phi_n] \tag{2-60}$$

The frequencies contained in $x(t)$ and $y(t)$ are at most half the bandwidth of $v(t)$ and are by hypothesis small compared with f_c. Hence $x(t)$ and $y(t)$ vary slowly compared with $\cos 2\pi f_c t$ and $\sin 2\pi f_c t$. Equations of the form (2-58) occur very often in signal-transmission problems. Representation in terms of envelope and phase is accomplished by the useful trigonometric identity:

$$A \cos \theta - B \sin \theta = (A^2 + B^2)^{1/2} \cos \left(\theta + \arctan \frac{B}{A} \right) \qquad (2\text{-}61)$$

The result in this case is

$$v(t) = \rho(t) \cos [2\pi f_c t + \theta(t)] \qquad (2\text{-}62)$$

where

$$\rho^2(t) = x^2(t) + y^2(t) \qquad (2\text{-}63)$$

and

$$\tan \theta(t) = \frac{y(t)}{x(t)} \qquad (2\text{-}64)$$

The function $\rho(t)$ is called the *envelope* of $v(t)$, and the function $\theta(t)$ is called the *phase deviation* or more simply the *phase*, when the frequency f_c is specified. The waves designated by $x(t)$ and $y(t)$ are called the *in-phase* and *quadrature* components, respectively.

We note that Eqs. (2-59) and (2-60) contain both positive and negative frequencies. To express $x(t)$ and $y(t)$ in terms of positive frequencies only, we rearrange the sums on the assumption that N is an even number. We thus obtain pairs of components with equal frequencies and random phase differences. The details are tedious but straightforward. We write

$$x(t) = \sum_{n=(N+2)/2}^{N} a_n \cos [2\pi(f_n - f_c)t + \phi_n]$$
$$+ \sum_{n=1}^{N/2} a_n \cos [2\pi(f_c - f_n)t - \phi_n]$$

Substitution of $n = m + N/2$ in the first summation and $n = 1 - m + N/2$ in the second yields

$$x(t) = \sum_{m=1}^{N/2} \{ a_{m+N/2} \cos [2\pi(f_{m+N/2} - f_c)t + \phi_{m+N/2}]$$
$$+ a_{1-m+N/2} \cos [2\pi(f_c - f_{1-m+N/2})t - \phi_{1-m+N/2}] \}$$

Since $f_{n+1} - f_n = \Delta f$, $f_n = f_1 + (n - 1)\,\Delta f$. Hence

$$f_c = \frac{f_1 + f_1 + (N - 1)\,\Delta f}{2} = f_1 + \frac{(N - 1)\,\Delta f}{2}$$

$$f_{m+N/2} = f_1 + \left(m - 1 + \frac{N}{2} \right) \Delta f$$

and

$$f_{1-m+N/2} = f_1 + \left(\frac{N}{2} - m\right) \Delta f$$

It follows that

$$f_{m+N/2} - f_c = f_c - f_{1-m+N/2} = (m - \tfrac{1}{2}) \Delta f \tag{2-65}$$

$$x(t) = \sum_{m=1}^{N/2} \{a_{m+N/2} \cos [2\pi(m - \tfrac{1}{2}) \Delta ft + \phi_{m+N/2}]$$

$$+ a_{1-m+N/2} \cos [2\pi(m - \tfrac{1}{2}) \Delta ft + \phi_{1-m+N/2}]\} \tag{2-66}$$

We can now find the spectral density function of $x(t)$ as a limit approached as N goes to infinity and Δf goes to zero. Two components of frequency $f_m = (m - \tfrac{1}{2}) \Delta f$ appear in $x(t)$. Their phases are random, and hence their mean-square amplitudes are additive. From (2-54)

$$a_{m+N/2}^2 = 2\Delta f \, w_v(f_{m+N/2}) = 2\Delta f \, w_v(f_c + f_m) \tag{2-67}$$
$$a_{1-m+N/2}^2 = 2\Delta f \, w_v(f_{1-m+N/2}) = 2\Delta f \, w_v(f_c - f_m) \tag{2-68}$$

The average power in bandwidth Δf is given by half the sum of (2-67) and (2-68). Hence dropping the subscript m for the limiting case in which Δf approaches zero, we have

$$w_x(f) = w_v(f_c + f) + w_v(f_c - f) \tag{2-69}$$

It should be clear that the same operations applied on $y(t)$ yield the same result, and hence that

$$w_y(f) = w_x(f) \tag{2-70}$$

The central limit theorem shows that both $x(t)$ and $y(t)$ become gaussian as $N \to \infty$ and $\Delta f \to 0$. We note, however, that the envelope $\rho(t)$ is a nonlinear function of $x(t)$ and $y(t)$ and hence is nongaussian. We can find the probability density function of the envelope by a transformation from the rectangular coordinates (x,y) to the polar coordinates (ρ,θ).

To do this, we first remark that the independence of x and y can be demonstrated from (2-59) and (2-60) by showing that $\mathbf{E}(xy) = 0$, a sufficient condition for the independence of gaussian processes. The joint probability $p(x,y)$ that $x(t)$ is in dx at x and $y(t)$ is in dy at y is therefore equal to $dx\,dy$ times the product of the pdf's of $x(t)$ and $y(t)$. Equation (2-70) shows that the standard deviation is the same for x as for y, since

$$\sigma_x{}^2 = \mathbf{E}x^2 = \int_0^\infty w_x(f)\,df = \int_0^\infty w_y(f)\,df = \mathbf{E}y^2 = \sigma_y{}^2 = \sigma^2 \tag{2-71}$$

Therefore, by multiplying two gaussian pdf's with mean zero and variance σ,

$$p(x,y)\ dx\ dy = \frac{1}{2\pi\sigma^2}\ e^{-(x^2+y^2)/2\sigma^2}\ dx\ dy \tag{2-72}$$

Equations (2-63) and (2-64) are the transformation equations from rectangular to polar coordinates and can be inverted to give

$$\begin{aligned} x &= \rho \cos \theta \\ y &= \rho \sin \theta \end{aligned} \tag{2-73}$$

with $dx\ dy = \rho\ d\rho\ d\theta$. Therefore,

$$\frac{1}{2\pi\sigma^2}\ e^{-(x^2+y^2)}\ dx\ dy = \frac{\rho e^{-\rho^2/2\sigma^2}\ d\rho\ d\theta}{2\pi\sigma^2} = p_\rho(\rho)\ d\rho\ p_\theta(\theta)\ d\theta \tag{2-74}$$

where

$$p_\rho(\rho) = \frac{\rho}{\sigma^2}\ e^{-\rho^2/2\sigma^2} \tag{2-75}$$

$$p_\theta(\theta) = \frac{1}{2\pi} \tag{2-76}$$

Equation (2-75) gives the pdf of the envelope of narrow-band gaussian noise. This pdf defines the *Rayleigh* distribution. Since ρ is restricted to nonnegative values, the PDF is

$$P_\rho(\rho) = \frac{1}{\sigma^2} \int_0^\rho \rho e^{-\rho^2/2\sigma^2}\ d\rho = 1 - e^{-\rho^2/2\sigma^2} \tag{2-77}$$

Equation (2-76) shows that the phase has a rectangular distribution with all angles equally likely.

A case of considerable practical importance is that of the envelope of the sum of a sine wave and narrow-band noise. Without loss of essential generality, we can consider the added sine wave $s_0(t) = a \cos 2\pi f_c t$. We write

$$\begin{aligned} s_0(t) + v(t) &= a \cos 2\pi f_c t + x(t) \cos 2\pi f_c t - y(t) \sin 2\pi f_c t \\ &= \rho(t) \cos [2\pi f_c t + \theta(t)] \end{aligned} \tag{2-78}$$

where now

$$\rho^2(t) = [a + x(t)]^2 + y^2(t) \tag{2-79}$$

$$\tan \theta(t) = \frac{y(t)}{a + x(t)} \tag{2-80}$$

A useful simplification occurs if a is large compared with $v(t)$ and hence also large compared with $x(t)$ and $y(t)$. We can then use the binomial series to obtain

$$
\begin{aligned}
\rho(t) &= [(a+x)^2 + y^2]^{1/2} = a\left[1 + \frac{2ax + x^2 + y^2}{a^2}\right]^{1/2} \\
&= a\left[1 + \frac{1}{1!}\frac{1}{2}\frac{2ax + x^2 + y^2}{a^2} \right. \\
&\qquad \left. + \frac{1}{2!}\left(\frac{1}{2}\right)\left(-\frac{1}{2}\right)\left(\frac{2ax + x^2 + y^2}{a^2}\right)^2 + \cdots\right] \\
&\approx a\left(1 + \frac{x}{a}\right) = a + x(t)
\end{aligned}
\tag{2-81}
$$

$$
\begin{aligned}
\theta(t) &= \arctan\frac{y}{a+x} = \frac{y}{a+x} - \frac{1}{3}\left(\frac{y}{a+x}\right)^3 + \cdots \\
&\approx \frac{y(t)}{a}
\end{aligned}
\tag{2-82}
$$

In the low-noise case, Eq. (2-81) shows that the envelope of a sine wave plus narrow-band gaussian noise is approximately gaussian with mean equal to a, the amplitude of the sine wave. The spectral density is given by Eq. (2-69) with f_c equal to the frequency of the sine wave. Equation (2-82) shows that under the same conditions the phase becomes approximately gaussian with zero mean and spectral density equal to $w_y(f)/a^2$. These results will be found useful in evaluating signal-to-noise ratios in signal-transmission systems of reasonably good quality.

2-5 THERMAL NOISE

As previously stated, thermal noise is the name given to the electrical noise originating from the random motion of electrons in a conductor. Since the number of electrons is large and their motions are practically independent of each other, the central limit theorem predicts a gaussian distribution. According to the kinetic theory of heat, thermal energy is stored in a body in the form of kinetic energy of the molecules. In the case of a conductor, there is a cloud of free electrons moving in equilibrium of energy exchange with the molecules. Description of this motion would require an exceedingly large number of coordinates. Such a problem comes within the province of statistical mechanics.

A statistical solution of a large mechanical system is found by introducing the *phase space*, which has a number of dimensions equal to the number of coordinates required to specify the state of the system. If the system is ergodic, we can identify relative volume in phase space with probability of assuming the corresponding states in time. A famous result obtained in this way is the *equipartition theorem* of classical statis-

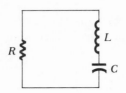

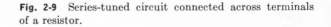

Fig. 2-9 Series-tuned circuit connected across terminals of a resistor.

tical mechanics. This theorem states that when the number of degrees of freedom is large, the average energy stored in each degree of freedom is $kT/2$, where k is Boltzmann's constant equal to 1.38×10^{-23} joules/°C and T is the absolute temperature. A degree of freedom is associated with every coordinate on which the energy depends quadratically.

Consider a conductor with resistance R. We propose to measure the spectral density of the thermal noise originating in the conductor by connecting a series-tuned circuit with inductance L and capacitance C across the terminal as shown in Fig. 2-9. We wait until thermal equilibrium is reached at some absolute temperature T. We note that we have added two new coordinates to the vast number already possessed by the resistor. The new coordinates may be chosen as the current i in the inductance L and the charge q of the capacitance C. The energy stored in the inductance is $Li^2/2$, and the energy stored in the capacitance is $q^2/(2C)$. Since the energy is a quadratic function of both these coordinates, each represents a degree of freedom. The equipartition theorem then says that

$$\frac{\mathbf{E}Li^2}{2} = \frac{\mathbf{E}q^2}{2C} = \frac{kT}{2} \tag{2-83}$$

Let us apply Thévenin's theorem from linear circuit theory to represent the conductor as a noise voltage source $v(t)$ in series with resistance R. The tuned circuit represents the analyzing filter, and the output voltage $v_n(t)$ is the voltage $Ri(t)$ across R. From (2-83)

$$\mathbf{E}v_n{}^2 = R^2\mathbf{E}i^2 = \frac{kTR^2}{L} \tag{2-84}$$

The transmittance function $H_n(f)$ turns out to be the function $RH(f)$, where $H(f)$ is the function defined by Eq. (1-84) of Chap. 1, with f_0 replaced by f_n; that is,

$$H_n(f) = \frac{jf/f_n}{Q(1 - f^2/f_n{}^2) + jf/f_n} \tag{2-85}$$

where

$$f_n = 2\pi(LC)^{-\frac{1}{2}} \quad \text{and} \quad Q = \frac{2\pi f_n L}{R} \tag{2-86}$$

Since $H_n(f_n) = 1$, the equivalent bandwidth of the measuring circuit, Eq. (2-38), is

$$\Delta f = \int_0^\infty |H_n(f)|^2 \, df = f_n \int_0^\infty \frac{x^2 \, dx}{Q^2(1 - x^2)^2 + x^2}$$

$$= f_n \int_0^\infty \frac{dx}{1 + Q^2(x - 1/x)^2} = f_n \int_{-\infty}^\infty \frac{e^z \, dz}{1 + Q^2(e^z - e^{-z})}$$

$$= f_n \int_{-\infty}^\infty \frac{(\cosh z + \sinh z) \, dz}{1 + 4Q^2 \sinh^2 z}$$

$$= \frac{f_n}{2Q} \int_{-\infty}^\infty \frac{d(2Q \sinh z)}{1 + (2Q \sinh z)^2} + f_n \int_{-\infty}^\infty \frac{\sinh z \, dz}{1 + 4Q^2 \sinh^2 z}$$

$$= \frac{f_n}{2Q} [\arctan (2Q \sinh z)]_{-\infty}^\infty = \frac{\pi f_n}{2Q} = \frac{R}{4L} \tag{2-87}$$

Substituting (2-84) and (2-87) in (2-37), we obtain finally

$$w_v(f) = \frac{kTR^2}{L} \frac{4L}{R} = 4kRT \tag{2-88}$$

This result, which was first discovered experimentally by J. B. Johnson[4] and derived theoretically by H. Nyquist,[5] is commonly stated in the form

$$\mathbf{E}v^2 = 4kRT \, \Delta f \tag{2-89}$$

where $\mathbf{E}v^2$ is the mean-square thermal noise voltage measured in a band of width Δf across a resistance R at absolute temperature T. The maximum amount of average power which the noise source can deliver to an external load is obtained when the resistor is terminated with an equal resistance R. This amount, which is called the available noise power in bandwidth Δf, is

$$\frac{\mathbf{E}v^2}{4R} = kT \, \Delta f \tag{2-90}$$

Equation (2-90) states that a resistor at a temperature of $T°K$ contains a source of available noise power with long-time average equal to $1.38 \times 10^{-23} \, T$ W/Hz of bandwidth throughout a very considerable range of frequencies. At a temperature of 17°C, the available power is 4×10^{-21} W/Hz. The formula indicates that the noise is white and that the total power is infinite. This is an example of the "ultraviolet catastrophe," which forced a modification of classical statistical mechanics to conform with reality. Quantum statistical mechanics has replaced the equipartition law by the Planck distribution function which multiplies kT by $hf/(e^{hf/kT} - 1)$, where h is Planck's constant equal to 6.6×10^{-27} erg-sec. The corrected version of (2-89) is

$$\frac{\mathbf{E}v^2}{4R} = \frac{hf \, \Delta f}{e^{hf/kT} - 1} \tag{2-91}$$

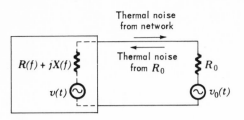

Fig. 2-10 General linear time-invariant network as a thermal noise source.

At room temperatures the correction is insignificant below 1 THz or 10^{12} Hz, but at $1°$K an appreciable difference begins at frequencies of 5 GHz or 5×10^9 Hz. At optical frequencies the thermal noise tends to disappear, and a different noise source associated with the corpuscular behavior of radiation becomes dominant.

In the range of temperatures and frequencies for which Eq. (2-90) holds, we can evaluate the mean-square total thermal noise voltage across any component of a linear time-invariant system by inserting voltage generators of mean-square value $4R_m kT \,\Delta f$ in series with every resistance R_m and summing the mean-square values thereby produced across the component. A simplified procedure derived originally by Nyquist represents any portion of the network by an equivalent noise generator in series with the open-circuit impedance of that portion. To derive the method, consider the circuit of Fig. 2-10 in which a resistance R_0 is connected across the terminals of a network with internal impedance $Z(f) = R(f) + jX(f)$. We insert a noise source with mean-square voltage $4R_0 kT \,df$ in series with R_0 and a noise source of mean-square voltage $w_z(f) \,df$ in series with $Z(f)$. We could calculate $w_z(f)$ if we knew the complete structure of the network, but as shown by Nyquist the second law of thermodynamics yields the desired result without specifying the structure. If the system is in equilibrium, the average noise power transmitted from left to right must be the same as that transmitted from right to left. This balance must hold not only for the total power but also for the average power flow in any band of frequencies. If there were any frequency interval in which an unbalance existed, insertion of a resonant circuit sharply tuned to pass only the frequencies in that interval would make perpetual motion possible.

A voltage $E_1 e^{j2\pi ft}$ in series with $Z(f)$ produces a current equal to $E_1 e^{j2\pi ft}/[Z(f) + R_0]$, thereby delivering to R_0 the average power $R_0|E_1|^2/|Z(f) + R_0|^2$. A voltage $E_2 e^{j2\pi ft}$ in series with R_0 produces a current equal to $E_2 e^{j2\pi ft}/[Z(f) + R_0]$, thereby delivering to $Z(f)$ the average power $R(f)|E_2|^2/|Z(f) + R_0|^2$. If we write $|E_1|^2 = w_z(f) \,df$ and $|E_2|^2 = 4R_0 kT \,df$, we obtain from the equality of the two values of average power dissipation that

$$\frac{R_0 w_z(f) \,df}{|Z(f) + R_0|^2} = \frac{4R(f)R_0 kT \,df}{|Z(f) + R_0|^2}$$

and hence

$$w_z(f) = 4R(f)kT \tag{2-92}$$

If a thermal noise source with internal impedance

$$Z(f) = R(f) + jX(f)$$

is applied as input to a linear time-invariant system as shown in Fig. 2-11, the average square of the resulting output noise current i is given by

$$\mathbf{E}i^2 = \int_0^\infty w_z(f)|Y(f)|^2 \, df$$
$$= 4kT \int_0^\infty R(f)|Y(f)|^2 \, df \tag{2-93}$$

where $Y(f)e^{j2\pi ft}$ is the output current produced by a voltage $e^{j2\pi ft}$ acting in series with $Z(f)$. Equation (2-93) gives only the noise contributed by $Z(f)$. If there are other noise sources in the system, their contributions must also be evaluated to find the total output noise power.

Although the total amount of thermal noise power is very small even when the band is wide, the effect becomes appreciable relative to the signal wave at the output of a channel if the channel attenuates the signal severely. If there were no noise, transmission could take place over an indefinitely great distance, and the signal could be made observable at the output by use of an amplifier with a sufficiently high gain. Thermal noise places a theoretical limit on how weak a recoverable signal can be. The theoretical limit is attainable only by an *ideal amplifier*, which amplifies the signal and noise impressed on its input circuit without introducing any new noise. Actual amplifiers are plagued by internal noise sources such as thermal noise from resistive components and shot noise due to irregular arrival times of discrete charge carriers. The resulting performance is worse than would be dictated by the thermal noise in the input circuit.

A convenient criterion for rating an amplifier relative to ideal noise performance is furnished by the *noise factor*, or *noise figure*, introduced by H. T. Friis.[6] Before explaining this widely used measure, we review some basic theorems and definitions pertaining to linear circuits. Consider the general case shown in Fig. 2-12 in which a source of signal and noise waves forms the input to an amplifier. By Thévenin's theorem,

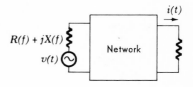

Fig. 2-11 Response of general linear time-invariant network to a thermal noise source.

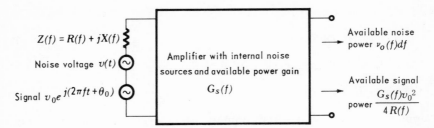

Fig. 2-12 Amplification of signal and noise.

the source can be represented by its open-circuit voltage acting in series
with the internal impedance $Z(f) = R(f) + jX(f)$. The maximum power
which the source can deliver to an external load is obtained when the
resistance is matched and the reactance is tuned out, i.e., when the load
impedance is $R(f) - jX(f)$. Alternatively, we could use Norton's theorem to represent the source by its short-circuit current acting in parallel
with the internal admittance $Y(f) = 1/Z(f)$.

We define the *available signal power* W_s from a source as the maximum average signal power which can be obtained. For the case of a
single-frequency signal component with open-circuit voltage $v_0 e^{j(2\pi ft + \theta_0)}$,

$$W_s = \left[\frac{v_0}{2R(f)} \right]^2 R(f) = \frac{v_0^2}{4R(f)} \tag{2-94}$$

Likewise, the *available noise power* $\nu(f)\,df$ in a band of width df centered
at f is the maximum obtainable average noise power in this band. If
the open-circuit noise voltage has spectral density $w(f)$,

$$\nu(f)\,df = \frac{w(f)\,df}{4R(f)} \tag{2-95}$$

For the case of thermal noise in a circuit at temperature T, $w(f)$ is given
by $w_z(f)$ in Eq. (2-92), and

$$\nu(f) = kT \tag{2-96}$$

The *available signal-to-noise ratio* ρ_s of the source in bandwidth f_1 to f_2 is
now defined by

$$\rho_s = \frac{W_s}{\int_{f_1}^{f_2} \nu(f)\,df} \tag{2-97}$$

For thermal noise at temperature T and bandwidth $f_2 - f_1 = b$,

$$\rho_s = \frac{W_s}{kTb} \tag{2-98}$$

When $\nu(f)$ is not constant, we can write for a narrow band of width Δf centered at f,

$$\rho_s(f) = \frac{W_s}{\nu(f)\,\Delta f} \tag{2-99}$$

We next introduce an appropriate set of terms describing the performance of an amplifier driven by the source for which we have defined the signal and noise parameters. We point out that there is no need of matching the amplifier input impedance to that of the source. In fact, most amplifiers operate as voltage- or current-controlled devices which absorb very little power from the input circuit. From the practical standpoint, it has been found best to include the input impedance conditions by defining the *available-power gain* of the amplifier for the specific input configuration used. The *available-power signal gain* $G_s(f)$ at frequency f is the ratio of *available signal power* $W_o(f)$ at the output of the amplifier to the *available signal power* $W_s(f)$ of the input circuit when the signal is a sinusoidal wave of frequency f; that is,

$$G_s(f) = \frac{W_o(f)}{W_s(f)} \tag{2-100}$$

Since a linear amplifier has no way of distinguishing between signal and noise waves, the noise input from the source is treated by the amplifier as a signal component. The result is an amplified noise component represented in the output by available noise power $G_s(f)\nu(f)\,df$ in bandwidth df at f. This is not the total amount of noise power in the amplifier output, however, because there are other noise sources inherent in the amplifying process. Let the density of the total available noise power of the amplifier output be $\nu_o(f)$, which is, in general, greater than $G_s(f)\nu(f)$. We then define the *spot noise factor*, or *spot noise figure*, $F(f)$ of the amplifier by

$$F(f) = \frac{\nu_o(f)}{G_s(f)\nu(f)} \tag{2-101}$$

For actual amplifiers $F(f) \geq 1$, and the merit of the amplifier at frequency f can be judged by how close the value of $F(f)$ is to unity. It is also common practice to express the noise factor in decibels (db) by $10\log_{10} F$. The best attainable value is then 0 db.

In practical situations the performance of the amplifier over a band of frequencies is important. This can be expressed by the *average noise figure*

$$F_0 = \frac{\displaystyle\int_0^\infty F(f)G_s(f)\,df}{\displaystyle\int_0^\infty G_s(f)\,df} \tag{2-102}$$

In the case of white noise and constant gain throughout a fixed band with zero gain at other frequencies, we can replace the functions of frequency by constants and obtain

$$F_0 = F = \frac{\nu_o}{G_s\nu} \tag{2-103}$$

The term *noise factor* is used in this case to mean either spot or average noise factor. In the case of thermal noise in the input circuit at absolute temperature T, the value of ν is kT, provided that hf/kT is small. If the bandwidth of the amplifier is b and the total available output noise power $\nu_o b$ is equal to N_o, we then find

$$F = \frac{N_o}{G_s kTb} \tag{2-104}$$

The term *standard noise factor* is applied when the value of T is 290°K.

Referring to Eq. (2-99), we see that the available signal-to-noise ratio $\rho_o(f)$ of the amplifier output in a narrow band of width Δf centered at f is given by

$$\rho_o(f) = \frac{G_s(f)W_s}{\nu_o(f)\Delta f} = \frac{G_s(f)W_s}{G_s(f)\nu(f)F(f)\,\Delta f} = \frac{\rho_s(f)}{F(f)} \tag{2-105}$$

The spot noise figure can thus be given the alternate definition

$$F(f) = \frac{\rho_s(f)}{\rho_o(f)} \tag{2-106}$$

which is a ratio of available signal-to-noise ratios at the input and output, respectively. Since $F(f) \geq 1$, the signal-to-noise ratio cannot increase, and usually decreases, with amplification.

It is often convenient to define an equivalent excess-noise input contribution $\nu_i(f)$ for an amplifier by

$$\nu_o(f) = G_s(f)[\nu(f) + \nu_i(f)]$$

or

$$\nu_i(f) = \frac{\nu_o(f)}{G_s(f)} - \nu(f) \tag{2-107}$$

From Eq. (2-101),

$$F(f) = 1 + \frac{\nu_i(f)}{\nu(f)} \qquad \text{and} \qquad \nu_i(f) = [F(f) - 1]\nu(f) \tag{2-108}$$

Insertion of the excess-noise component in the input circuit enables the amplifier to be treated as noiseless, i.e., with noise factor of unity.

Amplifiers commonly consist of successive stages. The principal impairment of signal-to-noise ratio occurs in the initial stages, where the signal is weak. We can treat the stages as individual amplifiers cascaded

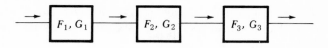

Fig. 2-13 Cascaded amplifier stages.

as shown in Fig. 2-13 with the nth stage having noise factor F_n and available signal-power gain G_n. The $(n + 1)$st stage has for its input a source with available noise power ν_{on} equal to the available noise power in the output of the nth stage. The amplifiers can be regarded as noiseless if we add the equivalent excess noise $\nu_{in} = (F_n - 1)\nu$ of Eq. (2-108) to the available noise power in the input to the nth stage. It follows that

$$\nu_{on} = G_n(\nu_{o,n-1} + \nu_{in}) = G_n[\nu_{o,n-1} + (F_n - 1)\nu] \qquad (2\text{-}109)$$

and the noise factor for the n-stage amplifier is

$$F = \frac{\nu_{on}}{G_1 G_2 \cdots G_n \nu} \qquad (2\text{-}110)$$

Beginning with $\nu_{o1} = G_1 F_1 \nu$ from Eq. (2-101), we compute successively

$$\begin{aligned}
\nu_{o1} &= G_1 F_1 \nu \\
\nu_{o2} &= G_2(G_1 F_1 + F_2 - 1)\nu \\
\nu_{o3} &= G_3[G_2(G_1 F_1 + F_2 - 1) + F_3 - 1]\nu \qquad \text{etc.}
\end{aligned} \qquad (2\text{-}111)$$

and find the general rule

$$F = F_1 + \frac{F_2 - 1}{G_1} + \frac{F_3 - 1}{G_1 G_2} + \cdots \qquad (2\text{-}112)$$

Equation (2-112) shows that if the first stage of the amplifier has a high gain, the noise figure for the complete amplifier is practically the same as that of the first stage. A first stage with low gain makes the noise figure of the second stage important, and if the combined gain of the first and second stages is low, the noise figure of the third stage must be considered. The argument proceeds progressively until sufficient gain is built up to make further excess-noise contributions negligible.

2-6 STATISTICAL REPRESENTATION OF NOISE IN THE TIME DOMAIN

We previously remarked that second-order statistics of noise can be more simply treated in the frequency domain than in the time domain. However, statisticians dealing with time series which have noise-like properties have developed a time-domain treatment with interesting features complementing the frequency-domain theory. Let $v(t)$ represent a member of an ergodic ensemble of noise waves which could exist in a system. We introduce the two-dimensional probability distribution function $P(v_1, v_2)$

representing the joint probability that $v(t_1)$ and $v(t_2)$ are not greater than v_1 and v_2, respectively. The stationarity of the process ensures that $P(v_1,v_2)$ does not depend on t_1 and t_2 separately but only on their difference $\tau = t_2 - t_1$. We also introduce a joint probability density function $p(v_1,v_2)$ which when multiplied by $dv_1\, dv_2$ gives the joint probability that $v(t_1)$ and $v(t_2)$ are in intervals of width dv_1 and dv_2 centered at v_1 and v_2, respectively. Analogous to the first-order probability relations, we have the equations

$$P(v_1,v_2) = \int_{-\infty}^{v_1} \int_{-\infty}^{v_2} p(v_1,v_2)\, dv_1\, dv_2$$

$$p(v_1,v_2) = \frac{\partial^2 P(v_1,v_2)}{\partial v_1\, \partial v_2}$$

$$P(-\infty,-\infty) = 0 \qquad P(\infty,\infty) = 1 \tag{2-113}$$

$$\mathbf{E}F(v_1,v_2) = \int_{-\infty}^{\infty} \int_{-\infty}^{\infty} F(v_1,v_2)p(v_1,v_2)\, dv_1\, dv_2$$

An important second-order statistical property in the time-domain description of noise is the mathematical expectation of the product $v_1 v_2$. For an ergodic process, we can calculate this expectation in two ways. We can let t_1 and t_2 be fixed and average over the ensemble of all possible noise waves to obtain the result

$$\mathbf{E}v_1 v_2 = \int_{-\infty}^{\infty} p(v_1,v_2)v_1 v_2\, dv_1\, dv_2 \tag{2-114}$$

We can also consider t_1 and t_2 given all possible values for a single noise wave $v(t)$ and obtain

$$\mathbf{E}v_1 v_2 = \lim_{T \to \infty} \frac{1}{T} \int_{-T/2}^{T/2} v(t)v(t + \tau)\, dt \tag{2-115}$$

We recall that in Sec. 1-3 we defined the autocorrelation function $R_{xx}(\tau)$ for a finite-energy signal $x(t)$ as the integral of $x(t)x(t + \tau)$ over all time. In the case of a noise wave, the integral does not converge, but the limiting process of Eq. (2-115), in which the integral over a finite interval is divided by the width of the interval, does approach a finite value if $v(t)v(t + \tau)$ has a finite average. We therefore extend the nomenclature of Sec. 1-3 by defining $\mathbf{E}v_1 v_2$ as $R_v(\tau)$, the autocorrelation function of the noise source $v(t)$.

It was deduced from Sec. 1-3, Eq. (1-35), that $R_{xx}(\tau)$ was the Fourier transform of $|X(f)|^2$. In the case of a noise wave, the Fourier transform does not exist. However, $|V_T(f)|^2/T$ is the Fourier transform of the integral of $v_T(t)v_T(t + \tau)/T$, where $v_T(t)$ is the noise wave truncated to an interval of width T. We write this statement as

$$\frac{R_{v_T v_T}(\tau)}{T} = \frac{1}{T} \int_{-\infty}^{\infty} |V_T(f)|^2 e^{j2\pi f \tau}\, df \tag{2-116}$$

As noted in Sec. 2-3, we cannot take the limit of this equation directly as T goes to infinity. We must first average over the ensemble of noise waves to obtain

$$\frac{\mathbf{E}R_{v_T v_T}(\tau)}{T} = \frac{1}{T} \int_{-\infty}^{\infty} \mathbf{E}|V_T(f)|^2 e^{j2\pi f\tau} \, df \tag{2-117}$$

The limit for infinite T then gives

$$R_v(\tau) = \int_{-\infty}^{\infty} u_v(f) e^{j2\pi f\tau} \, df \tag{2-118}$$

where

$$u_v(f) = \lim_{T \to \infty} \frac{\mathbf{E}|V_T(f)|^2}{T} \tag{2-119}$$

By comparison with (2-45), we see that $u_v(f)$ is half of the one-sided spectral density function $w_v(f)$. Hence the autocorrelation function is the Fourier transform of the two-sided spectral density function. By inversion

$$u_v(f) = \int_{-\infty}^{\infty} R_v(\tau) e^{-j2\pi f\tau} \, d\tau \tag{2-120}$$

PROBLEMS

2-1. A noise wave has probability density function $p(v) = ke^{-|v|/v_0}$ with $v_0 > 0$.
    (a) Express k in terms of v_0.
    (b) What is $P(v)$?
    (c) Find $\mathbf{E}v$.
    (d) Find $\mathbf{E}v^2$.
    (e) Find $\mathbf{E}\cos(v/v_0)$.

2-2. A rectangular wave $v(t)$ alternates between the values v_1 and v_2. A sample taken at random has probability p_1 of having the value v_1.
    (a) What is the probability that a random sample is equal to v_2.
    (b) Making use of the δ function, write an expression for the probability density function of $v(t)$.
    (c) What is the PDF?
    (d) Calculate $\mathbf{E}v$ and $\mathbf{E}v^2$.

2-3. Given two independent noise waves $x(t)$ and $y(t)$, with probability distribution functions $P_1(x)$ and $P_2(y)$ defined by

$$P_1(x) = \begin{cases} 0 & x < -a \\ \dfrac{1}{2}\left(1 + \sin\dfrac{\pi x}{2a}\right) & -a < x < a \\ 1 & a < x \end{cases}$$

$$P_2(y) = \begin{cases} 0 & y < -a \\ \dfrac{1}{2}\left(1 + \dfrac{y}{a}\right) & -a < y < a \\ 1 & a < y \end{cases}$$

find the mean value and the variance of $z(t) = x(t) + y(t)$.

2-4. What is the mean value and variance of the envelope of narrow-band zero-mean gaussian noise with variance σ^2?

2-5. What is the rms thermal noise voltage across the parallel combination of a 1000-ohm resistor, a 1-H inductor, and a 1-μF capacitor at a temperature of 23°C?

2-6. If the thermal noise in a resistor is represented by Norton's theorem as a short-circuit current $i(t)$ in parallel with the conductance $G = 1/R$, what is the spectral density function $w_i(f)$ of $i(t)$?

2-7. The first stage of a two-stage amplifier has a gain of 10 and a noise factor of 1.1. The second stage has a gain of 5 and a noise factor of 1.5.

  (a) What is the noise factor of the amplifier?

  (b) What would the noise factor be if the order of the stages were interchanged?

2-8. What is the noise factor of a purely resistive attenuator which when connected to a source has available signal output power equal to $1/A$ times that of the source?

REFERENCES

1. Bennett, W. R.: "Electrical Noise," McGraw-Hill, New York, 1960.
2. Bennett, W. R.: Methods of Solving Noise Problems, *Proc. IRE*, vol. 44, pp. 609–638, May, 1956.
3. Cramer, H.: "Mathematical Methods of Statistics," Princeton University Press, Princeton, N.J., 1951.
4. Johnson, J. B.: Thermal Agitation of Electricity in Conductors, *Phys. Rev.*, vol. 32, pp. 97–109, July, 1928.
5. Nyquist, H.: Thermal Agitation of Electric Charge in Conductors, *Phys. Rev.*, vol. 32, pp. 110–113, July, 1928.
6. Friis, H. T.: Noise Figures of Radio Receivers, *Proc. IRE*, vol. 32, pp. 419–422, July, 1944.

3
Baseband Transmission of Telephone Signals

Basic communication between human beings takes place by means of sound and light waves which constitute signals of the continuous type. These continuous signals are typically used, however, to express words or signs which have a discrete set of meanings. In the early history of communication over distances too great for conventional conversation, discrete coding methods were established to represent the desired words or signs by drumbeats, smoke puffs, or light flashes suitable for remote observation. The first electrical transmission of signals was naturally a continuation of the coding method and led to the development of electric telegraphy, which is based on the transmission and reception of discrete symbols. Analog transmission, in which the original signal waves are represented by electrical replicas, was introduced with the invention of the telephone and has since been developed as the general method of dealing with acoustic and visual information. The principles will be made clearer by examining in detail the nature of the signals in the three important categories of telegraphy, telephony, and television.

We use the term *baseband*, originally suggested by Goodall, to designate the band of frequencies representing the original signal as delivered by the source.   In baseband transmission the frequency range of the channel is the same as that of the signal, and no frequency translation such as used in carrier systems is needed.   In the case of telegraph signals, the baseband consists of the band of frequencies emitted by the telegraph transmitter.   In telephony the baseband is the voice band or audio band, and in television the baseband is the video band.

If we were to follow the historical order of development, our first study of communication systems would deal with telegraphy.   However, mature understanding of the telegraph problem did not actually evolve until considerable progress had been made in the transmission of analog signals.   Although present-day knowledge provides a satisfactory basis for an introduction to communication by way of digital signaling, the description of pulse transmission in terms of the frequency domain is initially more difficult than the corresponding discussion of analog signals. Accordingly, we shall begin with telephony and defer telegraphy to the following chapter.

In telephonic communication the signals to be transmitted are of the continuous or analog type.   The principal source is the sound produced by the human voice, and the ultimate destination is the human ear.   The sound waves are converted into electric waves by a *microphone* or *telephone transmitter* placed near the speaker's mouth, and the electric waves are converted back into acoustic form by a *reproducer* or *telephone receiver* near the listener's ear.   The goal of the transmission system is to deliver signals which make the telephone channel an acceptable substitute for face-to-face conversation.

3-1 EFFECT OF BANDWIDTH ON TELEPHONE QUALITY

The primary standards for measuring the quality of a telephone channel depend on subjective tests.   The problem can be separated into basic parts by study of (1) the waves which various human voices can produce, (2) the waves which human ears can hear, and (3) the fidelity with which the waves must be reproduced to enable satisfactory communication by telephone.   It should be noted with regard to item 2 that the ear can hear a wider variety of sounds than the human vocal apparatus generates and that electrical transmission of these other sounds is also an important problem, particularly in the entertainment field.   The term *program channel* is customarily applied to facilities which transmit music and other audible waves in addition to voice.   The requirements on a program channel are typically more severe than on a *voice* or *message* channel.

Transmission of audio signals can conveniently be described in terms of response to sinusoidal components.   The spectrum of a speech wave is not a very definite thing because of the wide variations between individual talkers and between the different sounds emitted by a single talker. Laboratory measurements of the spectral density function and the spectral distribution function of speech waves have been made by inserting narrow bandpass filters followed by average-power-indicating meters in the microphone output circuit. These readings have then been averaged for different talkers.

The terms spectral density and spectral distribution are applied here to speech waves in the same way as was defined for noise in the preceding chapter. Figure 3-1, which includes results for three male and three female voices, is a rudimentary example of the sort of results[1] which have been obtained. It will be noted that the average spectral density for the measured voices approaches zero at zero frequency and is peaked in the neighborhood of a few hundred hertz. However, the relative importance of the different components is not necessarily revealed by such measurements.

The properties of the ear are illustrated by experimental curves of threshold of hearing and feeling such as shown in Fig. 3-2. Data for these curves are obtained from tests in which different individuals listen to single-frequency tones in a quiet room. The sound pressure of each tone is varied over a sufficient range to determine the minimum intensity at which the tone can be heard and the intensity at which the sensation

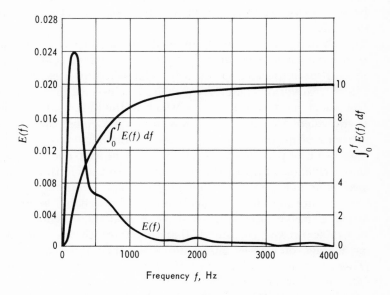

Fig. 3-1 Average of energy-versus-frequency distribution for representative talkers. $E(f)\, df$ is energy in band of width df at frequency f.

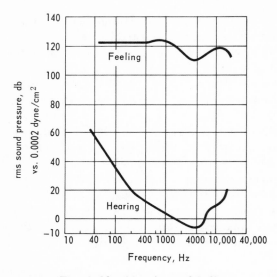

Fig. 3-2 Thresholds of hearing and feeling.

of hearing is replaced by one of pain. Hearing occurs in the region bounded by the two curves, which are designated as the *threshold* of *hearing* and the *threshold* of *feeling*, respectively. If the capabilities of the ear are to be fully utilized, the intensity and frequency ranges comprised between the two thresholds must be within the capabilities of the channel.

As we have previously implied, satisfactory voice transmission can be accomplished without delivering all the sounds that the ear can hear. Quantitative specifications can be established by listening tests in which filters with various cutoff frequencies are inserted in a substantially perfect telephone system; i.e., one which in the judgment of expert listeners is equivalent to a direct transmission path through the air. A practical criterion of telephone quality is the intelligibility of the received speech. Tests can be performed on intelligibility of sentences, words, and syllables. Syllables furnish the most severe test since the influence of context as an aid in recognition is minimized.

Figure 3-3 shows typical results of a syllabic articulation test in which a speaker pronounces the syllables at the transmitter, and a group of listeners record the sounds that they think the receiver delivers. The percentage of correct observations is called the "sound articulation." This would not necessarily be 100 percent for direct transmission by air. The curve marked "high pass," obtained by varying the cutoff frequency of a high-pass filter inserted in the channel, shows the effect of removing the low-frequency components of the speech. The indication is that the frequencies below 300 Hz are not very important. The curve marked "low pass" exhibits the effect of suppressing the high frequencies and indicates that not much additional articulation efficiency is contributed above 3500 Hz.

It appears from the curves of Fig. 3-3 that a band from say 300 to 3500 Hz gives very good articulation. Indeed, it is found that telephone circuits which respond well to this range of frequencies give quite satisfactory commercial telephone service. Many circuits in use today transmit a considerably narrower band. There is, of course, some loss in naturalness of the speaker's voice because some component frequencies are either lacking or greatly attenuated. A satisfactory reproduction of music requires a considerably wider range including both lower and higher frequencies. For this reason special program-transmission channels are provided for services needing greater fidelity in the restoration of the original sound waves than suffices for mere intelligibility of speech. The band of frequencies for high-quality program facilities may extend from frequencies as low as 30 Hz to frequencies as high as 15 kHz.

The fact that the frequencies from zero to a few hundred Hz do not contribute much to intelligibility is of great importance in telephone transmission, for it enables the use of circuits containing transformers and blocking condensers of reasonably small size. These components perform very useful functions in matching impedances and in isolating

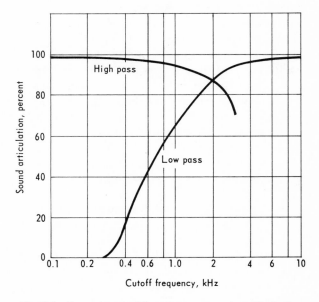

Fig. 3-3 Importance of frequency range in articulation.

battery potentials. Their use with considerable impunity in telephone circuits contrasts with telegraph practice, in which frequencies down to and including zero frequency are often essential. We shall also see later that trimming off the low-frequency edge of the band is of great utility in single-sideband transmitter design.

3-2 INFLUENCE OF PHASE IN TELEPHONE TRANSMISSION

The curves of Figs. 3-1 to 3-3 express only magnitude-vs.-frequency relationships. The relation between phase and frequency, which is of great importance in waveform preservation, is not of first-order significance in telephony because of the way in which the human ear operates. There is considerable experimental evidence that a spatial separation of the positions of maximum response to different frequencies exists along the basilar membrane, somewhat as shown in Fig. 3-4. The result may be roughly described by saying that the ear hears tones of different frequencies independently and is not influenced by the instantaneous waveform of the sum. A law sometimes ascribed to Ohm and sometimes to Helmholtz embodies this phenomenon in the statement that the sensation of the ear from a set of superimposed sine waves of different frequencies is independent of the phase relationships between the components. The law is not to be regarded as rigorously exact and was not so stated by either of the original proponents. It has been demonstrated experimentally that certain special kinds of waveforms exist in which a single ear can detect the phase relationship between steady-state components. It is well known also that binaural hearing properties enabling spatial location of sound sources depend on phase-sensitive response of the two ears. Duplication of these effects would require separate transmission channels for each ear and have as yet not become important in telephony.

A more serious exception is the case in which the phase distortion, or departure from linear variation of phase with frequency, is very large. As discussed in Sec. 1-6, a distortionless channel has a delay between the

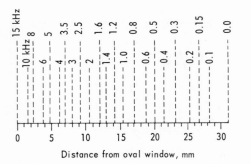

Fig. 3-4 Characteristic frequency regions of the basilar membrane.

received and incident signals equal to the slope of the curve of phase shift in radians plotted against frequency in radians per second. When the distortionless conditions do not hold, we can divide the spectrum into small elements over which linear phase shift and uniform transmission approximately exist. It appears then that if the slope of the phase curve varies widely with frequency, the different elementary portions of the spectrum will actually arrive at the destination at different times. Under such conditions the spectrum of a speech syllable might be drawn out along the time scale to such an extent that the ear actually hears different parts of the syllable at different times. Effects of this type are observed, for example, on long loaded-cable circuits, in which the arrival of the high-frequency components is appreciably retarded. A syllable or other impulsive excitation is then accompanied by a whistling sound resembling the chirping of birds. Experimental investigation has shown that the total variation of phase slope over the speech band must be at least several milliseconds before the effect can be recognized by an observer, and that considerably greater variation could take place before an appreciable diminution in articulation efficiency occurs. It is important to recognize, however, that phase distortion must be kept within bounds even on telephone circuits.

The relative immunity of telephonic performance to moderate amounts of phase distortion has greatly simplified the general problem of providing adequate circuits over a variety of conditions. As a result there is today a considerable lack of uniformity in phase characteristics of telephone channels. There would be no point in specifying any more rigid control over phase than now exists as long as the use of the circuits is confined to voice transmission. The prospective customer who wishes to send telegraph pulses over a dialed telephone channel must resign himself to a substantially slower signaling rate than indicated by the nominal bandwidth in terms of magnitude alone.

While on the subject of phase shift, we should further remark that the absolute delay which would be incurred because of a linear-phase shift in transmission is also of interest. A telephone conversation is a two-way affair, and the talker and listener exchange roles at intervals of time. It is disturbing if the time delay is so great that each participant thinks the other unnaturally sluggish in replying. For this reason transmission delays greater than about 250 msec are regarded as intolerable in telephone systems. This requirement has an important bearing on theoretical means of improving the information rate by exploiting the statistical properties of speech signals. In order to be permissible, such procedures must be carried out with sufficient speed to keep the total transmission delay within the allowed limit. Also, since regularity in statistics requires a certain minimum number of samples, we might not be able to accumulate enough data within the allowed time for making the process effective without combining signals from a considerable number of channels.   Hence it would be expected that statistical methods have more potential value on a large multiplex than on a system with a small number of channels.

In yet another aspect, the amount of delay has a profound influence upon telephone plant design.   This is the effect of what is known as "talker echo."   It occurs on any low-loss circuit when, as usually is the case, the far end or some intermediate point presents an impedance discontinuity that reflects part of the energy of the oncoming speech waves.   A person speaking into the telephone will then hear a delayed version of his own voice.   This has been found to be extremely annoying to the talker.   Curves have been plotted from experiments with groups of people to show the tolerable echo delay as a function of the intensity of the echo which is heard.   One way of minimizing the difficulty is to increase the loss in the talking path.   Thus a 6-db increase in loss will decrease the echo 12 db because it encounters both the "go" and "return" paths.   Increase of loss is undesirable from the standpoint of the listener, however, and cannot be carried very far.   On long circuits where the echo delay would be intolerable, independent paths are provided for the two directions of transmission, and the path not in use is disabled by *echo suppressors* actuated by voice-operated relays.

3-3 EFFECT OF NOISE IN TELEPHONE CHANNELS

Since a voice signal is an analog wave, the concept of an error rate caused by noise in the channel is inapplicable.   The effect of noise is subjective and requires experimental evaluation.   It is appropriate to describe the results of experiments in terms of the ratio of signal power to noise power, but a considerable question arises with regard to what measure of signal power should be used.   The short-term average speech power varies widely for different sounds and for different speakers.

As a general principle, averaging operations performed on an intermittent process such as speech should take into account the nature of the intended receiver.   The human ear requires about 0.2 sec to register the full effect of a suddenly applied tone.   This suggests that an integration time of 0.2 sec is appropriate for sound meters.   A type of instrument in widespread use for measurement of speech and music is the *volume indicator* or *vu meter*, which is calibrated in *volume units*, abbreviated as vu and pronounced "vee-you."   The vu meter includes a full-wave rectifier, a weighting network, a calibrated attenuator, and a d-c meter. The dynamic response to tones of short duration is matched to the properties of the ear and is not translatable, in general, to an average power measurement. For a steady tone at a frequency of 1 kHz, the meter reads a steady value of 0 vu when the mean power is 1 mW, and, in general, the volume in vu of a 1-kHz tone is equal to the mean power in *dbm*, or "decibels above 1 milliwatt." This equivalence is, in fact, approximately valid for single-frequency tones throughout the entire range from 25 Hz to 16 kHz. When speech or music is applied, the reading fluctuates and the attenuator is adjusted until the peak deflections just reach the 0-vu mark. The corresponding attenuator setting is read as the volume in vu.

The vu meter is also used to measure noise, with or without a frequency-weighting network to evaluate the interfering effects of the various components. One standard of reference is the interfering effect of a tone with a frequency of 1 kHz and an average power of 1 $\mu\mu$W (10^{-12} W). This tone is called "reference noise" or "rn." Noise waves are measured in "decibels above reference noise" (dbrn) by determining the loss in decibels which must be inserted between the noise source and the point of observation to make the interfering effect equivalent to that of reference noise. Frequency-weighting networks which can be used with the vu meter to make the reading in vu convertible to dbrn are determined experimentally by judgment tests with many observers.

The speech volume as registered by the vu meter at a specified point in a telephone channel varies widely among different talkers. It is often convenient to refer instead to the average power of a full-load sine wave at that point. In any physical approximation to a linear system, the input amplitude cannot be increased indefinitely without causing an observable departure from linearity. Nonlinearity in a telephone channel can originate in various components, e.g., the transmitter, receiver, amplifiers, and iron-cored inductors. The onset of overload is more or less gradual and can be defined precisely only by an arbitrary specification of a critical amount of nonlinearity. The definition often used is the "1-decibel compression point" for a 1-kilohertz tone. The measurement is made by applying a 1-kHz sine wave at various input power levels and using a frequency analyzer to determine the amount of average output power at 1 kHz. Overload is said to occur when the ratio of average output power to average input power is 1 db less than when the input power is low.

The full-load power appropriate for a satisfactory voice channel depends on the loudness of the talker, the nature of the telephone instruments, the lengths of the lines between the telephone stations and the central office, and the noise present on the channel. Empirical judgments based on tests of the population of talkers and channels are necessary to establish requirements. A representative value for the standard full-load 1-kHz test tone at a switching point, i.e., where connections would be made between the circuits of two talkers, is 9.5 db above 1 mW or 9.5 dbm. The speech volumes at this point have approximately a gaussian distribution with a mean of -10 vu and a standard deviation of 6 vu. Loud talkers with a volume of as much as 7 vu may be occasionally encountered, and it is better that they overload the system somewhat rather than allow the extremely weak talkers to be obliterated by noise.

It would be a considerable advantage in the operation of a telephone system if the variations in the volume of different talkers or in the volume of a single talker at different times could be substantially reduced. One device which has been developed for this purpose is the *vogad* or *voice-operated gain adjuster*. A vogad includes circuitry for continuous measurement of the short-term average signal power and derivation of a corresponding electrical control signal to regulate either the gain of an amplifier or the loss of an attenuator in the voice path. The cost and complication of a vogad would be justified in an expensive transoceanic radio or cable channel in which nearly constant input volume is a very important requirement. The smoothing out of the variations deprives the listener of the emotional impact which the changes in loudness might imply, but does not affect intelligibility.

One important advantage obtainable by regulating the power in voice waves is an improvement in the signal-to-noise ratio for weak signals. The loudest talkers naturally get the benefit of the highest signal-to-noise ratio provided by the system. A comparable performance for weak talkers can be attained by increasing the gain of a transmitting amplifier to a value at which the system approaches overload when the signal is weak. For best results, the gain would be adjusted continuously with minimum gain for high volume and maximum gain for low volume. A device which operates in this way is called a *compressor* because it compresses the range of variation in signal power. A complementary device which has more gain for strong signals than for weak is called an *expander*. A compressor at the transmitter and a complementary expander at the receiver form a *compandor*, which can be designed to deliver the full variation in the original signal at the destination. The object of the compandor is to provide an increased signal-to-noise ratio for weak signals.

A compandor is an example of a combination of nonlinear devices capable of linear behavior when viewed from the input and output terminals. Compandors can be classified as *instantaneous* or *syllabic*. Instantaneous compressors and expanders are zero-memory nonlinear devices specified by response-vs.-stimulus characteristics of form

$$r(t) = F[s(t)] \tag{3-1}$$

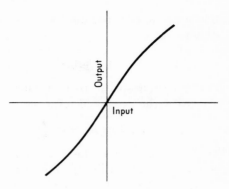

Fig. 3-5 Typical characteristic of a compressor.

The nature of the function $F(x)$ is shown in Fig. 3-5 for a compressor and in Fig. 3-6 for an expander. Since amplification is proportional to the slope of $F(x)$, the essential identifying feature of a compressor is that the derivative $F'(x)$ decreases as $|x|$ increases. Similarly, for an expander, $F'(x)$ increases as $|x|$ increases.

An example of a compressor characteristic is

$$F(x) = a|x|^{1/\nu}\operatorname{sgn} x \qquad \nu > 1 \qquad a > 0 \tag{3-2}$$

(See Prob. 1-2 for a definition of the signum function.)

$$F'(x) = \frac{a}{\nu}|x|^{(1-\nu)/\nu} \qquad x \neq 0 \tag{3-3}$$

Since $1/\nu < 1$, $F'(x)$ decreases as $|x|$ increases. A corresponding example for an expander is

$$F(x) = b|x|^{\nu}\operatorname{sgn} x \qquad \nu > 1 \qquad b > 0 \tag{3-4}$$

with

$$F'(x) = b\nu|x|^{\nu-1} \qquad x \neq 0 \tag{3-5}$$

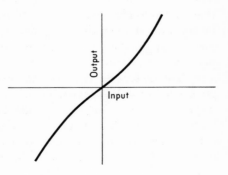

Fig. 3-6 Typical characteristic of an expander.

If $s(t)$ is applied as input to the compressor defined by Eq. (3-2), the response is

$$r_c(t) = a|s(t)|^{1/\nu} \operatorname{sgn} s(t) \tag{3-6}$$

If this response is, in turn, applied as input to the expander defined by Eq. (3-4), the expanded response is

$$r_e(t) = b|r_c(t)|^\nu \operatorname{sgn} r_c(t) = ba^\nu|s(t)| \operatorname{sgn} s(t) = ba^\nu s(t) \tag{3-7}$$

The combination of the $1/\nu$- and ν-power laws thus produces a companding system which is linear between input and output terminals. The amount of compression and expansion increases with ν. For very large values of ν, the transmitted signal is compressed to an almost rectangular wave, but enough variation remains to allow complete recovery when the very large complementary expansion is applied.

The suppression of noise can be illustrated in the general case by assuming complementary functions of the form $F(x)$ for the compressor and $G(x)$ for the expander, where

$$G[F(x)] = x \tag{3-8}$$

Then if a noise wave $v(t)$ is added in the channel,

$$r_e(t) = G\{F[s(t)] + v(t)\} \tag{3-9}$$

In useful voice channels the additive noise in the channel should be small relative to the signal most of the time. If $|v(t)|$ is small relative to $|F[s(t)]|$, a Taylor's series expansion about the point at $F[s(t)]$ gives the approximation

$$r_e(t) \approx G\{F[s(t)]\} + \frac{dG\{F[s(t)]\}}{dF[s(t)]} v(t) = s(t) + \frac{v(t)}{F'[s(t)]} \tag{3-10}$$

The additive noise is thus divided by the factor $F'[s(t)]$, which increases as $|s(t)|$ decreases. In effect, the gain of the receiver to noise picked up in the channel is controlled by the signal and becomes low when the signal is weak. This action is possible because the externally linear system is nonlinear for internally applied waves. The noise must be initially smaller than the signal; the compandor can then make the noise still smaller and thereby convert poor performance into good performance.

The listener's reaction to noise varying with signal strength is governed by the psychological masking effect which loud sounds impress on weak sounds. When the signal is faint, the ear can hear low-level noise, but when the intensity of the signal is increased, the ear becomes insensitive to a higher noise background. Therefore, the compandor works in the right direction to improve reception of speech in the presence of noise.   The most disturbing noise is that heard when the speech is weak or even absent altogether, and the compandor reduces this noise to a very low level.   When the speech is louder, the noise also becomes louder, but since the loud speech masks the noise increment, the listener is unaware of the change in noise.

The difficulty with instantaneous companding is that the compressed wave must be transmitted through the channel without distortion of waveform.   Otherwise the expansion function would not recover $s(t)$. The bandwidth occupied by $F[s(t)]$ is, in general, greater than that of $s(t)$ because a nonlinear operation on sinusoidal components produces harmonics as well as sum and difference products outside the original band.   Straightforward transmission of the compressed signal through a band of the same width as that of the original signal removes the out-of-band products, and complementary expansion is no longer possible.   By a theorem of Beurling,[2] it is possible to recover the uncompressed signal uniquely from the band-limited response to the compressed signal, but this requires an iterative approximation imposing a considerable delay. Also, if samples of $F[s(t)]$ can be transmitted at a rate equal to twice the bandwidth of $s(t)$, the signal can be recovered by expanding the samples, as will be discussed in a later chapter on pulse modulation.   Both these methods require a distortionless channel and, therefore, introduce a stringent requirement on phase linearity foreign to widespread practice in analog voice transmission.

In a syllabic compandor the gain changes are made slowly under control of the envelope of the speech wave rather than the instantaneous values.   The bandwidth of the compressed signal is only slightly increased, and no new requirements on waveform preservation are introduced.   The operation can be illustrated by considering an idealized case in which a signal is represented over a finite time interval by a sine wave, say,

$$s(t) = A \cos \omega_s t \tag{3-11}$$

A syllabic compressor is designed to give a response of form $F(A) \cos \omega_s t$ to this wave instead of $F(A \cos \omega_s t)$ as would occur in an instantaneous compressor.   The syllabic device has the advantage that no harmonics of ω_s are produced.   If A changes slowly with time, there is only a slight spreading of the spectrum of the compressed wave about the frequency ω_s.

The essential ingredients of a syllabic compressor include an envelope detector for recovering the slowly varying amplitude of a speech wave and a device with variable loss or gain controlled by the speech envelope to give less gain when the envelope is large.   A syllabic expander is similar except that the gain is increased when the envelope is large.

Even a short segment of a speech wave cannot be represented by such a simple function as indicated by Eq. (3-11).   However, from the physiological nature of speech production, the rates at which changes are made in the vocal tract are inherently slow compared with the oscillation frequencies emitted by the larynx. This suggests that an appropriate short-term representation of form

$$s(t) = A(t) \cos [\omega_s t + \phi(t)] \tag{3-12}$$

is justifiable for the part of the voice spectrum in which most of the energy is concentrated. The amplitude and phase functions $A(t)$ and $\phi(t)$ are composed of frequencies which are relatively small compared with ω_s, which is centrally located in a high-energy part of the voice band.

A mathematical demonstration of the intuitively evident fact that the syllabic compandor reduces noise when the signal is weak is more complicated in detail than the corresponding argument for instantaneous companding. It is necessary to show how the envelope is affected by the noise. The solution of this problem has been given in Sec. 2-4 for the case of gaussian noise. In Eq. (2-78), we can replace $s_0(t)$ by the compressed signal $F[A(t)] \cos [\omega_s t + \phi(t)]$, which enables us to identify a with $F[A(t)]$ and $2\pi f_c t$ with $\omega_s t + \phi(t)$. The response of the expander to the compressed signal with additive gaussian noise is then given by

$$r_e(t) = G[\rho(t)] \cos [\omega_s t + \phi(t) + \theta(t)] \tag{3-13}$$

where $\rho(t)$ and $\theta(t)$ are defined by Eqs. (2-79) and (2-80), respectively, with $F[A(t)]$ substituted for a. When the magnitudes of the noise wave are small relative to $F[A(t)]$, the approximations of (2-81) and (2-82) hold and

$$\rho(t) \approx F[A(t)] + x(t)$$
$$\theta(t) \approx \frac{y(t)}{F[A(t)]} \tag{3-14}$$

Then

$$G[\rho(t)] \approx G\{F[A(t)] + x(t)\} \approx G\{F[A(t)]\}$$
$$+ G'\{F[A(t)]\}x(t) = A(t) + \frac{x(t)}{F'[A(t)]} \tag{3-15}$$

Then by retaining only first-order terms in the in-phase and quadrature noise components, we calculate

$$r_e(t) \approx \left\{ A(t) + \frac{x(t)}{F'[A(t)]} \right\} \cos \left\{ \omega_s t + \phi(t) + \frac{y(t)}{F[A(t)]} \right\}$$
$$\approx A(t) \cos [\omega_s t + \phi(t)] + \frac{x(t)}{F'[A(t)]} \cos [\omega_s t + \phi(t)]$$
$$- \frac{A(t)y(t)}{F[A(t)]} \sin [\omega_s t + \phi(t)] \approx s(t) + \frac{v(t)}{F'[A(t)]}$$
$$+ \left\{ \frac{1}{F'[A(t)]} - \frac{A(t)}{F[A(t)]} \right\} y(t) \sin [\omega_s t + \phi(t)] \tag{3-16}$$

Comparison with the corresponding equation, (3-10), for the instantaneous compandor shows that the effect of noise on the envelope introduces an extra noise component in the output of the syllabic compandor. However, we should also note that the dependence on $F'(A)$ instead of $F'[s(t)]$ gives a more powerful noise reduction because there is no breakdown of effectiveness when the instantaneous values of $|s(t)|$ are not larger than $|v(t)|$.

The masking effect which loud signals exert on noise is weakened when the noise components extend over a very wide band. For this reason, simple companding applied to a program channel encounters the so-called "hush-hush" effect, in which the intensity of high-frequency noise is heard to rise and fall under control of high-energy, low-frequency signal components. This difficulty can be remedied by use of a "split-band" compandor, which compands the high- and low-frequency ranges separately.

An interesting application of companding to program channels is obtainable by making the range of expansion greater than the range of compression. So-called "enhanced music" has been created in this way.[3] Compression is used in a recording process to obtain a good margin over noise for the weakest sounds. When more than complementary expansion is used in reproduction, a dynamic range of sound effects unattainable with a physical orchestra can be produced.

3-4 BANDWIDTH REDUCTION SCHEMES

Although the empirical procedures described in this chapter for analyzing the bandwidth requirements of telephony have been successful in establishing specifications for telephone channels of good quality, they do not preclude the existence of methods employing narrower bands. The word "bandwidth" implies some sort of a spectrum, and our mathematical definition of a spectrum is based on values of the signal specified over a long interval of time. Actually we recognize individual speech sounds by making observations which are localized in time to a considerable extent; we do not take into account much of the past or future of the signal wave. The spectrum of interest is thus not what would be calculated from a long sequence of sentences or words, since this would include effects from a considerable variety of distinct sounds, and individual sounds would tend to lose their identifying features. A more important spectrum would be that calculated for the part of the wave associated with one speech sound. The values of the wave in the remote past and future would be set equal to zero in this calculation. A physical bank of bandpass filters with regularly spaced midband frequencies actually performs such a selective analysis in time; the response induced by earlier portions of the input wave gradually decays, and the heaviest weighting applies to the most recent part. We shall call the resulting function of frequency a *short-term spectrum* to distinguish it from the mathematical spectrum defined for a long time interval. A short-term spectrum of speech may be expressed as a function of frequency which changes as the sounds succeed each other in time. Since the ear is insensitive to phase, only the amplitude of the spectrum is significant.

We can describe the speech transmission problem with fair accuracy as one of delivering the data defining a *short-term amplitude spectrum* which varies with time. The basic concepts of conventional speech transmission stress the frequency range included by the short-term spectrum and pay little attention to the rate of variation of the spectrum with time. The systems thereby called for are sufficient but may be better than necessary. They may be capable of transmitting waves which the human voice cannot produce and from which the human ear cannot derive unique information. Our vocal generators have mechanical limitations on the speed with which transitions between successive sounds can occur, and likewise our ears do not follow in detail highly rapid changes from one sound to another. The *vocoder*, invented by Homer Dudley,[4] takes practical advantage of these properties to transmit speech with high intelligibility over a considerably narrower band than the spectral data imply.

Figure 3-7 shows a schematic diagram of a vocoder which reduces the channel bandwidth for transmitting intelligible speech to approximately one-tenth of that required in conventional telephony. A bank of bandpass filters resolves a 3-kHz voice band into 10 subbands, 300 Hz wide. A rectifier and a 25-Hz low-pass filter in the output of each bandpass filter produces a short-term average indication of the amplitude in each narrow band. The resulting slowly varying signals are transmitted to the receiver. Since each has a bandwidth of 25 Hz, the total bandwidth required is 250 Hz.

The 10 low-frequency signals convey the information concerning the approximate distribution of the speech energy with frequency. To synthesize speech from these control signals, the receiver is provided with a bank of 10 bandpass filters identical with those at the transmitter. If this bank of filters is driven by a "hiss source," which is a noise source with a uniform spectral distribution, the 10 outputs can be controlled individually by the 10 corresponding low-frequency control signals to recreate intelligible speech. However, the harmonic frequency structure which gives the voice the property of pitch will be missing, and the quality will be that of whispered speech. Pitch can be introduced by replacement of the hiss source by a "buzz source," which is the output of

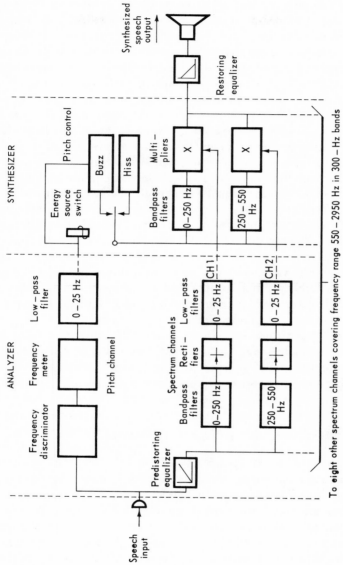

Fig. 3-7 Schematic circuit of a vocoder.

a relaxation oscillator or multivibrator rich in harmonics, but this also gives an unnatural effect because of the monotone character.

To reproduce an approximation to normally voiced speech, the pitch must be measured at the transmitter and an eleventh channel must be provided to send the measured-pitch data to the receiver.   As shown in Fig. 3-7, the pitch-measuring circuit begins with a frequency discriminator, which has maximum response to the lowest frequencies.   The purpose is to ensure that the axis crossings are determined by the fundamental frequency and not by the harmonics.   A microphone with very good low-frequency response is necessary for satisfactory pitch measurement. Once the axis crossings have been made to occur at the fundamental frequency, a conventional frequency detector serves to deliver a slowly varying output proportional to the pitch.   This low-frequency current is used to control the fundamental frequency of the buzz source at the receiver.   When unvoiced sounds, which do not have pitch, occur, the frequency detector delivers a very low output corresponding to a very low average repetition frequency.   A relay is provided at the receiver to switch from the buzz source to the hiss source when no indication of pitch is received.

Although the vocoder can deliver intelligible speech over a channel with substantially less bandwidth than conventional methods require, there are only very special circumstances which warrant its use.   One reason for this is that high intelligibility is not sufficient in itself to make a voice channel satisfactory.   In spite of all the intensive work which has been done to improve the vocoder, there remain unpleasant and unnatural qualities which preclude its use except when there is no possibility of obtaining a telephone channel in any other way.

3-5   TASI—TIME ASSIGNMENT SPEECH INTERPOLATION

The vocoder illustrates the possibility of compensating for the inefficient way in which speech makes use of bandwidth.   A corresponding saving in the time domain has also been demonstrated in the form of a *time-assignment speech-interpolation system* abbreviated as *TASI*.   This scheme takes advantage of the fact that silent intervals occur in conversations. Sophisticated equipment can actually interleave speech waves from a number of different talkers and thereby provide for more simultaneous conversations than the number of available independent transmission channels.

The most substantial advantages of TASI occur in so-called "four-wire" systems, in which the oppositely directed speech waves from a two-person conversation travel on separate paths.   On the reasonable assumption that people listen as well as talk, each pair of a four-wire circuit is likely to be idle at least half of the time.   When normal pauses between phrases and syllables are taken into account, the fraction of silent time can be expected to be definitely more than one-half.

A first essential ingredient of a TASI system is a speech detector to determine whether or not a talker is active.   Setting the threshold of the detector is an important matter since if the threshold is too high, weak speech sounds may be lost, while if the threshold is too low, background noise may give a false indication of activity.   Empirical adjustment must be made to find an operating point which will obtain a significant reduction in channel demand time without objectionable clipping of the speech signal.   When the onset of a "talk-spurt" has been registered by the detector and a channel has been assigned, subsequent clipping can be significantly minimized if the talker is not required to relinquish the channel during pauses unless the channel is needed to serve another talker.   Clipping is thereby confined to the relatively infrequent periods of heavy simultaneous demands.

It is possible, of course, for the number of simultaneous talk-spurts to exceed the number of available channels and thereby cause "freeze-out" of some of the talkers.   This very undesirable condition must be held to a small probability of occurrence.   Design of a TASI system depends heavily on statistical data relating the "TASI gain" or "line-to-channel ratio" to the speech activity ratio, the freeze-out ratio, and the number of available channels.   A set of curves exhibiting these relations is given in Fig. 3-8.   Curve 3, for example, shows that 72 talkers individually and independently active 40 percent of the time can be served by 36 channels with 0.5 percent freeze-out.   It has been demon-

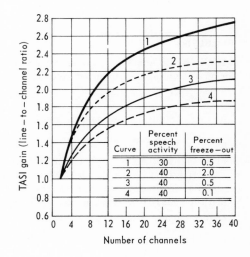

Fig. 3-8 Relations between TASI gain, speech activity, and freeze-out. (From E. F. O'Neill, *Bell Lab. Record*, vol. 37, p. 84, March, 1959.)

Curve	Percent speech activity	Percent freeze-out
1	30	0.5
2	40	2.0
3	40	0.5
4	40	0.1

strated experimentally[5] that even a critical listener is barely aware of the resulting disturbance of a conversation.

The TASI gain in number of connected talkers is not quite obtainable without channel alterations. Since the talkers are being moved around among the channels as dictated by unpredictable successive demands, the receiving terminal must follow the switching pattern at the transmitter in order to pair the talkers correctly in the intended conversations. This means that in addition to the actual speech signals, it is necessary to transmit the activity pattern identifying which talker is using each channel. The activity information is digital and can be coded into a fairly simple telegraph signal. Some additional bandwidth must be provided for this signal. In the illustrative 36-channel case, the equivalent of a 37th channel is the transmission penalty.

The complication and expense of TASI terminals are not justifiable except when the channels themselves are difficult to provide in sufficient number. Transoceanic submarine telephone cables furnish the one outstanding case in which TASI has been profitably employed. These cables provide a bandwidth adequate for a plurality of telephone channels by use of submerged intermediate amplifiers, which must be designed for long life. A four-wire system with one-way amplifiers duplicated for the two directions of transmission makes TASI attractive as a means of increasing the number of possible simultaneous telephone conversations without significant loss of speech quality. A doubling of the number at the cost of installing TASI terminals becomes substantially less expensive than achieving the same result by installing another cable system. Use of the vocoder could bring about an even greater increase in number of talkers, but unfortunately the subscribers would not be happy with the grade of service thereby offered.

PROBLEMS

3-1. Given a channel with nonlinearity described by a cubic term in the expression for output voltage versus input voltage,

$$E_2 = a_1 E_1 - a_3 E_1{}^3$$

The single-frequency gain is determined by applying a sine wave

$$E_1 = A \cos \omega t$$

and measuring the amplitude of the output component at frequency ω.

(a) Derive a formula for the single-frequency gain.

(b) How many decibels is the third harmonic down relative to the fundamental when the gain is 1 db less than the limiting value at $A = 0$?

3-2. Assume an instantaneous compandor with compression characteristic

$$F(x) = a|x|^{\frac{1}{2}} \operatorname{sgn} x$$

and expansion characteristic

$$G(x) = x^2 \, (\mathrm{sgn}\ x)/a^2$$

The system is to be tested with sine waves

$$s(t) = A \cos \omega_s t \qquad v(t) = B \cos (\omega_s + \nu)t$$

representing, respectively, the signal input to the compressor and the noise on the channel. Suppose it is specified that the instantaneous signal values on the channel are restricted to be within the range $-V$ to V. The amplitude of the sine wave input which produces full load on the channel is then equal to V when the compandor is not used and $(V/a)^2$ when the compandor is used. Let r represent the ratio of a test-tone amplitude to the maximum permitted value. Define the test signal-to-noise ratio $\rho(r)$ at a particular value of r as the ratio of mean power in the signal tone to mean power in the noise tone at the output of the system. Compare the values of $\rho(r)$ with and without the compandor.

3-3. Repeat Prob. 3-2 for a syllabic compandor.

3-4. Which of the following instantaneous response functions are suitable for compressors and which for expanders?

(a) $F(x) = (e^{x^2} - 1) \, \mathrm{sgn}\ x$

(b) $F(x) = \dfrac{e^x - 1}{e^x + 1}$

(c) $F(x) = \begin{cases} \log (1 + x) & x > 0 \\ -\log (1 - x) & x < 0 \end{cases}$

(d) $F(x) = x^3$

(e) $F(x) = \displaystyle\int_0^x e^{-z^2} \, dz$

3-5. Why are the predistorting and restoring equalizers used in the vocoder (see Fig. 3-7)?

REFERENCES

1. Fletcher, H.: "Speech and Hearing," D. Van Nostrand, Princeton, N.J., p. 79, 1929.
2. Schwartz, M., W. R. Bennett, and S. Stein: "Communication Systems and Techniques," McGraw-Hill, New York, p. 215, 1966.
3. Fletcher, H.: Stereophonic Reproduction from Film, *J. Soc. Motion Picture Engrs.*, vol. 34, pp. 606–613, June, 1940.
4. Dudley, H. W.: Remaking Speech, *J. Acoust. Soc. Am.*, vol. 11, pp. 169–177, October, 1939.
5. O'Neill, E. F.: TASI: Time Assignment Speech Interpolation, *Bell Lab. Record*, vol. 37, pp. 82–87, March, 1959.

4

Baseband Transmission of Telegraph Signals

In contrast to telephony, it would appear that telegraph signaling should be described in the time domain rather than in the frequency domain. However, the powerful concepts of Fourier analysis become almost indispensable when we get beyond the crude key-and-battery techniques of early digital signaling. The present chapter will demonstrate how the time and frequency domains supplement each other to produce a comprehensive theory with great versatility.

4-1 THE TELEGRAPH SIGNAL

Early inventors of electric telegraph systems were extravagant in the use of equipment. For example, methods in which a separate wire was provided for each letter of the alphabet were actually proposed. Such luxury was soon supplanted by assignment of codes to the letters in terms of electrical pulses, which were sequentially transmitted over one pair of wires or between one wire and ground. The Morse code introduced in America was based on combinations of long and short pulses. The code of Wheatstone and Cooke, which was adopted in Great Britain, employed positive and negative pulses. At the relatively slow speeds possible with manual keying, there was at first no appreciable difficulty from distortion of the electrical pulses by the transmission line. The main obstacle was a weakening of the current with distance. In telegraphy over land, this could be overcome by inserting *repeaters*, in which an electromechanical relay opened and closed a switch in series with a local sending battery and the outgoing line. The repeaters were spaced closely enough to prevent the received current from falling below the value necessary to operate the relay.

When telegraph signals were sent over long submarine cables, it was found that the pulses received were considerably prolonged in time compared with those sent. The resulting overlap made recognition difficult except when the sending rate was greatly reduced. The cause of the sluggishness of response was the distributed capacitance, which slowly charged and discharged through the resistance of the cable as the electrical pulses were applied. In more modern terminology the signaling rate had to be reduced to a value permitted by the bandwidth of the system. The same phenomena are found in land lines when signaling rates are increased above the early manual sending speeds. We shall investigate these matters in detail.

In manual telegraphy it is not necessary to send signals at a precisely constant rate since fairly substantial variations in spacing of symbols do not break up the group patterns. With machine telegraphy at higher speeds, exact time intervals become important and the receiver must be synchronized with the transmitter. In *start-stop systems* a special synchronizing signal precedes each set of symbols making up a letter. In what is known as *synchronous telegraphy*, the symbols of the entire message are transmitted sequentially with equal time-slot widths assigned to each symbol. This is the most commonly used method in modern high-speed data-transmission circuits.

Let $T = 1/f_s$ represent the duration of the elementary signaling interval in a synchronous telegraph system, and let $a_1, a_2, a_3, \ldots, a_M$ be the M values of electrical voltage or current chosen to represent M distinct symbols. Then a message consisting of $2N + 1$ sequentially selected symbols produces an output wave from the telegraph transmitter representable by

$$s(t) = \sum_{n=-N}^{N} b_n \, g(t - nT) \tag{4-1}$$

where each b_n can be any one of the M permissible values $a_1, a_2, \ldots, a_M$, and $g(t)$ is a standard pulse emitted by the transmitter when $b_0 = 1$ and all the other values of b_n are zero. The origin of time has been chosen without loss of essential generality to be the center of the message. The number N will usually be assumed large and will be made infinite when a useful simplification is thereby obtained.

The *signaling rate* $f_s = 1/T$ symbols/sec is also expressed as f_s *bauds*, a baud being a unit of signaling rate equal to one symbol per second. The most common case is that of binary signaling, defined by $M = 2$. In this case there are only two possible choices for each b_n, for example, 0 and 1, or $+1$ and -1. A choice between two equally likely symbols is defined as one *bit* of information, and if the successive choices are made independently, the binary message source produces information at the rate of f_s bits/sec. In practical telegraph transmission the channel is capable of handling input data at this rate, and no provision is made for saving channel time when the symbols from the source are not independently chosen and are not equally distributed between the two values. Hence it is standard in data transmission not to make any distinction between bits per second and binary symbols per second. The term *binits per second* is sometimes used for the latter when a distinction is desired. Note that a baud is equivalent to 1 bit/sec when binary transmission is used, but not when more than two signal levels are allowed. For example, in the case of quaternary transmission, the value of M is 4, and the possible levels can be identified with the four 2-bit sequences 00, 01, 10, and 11. Thus each symbol represents 2 bits, and 1 baud is equivalent to 2 bits/sec. Similarly, in a 2^m-level system, a baud is equal to m bits/sec.

A block diagram of the complete baseband telegraph transmission system is shown in Fig. 4-1. An input shaping network, or sending filter, with transmittance function $Y_1(f)$ is inserted between the telegraph transmitter and the channel input. The channel is assumed to have transmittance function $H(f)$. There is an output shaping network, or receiving filter, with transmittance $Y_2(f)$ between the channel output and the decision-making part of the receiver. The resolution of the telegraph signal into sinusoidal components can be simply performed at any point in the system in terms of the Fourier transform of the original signal

$$S(f) = \int_{-\infty}^{\infty} s(t)e^{-j2\pi ft}\,dt$$

$$= \sum_{n=-N}^{N} b_n\, G(f)e^{-j2n\pi fT} \tag{4-2}$$

The Fourier transforms of the signal at the other points are then $Y_1(f)S(f)$ at the output of the sending filter, $H(f)Y_1(f)S(f)$ at the channel output, and $Y_2(f)H(f)Y_1(f)S(f)$ at the receiving filter output. If we let

$$Q(f) = Y_2(f)H(f)Y_1(f)G(f) \tag{4-3}$$

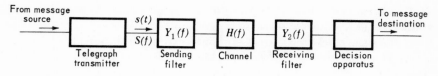

Fig. 4-1 Block diagram of a baseband telegraph system.

the signal from the receiving filter is given by

$$r(t) = \int_{-\infty}^{\infty} Y_2(f)H(f)Y_1(f)S(f)e^{j2\pi ft}\,df$$

$$= \sum_{n=-N}^{N} b_n \int_{-\infty}^{\infty} Q(f)e^{j2\pi f(t-nT)}\,df$$

$$= \sum_{n=-N}^{N} b_n\, q(t - nT) \tag{4-4}$$

It will be noted that the effect of the four different functions $Y_2(f)$, $H(f)$, $Y_1(f)$, and $G(f)$ are combined as a product to form one function $Q(f)$ which completely determines the wave from which the message is to be read. These functions are interchangeable as far as final effect is concerned. The channel function $H(f)$ is typically given as an initial condition. The Fourier transform $G(f)$ of the standard signal pulse $g(t)$ is associated with the switching process at the transmitter and can be modified to a limited extent. The remaining two functions are then to be adjusted to give the desired $Q(f)$.

4-2 NYQUIST'S FIRST CRITERION FOR DISTORTIONLESS TELEGRAPH TRANSMISSION

The object in telegraphy is to deliver the sequence of values b_n at the receiver. The transmission problem thus reduces to establishing means for recognizing the individual b_n's in the received signal wave of Eq. (4-4). One obstacle to be overcome is the *intersymbol interference* resulting from overlapping of the functions $q(t - nT)$ along the time scale. Control of intersymbol interference is accomplished in the time domain by controlling the function $q(t)$, or, in the frequency domain, by controlling the product of the four functions which form $Q(f)$. One way of adjusting $q(t)$ to reduce intersymbol interference is to make its values very small outside the range $-T/2$ to $T/2$. In fact, an ideal $q(t)$ would be the function $A\,\mathrm{rect}\,t/T$. However, as we observed in Chap. 1, this function requires a very wide band of frequencies. We are thus reminded that in choosing $q(t)$ we cannot ignore the channel transmittance function

$H(f)$, which is a factor of $Q(f)$, and for practical channels cannot have usable values for all values of f.

Basic methods for suppressing intersymbol interference when only a finite band of frequencies is available in the system were proposed and analyzed by Nyquist in 1928.[1] His first method, known as Nyquist I, requires that $q(0)$ is a nonzero constant A and that $q(mT)$ vanishes when m is any positive or negative integer. Each signaling pulse can then be sampled at an instant when all the other pulses pass through zero. In mathematical terms, Nyquist required

$$q(mT) = A \delta_{m0} \tag{4-5}$$

where δ_{mn} is the Kronecker delta defined as unity when $m = n$, and zero otherwise. If this condition is satisfied,

$$r(mT) = \sum_{n=-N}^{N} b_n \, q[(m-n)T] = A \sum_{n=-N}^{N} b_n \, \delta_{m-n,0}$$
$$= A b_m \tag{4-6}$$

Each b_m is then found by dividing the measured value of $r(mT)$ by the constant A. In the absence of noise, the reception is perfect.

A solution of Eq. (4-5) can be found in the frequency domain by noting that

$$q(mT) = \int_{-\infty}^{\infty} Q(f)e^{j2\pi fmT} \, df$$
$$= \sum_{n=-\infty}^{\infty} \int_{(2n-1)f_s/2}^{(2n+1)f_s/2} Q(f)e^{j2\pi mf/f_s} \, df$$
$$= \sum_{n=-\infty}^{\infty} \int_{-f_s/2}^{f_s/2} Q(f' + nf_s)e^{j2\pi m(f'+nf_s)/f_s} \, df'$$
$$= \int_{-f_s/2}^{f_s/2} e^{j2\pi mf/f_s} \sum_{n=-\infty}^{\infty} Q(f + nf_s) \, df \tag{4-7}$$

Equation (4-5) is satisfied if

$$\sum_{n=-\infty}^{\infty} Q(f + nf_s) = \frac{A}{f_s} \tag{4-8}$$

That Eq. (4-8) is not only sufficient but also necessary can be shown by assuming that the right-hand member is not a constant but a function $\phi(f)$. Then,

$$q(mT) = \int_{-f_s/2}^{f_s/2} e^{j2m\pi f/f_s}\phi(f) \, df \tag{4-9}$$

Since the left-hand member of (4-8) is periodic in f with period f_s, we expand $\phi(f)$ in a Fourier series, setting

$$\phi(f) = \sum_{m=-\infty}^{\infty} c_m e^{-j2m\pi f/f_s} \tag{4-10}$$

$$c_m = \frac{1}{f_s} \int_{-f_s/2}^{f_s/2} e^{j2m\pi f/f_s} \phi(f) \, df = \frac{1}{f_s} q(mT) \tag{4-11}$$

Therefore,

$$q(mT) = f_s c_m \tag{4-12}$$

To satisfy (4-5), we must then have

$$c_m = \frac{A \delta_{m0}}{f_s} \tag{4-13}$$

and hence

$$\phi(f) = \frac{A}{f_s} \sum_{m=-\infty}^{\infty} \delta_{m0} e^{-j2m\pi f/f_s} = \frac{A}{f_s} \tag{4-14}$$

Band-limited functions which satisfy the Nyquist I criterion can be constructed from Eq. (4-8). The narrowest band is obtained by permitting only one nonzero component in the series for each f in the range $-f_s/2$ to $f_s/2$, that is, by setting

$$Q(f) = \frac{A}{f_s} \operatorname{rect} \frac{f}{f_s} \tag{4-15}$$

from which

$$q(t) = A \operatorname{sinc} f_s t \tag{4-16}$$

by setting $f_s = 2f_0$ in Eqs. (1-51) and (1-52). It is readily verified that $q(t)$ as defined by Eq. (4-16) satisfies the condition for no intersymbol interference when the signaling rate is f_s and the samples are taken at multiples of $1/f_s$. The band required is exactly the range from $-f_s/2$ to $f_s/2$, which means that no frequencies of absolute value exceeding half the signaling rate are needed. The time function can be regarded as the impulse response of an ideal low-pass filter cutting off at $f = f_s/2$.

Although the solution expressed by Eqs. (4-15) and (4-16) achieves economy in bandwidth, there are practical difficulties which make it an undesirable objective for system design. The abrupt transition in $Q(f)$ at $f = \pm f_s/2$ is, of course, impossible to attain exactly, but this could be approximated within arbitrarily small nonzero error if the end result were worth the effort. We need not be deterred by the argument sometimes

given that a pulse with this spectrum is physically unrealizable because
the response anticipates the stimulus.   As explained in Sec. 1-6, we overcome this difficulty by replacing $q(t)$ with $q(t - \tau)$, which in the frequency
domain replaces $Q(f)$ by $Q(f)e^{-j2\pi f\tau}$.   The sampling times are then uniformly delayed by the amount τ.   As τ is made larger, the approximation
to the abrupt cutoff can be approached more nearly, and more of the
anticipatory part of the response is moved into the nonanticipatory delay
interval between $t = 0$ and $t = \tau$.   Of course, it would require an infinite
value of τ to obtain complete physical realization, and in the limit the
message would never be delivered.   However, a satisfactory approximation with a tolerable value of delay could be obtained.

The bad features of the minimum-bandwidth solution are associated
with the slow rate of decay of the function sinc $f_s t$.   One effect is that
there is practically no margin for error in sampling times.   Consider the
sample taken at $t = \epsilon$, where ϵ can be arbitrarily close but not equal to
zero.   We calculate

$$
\begin{aligned}
r(\epsilon) &= \sum_{n=-N}^{N} b_n\, q(\epsilon - nT) = A \sum_{n=-N}^{N} b_n\, \text{sinc } f_s(\epsilon - nT) \\
&= A \sum_{n=-N}^{N} b_n \frac{\sin \pi f_s(\epsilon - nT)}{\pi f_s(\epsilon - nT)} = A \sum_{n=-N}^{N} b_n \frac{\sin(\pi f_s\epsilon - n\pi)}{\pi(f_s\epsilon - n)} \\
&= A b_0 \frac{\sin \pi f_s\epsilon}{\pi f_s\epsilon} + A \frac{\sin \pi f_s\epsilon}{\pi} \sum_{n=\pm 1}^{\pm N} \frac{(-)^n b_n}{f_s\epsilon - n} \quad (4\text{-}17)
\end{aligned}
$$

The first term on the right of (4-17) measures the desired symbol, while
the remaining series represents the intersymbol interference caused by
incorrect sampling time.

For simplicity consider the binary case in which b_n can be either
$+1$ or -1.   Then a sequence exists in which all terms in the series of
(4-17) are positive.   This sequence is found by setting $b_n = +1$ if the
coefficient of b_n is positive and setting $b_n = -1$ if the coefficient of b_n is
negative.   For this sequence the intersymbol interference is

$$
I = A \frac{\sin \pi f_s\epsilon}{\pi} \sum_{n=1}^{N} \left(\frac{1}{|f_s\epsilon - n|} + \frac{1}{|f_s\epsilon + n|} \right) \qquad (4\text{-}18)
$$

If $|\epsilon| < 1/f_s$,

$$
I = A \frac{\sin \pi f_s\epsilon}{\pi} \sum_{n=1}^{N} \left(\frac{1}{n + f_s\epsilon} + \frac{1}{n - f_s\epsilon} \right)
$$

$$
= 2A \frac{\sin \pi f_s\epsilon}{\pi} \sum_{n=1}^{N} \frac{n}{n^2 - f_s^2\epsilon^2} \qquad (4\text{-}19)
$$

Since $n^2 - f_s^2\epsilon^2 < n^2$, it follows that

$$\sum_{n=1}^{N} \frac{n}{n^2 - f_s^2\epsilon^2} > \sum_{n=1}^{N} \frac{1}{n} > \int_1^N \frac{dx}{x} = \ln N \qquad (4\text{-}20)$$

Therefore, $I \to \infty$ as $N \to \infty$. This means that in very long messages even the slightest nonzero error in sampling time leads to very large intersymbol interference.

It could be argued that the sequences which produce catastrophic interference are very unlikely, and that, therefore, there need be only a negligibly small error rate in the received message when the amount of synchronizing error is moderate. The objection to this reasoning is that while the worst sequence may be improbable on the basis of random data, its simple systematic structure may cause its frequent selection for special signaling purposes. In the example just analyzed, the most hazardous situation is the detection of a negative value when both the preceding and succeeding sequences are alternatively positive and negative. To design a data transmission system in which such a simple sequence causes failure may place an unacceptable constraint on the mode of operation.

The disadvantages of the minimum-bandwidth system are not confined to the increased intersymbol interference. In the example analyzed, the large values of the message wave which can occur between multiples of T may be harmful even if they are not sampled. A physical channel does not maintain linearity over an indefinitely great range of signal inputs, and, in fact, may be destroyed if too high a voltage is impressed.

The method of modifying the minimum-bandwidth solution for practical usefulness was given by Nyquist, and can be deduced from Eq. (4-8) by extending the bandwidth from $f_s/2$ to an adjustable value between $f_s/2$ and f_s. Two components are then permitted in (4-8), which is now written

$$Q(f) + Q(f - f_s) = \frac{A}{f_s} \qquad |f| < \frac{f_s}{2} \qquad (4\text{-}21)$$

We note that if we specify $Q(f)$ arbitrarily for $0 < f < f_s/2$, the values in the range $-f_s < f < -f_s/2$ are determined from

$$Q[-(f_s - f)] = \frac{A}{f_s} - Q(f) \qquad (4\text{-}22)$$

The remaining values are then fixed by the condition $Q(-f) = Q^*(f)$ and the assumption that $Q(f) = 0$ for $|f| > f_s$. In particular, the values between $f_s/2$ and f_s are found from

$$Q(f_s - f) = \frac{A}{f_s} - Q^*(f) \qquad 0 < f < \frac{f_s}{2} \tag{4-23}$$

A discontinuity at $f = f_s/2$ can be avoided if the same value of $Q(f_s/2)$ is approached from both sides. By substituting $f = (f_s/2) - \epsilon$ in (4-23), we obtain

$$Q\left(\frac{f_s}{2} + \epsilon\right) = \frac{A}{f_s} - Q^*\left(\frac{f_s}{2} - \epsilon\right) \tag{4-24}$$

For continuity, we must have

$$\lim_{\epsilon \to 0} Q\left(\frac{f_s}{2} + \epsilon\right) = \lim_{\epsilon \to 0} Q\left(\frac{f_s}{2} - \epsilon\right) = \frac{A}{f_s} - \lim_{\epsilon \to 0} Q^*\left(\frac{f_s}{2} + \epsilon\right) \tag{4-25}$$

Equation (4-25) is satisfied if and only if

$$\mathrm{Re}\, Q\left(\frac{f_s}{2}\right) = \frac{A}{2f_s} \tag{4-26}$$

By the conjugate relationship between $Q(-f)$ and $Q(f)$, the discontinuity at $f = -f_s/2$ is also avoided if Eq. (4-26) is satisfied. We can, therefore, make $Q(f)$ continuous for all f and thereby prevent the very slow decay of the function $q(t)$ found in the minimum-bandwidth case. This in turn provides an allowable margin for error in the sampling time and assures finite bounds for ordinates of the signal wave between samples.

Figure 4-2 shows typical graphs for the real and imaginary components of $Q(f)$ when the conditions for continuity and the Nyquist I criterion are satisfied within a band of $\pm f_s$. It is convenient in the description of these curves to express them in terms of $x = (f_s/2) - f$. The conditions met in terms of x for $|x| < f_s/2$ are

$$\mathrm{Re}\, Q\left(\frac{f_s}{2} + x\right) + \mathrm{Re}\, Q\left(\frac{f_s}{2} - x\right) = \frac{A}{f_s}$$

$$\mathrm{Im}\, Q\left(\frac{f_s}{2} + x\right) = \mathrm{Im}\, Q\left(\frac{f_s}{2} - x\right) \tag{4-27}$$

A pictorial interpretation of the curve for the real part is that the contribution of the shaded area removed from the minimum-bandwidth function is made up by the equal area added above the frequency $f_s/2$. Note that the curve can be brought to zero at any point in the interval between $f_s/2$ and f_s, and that not only can the function be continuous for all f, but a finite number of derivatives can be made continuous. To maintain exactly zero as the value of the function at all frequencies out-

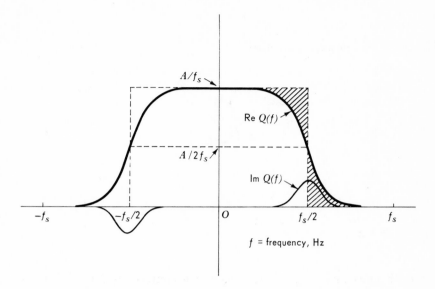

Fig. 4-2 Fourier transform $Q(f)$ of a signal pulse satisfying Nyquist's first criterion for suppression of intersymbol interference at a signaling rate of f_s bauds.

side a finite range is physically impossible, but a realizable approximation can be obtained which is not significantly different in performance from the unrealizable case. It should be kept in mind that these functions can be multiplied by $e^{-j2\pi f \tau}$ with no other effect than a delay τ.

One form of $Q(f)$ which embodies many desirable features is constructed by a so-called "cosine rolloff" as shown in Fig. 4-3. The real part of $Q(f)$ is constant at A/f_s for $|f| < f_1 < f_s/2$. The function is continued outside this range by junction with biased half-period cosine waves which have their positive peaks at $f = \pm f_1$, pass through the points $(\pm f_s/2, A/2f_s)$, and reach zero at $|f| = f_s - f_1$. The imaginary part of $Q(f)$ is set equal to zero. The ratio

$$\rho = \frac{f_s/2 - f_1}{f_s/2} = 1 - \frac{2f_1}{f_s} \tag{4-28}$$

is called the *rolloff factor*. A minimum-bandwidth function has rolloff factor equal to zero. The equation for $Q(f)$ is

$$Q(f) = \frac{A}{f_s} \begin{cases} 1 & |f| < f_1 \\ \frac{1}{2} + \frac{1}{2} \cos \frac{\pi(|f| - f_1)}{f_s - 2f_1} & f_1 < |f| < f_s - f_1 \\ 0 & |f| > f_s - f_1 \end{cases} \tag{4-29}$$

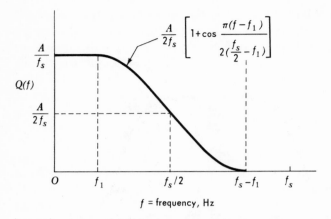

Fig. 4-3 Cosine rolloff meeting Nyquist I requirement for signaling speed of f_s bauds. $Q(-f) = Q(f)$.

Both $Q(f)$ and its first derivative are continuous for all f. The time function $q(t)$ is given by

$$q(t) = \frac{2A}{f_s} \int_0^{f_1} \cos 2\pi ft \; df$$

$$+ \frac{A}{f_s} \int_{f_1}^{f_s-f_1} \left[1 + \cos \frac{\pi(f - f_1)}{f_s - 2f_1} \right] \cos 2\pi ft \; df$$

$$= \frac{A \sin \pi f_s t \cos \pi(f_s - 2f_1)t}{\pi f_s t [1 - 4(f_s - 2f_1)^2 t^2]}$$

$$= \frac{A \cos \rho \pi f_s t}{1 - 4\rho^2 f_s^2 t^2} \; \text{sinc} \; f_s t \tag{4-30}$$

Since $q(t)$ contains sinc $f_s t$ as a factor, the nulls satisfy Nyquist I. There are additional nulls at $t = (2n + 1)/2\rho f_s$ for $n = 1, 2, 3, \ldots$, and $n = -2, -3, -4, \ldots$. Nulls do not occur for $n = 0$ or -1 because of the simultaneous vanishing of the denominator. For large $|t|$, the peaks of $q(t)$ vary as $1/|t|^3$, which as shown in Sec. 1-5 is a property of the Fourier transform of a continuous function with a continuous first derivative, but with discontinuities in the second derivative. The amount of intersymbol interference resulting from a given error in the sampling time, and the maximum value of the signal wave between sampling times both decrease as ρ is increased from zero to unity.

4-3 NYQUIST'S SECOND CRITERION

Nyquist's first method of overcoming the effects of intersymbol interference depends upon sampling the received signal wave at the midpoints of the signaling intervals.   This is a particularly effective procedure for accurate recognition of the symbols.   In a multilink system, regenerative repeaters can be inserted to transmit the decisions over succeeding links without carrying along accumulated timing errors and waveform distortion.   Many practical telegraph systems, however, operate without the precision in synchronization necessary to obtain the full advantages of regular sampling.   These systems make use of the instants of transition between unlike symbols in the received wave rather than centered samples.

Transition times are easily registered by an electromechanical relay or its modern electronic counterpart.   These devices change states at the instants when the current passes through the transition value, which, in the binary case, is nominally halfway between the values of current representing the two symbols.   Figure 4-4 illustrates a simple binary receiving circuit employing a relay.   The armature is deflected to the

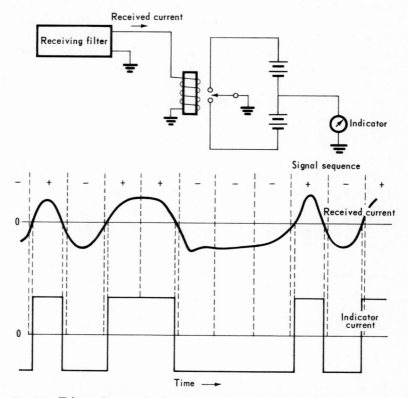

Fig. 4-4   Telegraph reception by observation of transition times.

right by positive received current, and positive battery is thereby connected to the ungrounded terminal of the local indicating device.   Similarly, deflection to the left by negative received current connects negative battery to the ungrounded indicator terminal.   The result is a local indicator current of rectangular wave shape with the same zero crossings as those of the received signal wave.   Accurate timing information is not necessary for reading this version of the message since the number of like symbols in sequence is given by the nearest whole number of symbol intervals in the time between adjacent transitions.   The relay-controlled indicator current can be treated as a repeater output to be sent over the next link in the system without use of any synchronizing control.   Distortion accumulates, of course, because displacements in the zero crossings are copied in the repeated wave.   Ultimately a symbol can be lost by continued shortening of the interval between transitions, and a spurious symbol can be added by a corresponding lengthening of the interval.

Nyquist showed how to design a synchronous telegraph system to operate over a finite-bandwidth channel without distortion of the transition times by intersymbol interference.   Ideally, the transitions should occur at the edges of the symbol intervals, that is, at all positive and negative odd multiples of $T/2$ in Eq. (4-4).   The value of the signal wave at each of these edges should be midway between the two adjacent symbol values.   Another way of stating this is that the response $q(t)$ to a standard symbol pulse should have the value $A/2$ at $t = \pm T/2$ and should have the value zero at all other odd multiples of $T/2$.   We therefore require

$$q\left[\frac{(2m-1)T}{2}\right] = \frac{A}{2}(\delta_{m0} + \delta_{m1}) \tag{4-31}$$

Performing a calculation similar to that used in obtaining Eq. (4-7), we find that in terms of the frequency-domain representation

$$q\left[\frac{(2m-1)T}{2}\right] = \int_{-f_s/2}^{f_s/2} e^{j\pi(2m-1)/f_s} \sum_{n=-\infty}^{\infty} (-)^n Q(f+nf_s)\, df \tag{4-32}$$

Equation (4-31) is then satisfied if

$$\sum_{n=-\infty}^{\infty} (-)^n Q(f+nf_s) = \frac{A}{2f_s}\left(e^{j\pi f/f_s} + e^{-j\pi f/f_s}\right)$$

$$= \frac{A}{f_s}\cos\frac{\pi f}{f_s} \tag{4-33}$$

By an argument similar to that used in the analysis of Nyquist's first criterion, this condition can be shown to be necessary as well as sufficient.

As in Nyquist I, the minimum-bandwidth solution is found in the range $-f_s/2 < f < f_s/2$, which permits only $n = 0$ in the series, and leads to

$$Q(f) = \begin{cases} \dfrac{A}{f_s} \cos \dfrac{\pi f}{f_s} & |f| < \dfrac{f_s}{2} \\[2mm] 0 & |f| > \dfrac{f_s}{2} \end{cases} \tag{4-34}$$

The corresponding signal pulse is

$$q(t) = \frac{2A \cos \pi f_s t}{\pi(1 - 4f_s^2 t^2)} \tag{4-35}$$

We note that $Q(f)$ is continuous but has a discontinuous first derivative at $f = \pm f_s/2$. Accordingly the peaks of $q(t)$ decay as $1/|t|^2$ for large t. We also observe that $Q(f)$ is zero at $f = \pm f_s/2$. This means that a periodic signal wave with fundamental frequency $f_s/2$ produces zero response at all times. In binary transmission, only the alternating sequence $b_n = (-)^n$ produces such a periodic signal. Hence the lack of output can be interpreted as a train of reversals. The difficulty with ambiguity of phase can be solved by using "transition" and "no transition" as the two binary code elements. Methods for signaling through a channel which does not pass the dotting signal were well known to telegraphers as far back as 1898.[2]

Again as in Nyquist I, the Nyquist II method can be more simply realized if the band is extended above $f_s/2$. The condition for rolloff into the range from $f_s/2$ to f_s is

$$Q(f) - Q(f - f_s) = \frac{A}{f_s} \cos \frac{\pi f}{f_s} \qquad |f| < \frac{f_s}{2} \tag{4-36}$$

from which

$$Q(f_s - f) = Q^*(f) - \frac{A}{f_s} \cos \frac{\pi f}{f_s} \tag{4-37}$$

In terms of $x = (f_s/2) - f$ with $|x| < f_s/2$,

$$\begin{aligned} \operatorname{Re} Q\left(\frac{f_s}{2} + x\right) &= \operatorname{Re} Q\left(\frac{f_s}{2} - x\right) - \frac{A}{f_s} \sin \frac{\pi x}{f_s} \\ \operatorname{Im} Q\left(\frac{f_s}{2} + x\right) &= -\operatorname{Im} Q\left(\frac{f_s}{2} - x\right) \end{aligned} \tag{4-38}$$

These functions can be constructed from the basic function of Eq. (4-34) by adding real components with even symmetry about $f = f_s/2$ and imaginary components with odd symmetry about $f_s/2$.

Comparing these equations with (4-27), we find that in order to satisfy both NyquistI and Nyquist II, the following conditions must hold:

$$\text{Re } Q(f) = \frac{A}{2f_s}\left(1 + \cos\frac{\pi f}{f_s}\right) \qquad |f| < f_s$$
$$\text{Im } Q(f) = 0 \tag{4-39}$$

This is the cosine rolloff with $\rho = 1$. The so-called 100 percent cosine rolloff is thus unique among continuous $Q(f)$ functions in attaining correct timing of both samples and transitions at a cost of no more than twice the minimum bandwidth.

4-4 THE EYE PATTERN

Intersymbol interference can be studied in detail experimentally by displaying the *eye pattern* on an oscilloscope. To form this pattern, the response of the system to a random data sequence is applied to the vertical deflection plates, and a sawtooth wave at the signaling frequency is applied to the horizontal. The waveforms in every signaling interval are thereby translated into one interval, where they form a family of traces. The different traces can be expressed by

$$r_k(t) = \sum_{n=-\infty}^{\infty} b_n\, q[t - (n-k)T] = \sum_{l=-\infty}^{\infty} b_{k+l}\, q(t - lT)$$
$$k = 0,\ \pm 1,\ \pm 2,\ \ldots \tag{4-40}$$

If the b_n's form a random sequence, the assignment of the different values of k produces all the permutations of the possible values of b_n. The oscilloscope display then shows all the possible response waves which can be observed in any signaling interval.

The nature of the eye pattern is most easily understood in the binary case. If intersymbol interference is small, the traces are grouped into two sets as shown in Fig. 4-5. One set tends to cluster near the value A at $t = 0$, and the other set near the value $-A$. Each of these sets of traces further subdivides into four subsets. In the upper set, there is one nearly horizontal family of traces corresponding to the sequences $\cdots + + + \cdots$. A second family is approximately horizontal at the left of $t = 0$ and then heads toward $-A$ at $t = T$, crossing zero in the neighborhood of $t = T/2$. These are the responses to the sequences $\cdots + + - \cdots$. A complementary subset representing $\cdots - +$ $+ \cdots$ rises from zero near $t = -T/2$ and becomes horizontal after passing near A at $t = 0$. The fourth subset represents $\cdots - + - \cdots$ and rises from zero near $t = -T/2$, reaches a value near to A at $t = 0$, and then drops to zero again near $t = T/2$. The lower set of traces passing near $-A$ at $t = 0$ forms a mirror image of the upper set since every sequence forming an upper trace is matched by another sequence

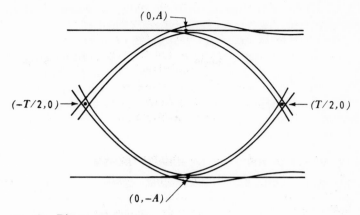

$(0,A)$

$(-T/2,0)$

$(T/2,0)$

$(0,-A)$

Fig. 4-5 Binary eye pattern.

with positive and negative values interchanged. The differences between the members of a subset are caused by the influence of the more remote data values. For example, the traces from the sequences $\cdots + + + + + \cdots$ are slightly different from those from $\cdots - + + + - \cdots$.

The eye pattern gets its name from its resemblance to an eye. The interior region free from traces is called the eye opening. The width of the opening indicates the range of time over which sampling can be performed without error from intersymbol interference, and the heights of the opening show what margin over noise exists if sampling is done at the corresponding times. The preferred time for sampling is the time at which the height of the opening is greatest. In cases of severe intersymbol interference, traces from the upper set cross traces from the lower set, and there may be no open region in the eye. If the eye is completely closed, it is impossible to avoid errors even when noise is absent.

The maximum height of the eye opening is indicative of the performance of the system as far as meeting Nyquist I is concerned. The deviation from Nyquist II is revealed by the spread of the zero crossings about the points $(\pm T/2, 0)$. Even in sampled reception, the transitions are important because they are often used as a source of timing information. Nonuniformity in their spacing can then cause jitter in the sampling instants.

Although the eye pattern for an actual channel is almost always more easily determined experimentally than by analysis, it is sometimes instructive to compute the eye pattern for isolated channel defects. To do this, a message length is adopted which is sufficient to make the influence of symbols outside the message negligible at the center of the message. Suppose this length consists of K intervals and that the system is binary. A computer can then be programmed to calculate the response in the central interval from each of the 2^K possible messages. It is possible to make the computer print out the eye pattern directly as well as the numerical values of the trace ordinates.

The eye pattern for multilevel signaling consists of a plurality of subsidiary eyes, each of which must be open to avoid errors from intersymbol interference. A quaternary eye pattern contains three eyes, and, in general, an M-level system should show $M - 1$ eyes.

4-5 EFFECT OF NOISE ON TELEGRAPH TRANSMISSION

We have shown how intersymbol interference can be controlled in a finite-bandwidth telegraph system to prevent errors arising from confusion of the successive symbols. Error-free transmission could thus be attained if the signal were the only wave delivered by the channel. Unfortunately, it is not physically possible to construct a channel which is completely free from extraneous disturbances. As explained in Chap. 2, the term *noise* is commonly used to designate the part of the channel response which is not related to the impressed signal wave. The more familiar concept of noise as an undesired acoustic wave is thereby extended to include unwanted electrical phenomena as well.

In electrical systems there is a basic noise component arising from random thermal motion of the electrons. This noise forms the ultimate limitation to performance in signal transmission. All other sources of interference, whether of natural origin such as lightning discharges or man-made electrical disturbances such as the arc between switching contacts, can in theory be avoided by suitable shielding and isolation of the channel path. Thermal noise, on the other hand, originates within the transmission circuit itself and is inescapable except at an absolute temperature of zero. It was shown in Sec. 2-5 how thermal noise could be represented as a mean-square voltage or current source in series or parallel, respectively, with the internal impedance or admittance of the input circuit. In passive linear circuits under ordinary conditions, the voltage or current itself has a gaussian probability distribution and a white spectral density. The spectral density function can be changed by frequency-selective amplifying circuits and by the introduction of noise from other than thermal sources. We shall assume here that the probability distribution remains gaussian.

The signal wave reaches its weakest values at the channel output. The receiving filter typically includes an amplifier, which we can assume either to be noiseless or to contain internal noise which can be added to that at the channel output. We therefore consider the case in which the only noise source in the telegraph system has spectral density $w(f)$ at the input of the receiving filter. The noise at the output of the receiving filter then has root-mean-square (rms) value σ, where

$$\sigma^2 = \int_0^\infty |Y_2(f)|^2 w(f)\, df \tag{4-41}$$

The probability of error in bipolar binary transmission can now be calculated. In the absence of intersymbol interference, the sampled voltage v_s at the output of the receiving filter is $v + A$ when a positive symbol is transmitted and $v - A$ when a negative symbol is transmitted. The value of v is a random sample of the noise voltage and has the distribution described by Eqs. (2-31) and (2-32). Assume a decision rule in which the symbol is called plus if v_s is positive and minus if v_s is negative. An error is made if $v + A < 0$ when the transmitted symbol is plus, or if $v - A > 0$ when the transmitted symbol is minus. If P_1 is the probability that the correct symbol is $+A$, the probability of error P_e is given by

$$
\begin{aligned}
P_e &= P_1 \int_{-\infty}^{-A} p(v)\, dv + (1 - P_1) \int_A^\infty p(v)\, dv \\
&= \int_{-\infty}^{-A} [P_1\, p(v) + (1 - P_1)p(v)]\, dv \\
&= \int_{-\infty}^{-A} p(v)\, dv = \frac{1}{2} - \frac{1}{2}\operatorname{erf} \frac{A}{\sigma \sqrt{2}} = \frac{1}{2}\operatorname{erfc} \frac{A}{\sigma \sqrt{2}}
\end{aligned} \tag{4-42}
$$

A graph of P_e versus A/σ is shown in Fig. 4-6. The monotonic decreasing property shows that minimization of the probability of error can be accomplished by maximization of the ratio of signal sample to rms noise. We cannot make A arbitrarily large because of limitations on the allowed size of signal input to the channel. There may be either a maximum allowable signal peak or a maximum allowable average signal power, depending on whether protection against high-voltage breakdown

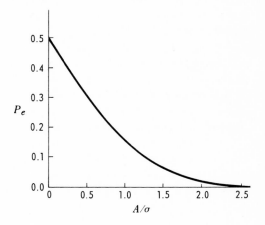

Fig. 4-6 Graph of Eq. (4-42), $P_e = \dfrac{1}{2}\operatorname{erfc} (A/\sigma)/\sqrt{2}$.

or heating damage is more important. Either requirement can be translated to the other by applying the *peak factor*, or ratio of peak to rms signal.

If we adopt an average signal-power limitation, we require a method of computing the mean-square value of the signal wave. To do this in the bipolar case, consider the signal wave of Eq. (4-1) with $b_n = \pm 1$. Results for this wave can be applied to the signal wave at any other point in the system by making the appropriate change in the standard pulse. Calculation of average values for random data can be conveniently performed by reference to the eye pattern, which translates all parts of the signal wave to the basic interval $-T/2 < t < T/2$. As previously pointed out, the traces can be arranged in pairs in which one trace is the exact negative of the other. The two traces of a pair are equally likely in random data. Since the point-by-point sum of the traces in a pair is zero, the average value of $s(t)$ must be zero.

The average square can be calculated by squaring the ordinates of each trace and averaging the resulting functions over all traces. The square of an individual trace is of form:

$$\Big[\sum_{l=-\infty}^{\infty} b_{k+l} g(t - lT) \Big]^2 = \sum_{l=-\infty}^{\infty} \sum_{m=-\infty}^{\infty} b_{k+l} b_{k+m} g(t - lT) g(t - mT)$$

$$k = 0, \pm 1, \pm 2, \ldots \qquad \frac{-T}{2} < t < \frac{T}{2}$$

$$(4\text{-}43)$$

A trace for a particular k is determined by the set of values $\ldots, b_{k-2}$, $b_{k-1}, b_k, b_{k+1}, b_{k+2}, \ldots$. A term $b_{k+l} b_{k+l}$ is always equal to $+1$ since b_{k+l} itself is either $+1$ or -1. A term $b_{k+l} b_{k+m}$ with $l \neq m$ can be either $+1$ or -1. However, for every value of k, another value k' can be found such that $b_{k'+l} b_{k'+m} = -b_{k+l} b_{k+m}$, and the two corresponding traces have equal probability of occurrence. Hence only the terms with coefficient $b_{k+l} b_{k+l}$ contribute to the average square, which means that the average square of $s(t)$ for random data is the average of

$$\xi(t) = \sum_{l=-\infty}^{\infty} g^2(t - lT) \tag{4-44}$$

over the values of t from $-T/2$ to $T/2$. Therefore,

$$\text{av } s^2(t) = \frac{1}{T} \int_{-T/2}^{T/2} \xi(t)\, dt = \frac{1}{T} \int_{-T/2}^{T/2} dt \sum_{l=-\infty}^{\infty} g^2(t - lT)$$

$$= \frac{1}{T} \sum_{l=-\infty}^{\infty} \int_{-T/2}^{T/2} g^2(t - lT)\, dt = \frac{1}{T} \sum_{l=-\infty}^{\infty} \int_{-T/2-lT}^{T/2-lT} g^2(t')\, dt'$$

$$= \frac{1}{T} \int_{-\infty}^{\infty} g^2(t)\, dt \tag{4-45}$$

From Parseval's theorem, Eq. (1-31),

$$\int_{-\infty}^{\infty} g^2(t)\, dt = \int_{-\infty}^{\infty} |G(f)|^2\, df \tag{4-46}$$

Therefore,

$$\text{av } s^2(t) = f_s \int_{-\infty}^{\infty} |G(f)|^2\, df \tag{4-47}$$

Assume a telegraph system with a constraint on the average power of the channel input. We accordingly set

$$W_1 = f_s \int_{-\infty}^{\infty} |Y_1(f)G(f)|^2\, df \tag{4-48}$$

where W_1 is the allowed value of mean-square signal, which is also the average power in a 1-ohm circuit, and $G(f)$ in Eq. (4-47) has been replaced by $Y_1(f)G(f)$ to represent the standard pulse spectrum at the channel input. The relation between $Y_1(f)G(f)$ and $Q(f)$, the required pulse spectrum at the receiving filter output, is given by Eq. (4-3). Therefore,

$$W_1 = f_s \int_{-\infty}^{\infty} \left| \frac{Q(f)}{Y_2(f)H(f)} \right|^2 df \tag{4-49}$$

Let us further assume that the Nyquist I condition for absence of intersymbol interference has been established by satisfying Eq. (4-27) with $Q(f)$ purely real. The result would not be changed, of course, if $Q(f)$ were multiplied by $e^{-j2\pi\tau f}$. Then the sampled signal values are $\pm A$, where

$$A = q(0) = 2 \int_0^{f_s} Q(f)\, df \tag{4-50}$$

For minimum probability of error, we must maximize the ratio A/σ, or equivalently A^2/σ^2, where σ^2 is given by Eq. (4-41). We assume that a definite real $Q(f)$ satisfying Nyquist I has been selected and that $H(f)$, the channel transmittance, is given. The only function which can be adjusted for optimization is then $Y_2(f)$, the transmittance function of the receiving filter, which is sometimes called the *front-end filter* of the receiver.

With $Q(f)$ real and equal to zero for $|f| > f_s$, Eq. (4-49) can be written

$$W_1 = 2f_s \int_0^{f_s} \frac{Q^2(f)}{|Y_2(f)H(f)|^2}\, df \tag{4-51}$$

The optimization problem can be formulated as finding a function $Y_2(f)$ which maximizes

$$\frac{A^2}{\sigma^2} = \frac{4 \left[\int_0^{f_s} Q(f)\, df \right]^2}{\int_0^{f_s} |Y_2(f)|^2 w(f)\, df} \tag{4-52}$$

subject to the constraint of Eq. (4-51). The upper limit on the integral in the denominator on the right-hand side of Eq. (4-52) has been set equal to f_s since nonzero values of $Y_2(f)$ for $f > f_s$ can only do harm by admitting more noise without contributing anything to the signal.

Since $Y_2(f)$ enters the problem only in the form of the square of its absolute value, it is convenient to let

$$X(f) = |Y_2(f)|^2 \tag{4-53}$$

Also, since the numerator of the right-hand side of Eq. (4-52) is a constant of the problem, the desired optimum $X(f)$ can equally well be defined as the function which minimizes the denominator subject to the constraint of Eq. (4-51).

If we let

$$\frac{Q(f)}{|H(f)|} = Z(f) \tag{4-54}$$

our problem reduces to finding a function $X(f)$ which gives a minimum value of the integral

$$I = \int_0^{f_s} X(f) w(f)\, df \tag{4-55}$$

when $X(f)$ is constrained to satisfy the auxiliary equation

$$\int_0^{f_s} \frac{Z^2(f)}{X(f)}\, df = \frac{W_1}{2f_s} \tag{4-56}$$

This is an elementary problem in the calculus of variations. For the benefit of the reader who is unfamiliar with the subject, we give the following explanation of the solution applicable to this particular case.

Consider the general problem of finding a function $y(x)$ which gives a maximum or minimum value of the integral

$$I = \int_{x_1}^{x_2} F(x,y)\, dx \tag{4-57}$$

Suppose a solution $y(x)$ exists. Then if $\delta y(x)$ is an arbitrarily chosen function of x which is sufficiently small in absolute value to permit expansion of $F(x, y + \delta y)$ in a Taylor's series in y at all points on the path of integration, we can write

$$
\begin{aligned}
I &= \int_{x_1}^{x_2} \left[F(x,y) + \frac{\partial F}{\partial y}\, \delta y(x) + \frac{1}{2} \frac{\partial^2 F}{\partial y^2}\, \delta^2 y(x) + \cdots \right] dx \\
&\approx \int_{x_1}^{x_2} F(x,y)\, dx + \int_{x_1}^{x_2} \frac{\partial F}{\partial y}\, \delta y(x)\, dx
\end{aligned}
\tag{4-58}
$$

when $\delta y(x)$ approaches zero. A necessary condition for I to have a maximum or minimum is that

$$\int_{x_1}^{x_2} \frac{\partial F}{\partial y} \, \delta y(x) \, dx = 0 \tag{4-59}$$

for arbitrary choice of $\delta y(x)$, and this can be satisfied only by setting

$$\frac{\partial F}{\partial y} = 0 \tag{4-60}$$

The condition (4-60) is not sufficient for a maximum. Investigation can proceed by calculating the sign of the second derivative. A maximum is obtained if the sign is negative and a minimum if the sign is positive. If the second derivative vanishes and the third derivative does not, the situation is analogous to that of a point of inflection on a curve, and neither a maximum nor a minimum is obtained. If the first three derivatives vanish, the fourth must be examined, and so on. In the typical case, the nature of the physical problem indicates whether a maximum, minimum, or neither exists.

Now consider the special case in which $F(x,y)$ is of the form

$$F(x,y) = F_0(x,y) + \lambda F_1(x,y) \tag{4-61}$$

where λ is a constant. The necessary condition for a maximum or minimum of I becomes

$$\frac{\partial F_0}{\partial y} + \lambda \frac{\partial F_1}{\partial y} = 0 \tag{4-62}$$

The solution of this equation for y is dependent on the parameter λ. A particularly interesting value of λ is obtained by specifying that the value of the integral

$$I_1 = \int_{x_1}^{x_2} F_1(x,y) \, dx \tag{4-63}$$

is a preassigned constant. The function y satisfying (4-62) with this special value of λ now meets necessary conditions for a maximum or minimum value of the integral of $F_0(x,y)$ with the integral of $F_1(x,y)$ constrained to be the constant I_1.

Applying the solution of the general variational problem to (4-55) and (4-56), we set $x = f$, $y = X(f)$, $x_1 = 0$, $x_2 = f_s$, $F_0(x,y) = w(f)X(f)$, $F_1(x,y) = Z^2(f)/X(f)$, and $I_1 = W_1/(2f_s)$. Then from (4-62),

$$w(f) - \frac{\lambda Z^2(f)}{X^2(f)} = 0$$

or

$$X(f) = \frac{\lambda^{1/2} Z(f)}{w^{1/2}(f)} \tag{4-64}$$

The value of λ is found from (4-63) and when substituted in (4-64) gives

$$X(f) = \frac{2f_s Z(f)}{W_1 w^{\frac{1}{2}}(f)} \int_0^{f_s} Z(f) w^{\frac{1}{2}}(f) \, df \qquad (4\text{-}65)$$

The presumed minimum value of I is then found by substituting (4-65) in (4-55) to obtain

$$I = \frac{2f_s}{W_1} \left[\int_0^{f_s} Z(f) w^{\frac{1}{2}}(f) \, df \right]^2 \qquad (4\text{-}66)$$

The corresponding maximum value of A/σ is

$$\frac{A}{\sigma} = \left(\frac{2W_1}{f_s}\right)^{\frac{1}{2}} \frac{\int_0^{f_s} Q(f) \, df}{\int_0^{f_s} Z(f) w^{\frac{1}{2}}(f) \, df} \qquad (4\text{-}67)$$

Verification that this is indeed a maximum is left as an exercise for the reader.

In the case of white noise, the noise power is uniformly distributed in frequency at the channel output, and we set

$$w(f) = w_0 \qquad (4\text{-}68)$$

The maximum value of A/σ is then

$$\frac{A}{\sigma} = \left(\frac{2W_1}{w_0 f_s}\right)^{\frac{1}{2}} \frac{\int_0^{f_s} Q(f) \, df}{\int_0^{f_s} Z(f) \, df} \qquad (4\text{-}69)$$

In a still simpler but important special case, the channel has uniform transmission with frequency, as well as a constant noise spectrum. Setting

$$|H(f)| = H_0 \qquad |f| < f_s \qquad (4\text{-}70)$$

in Eq. (4-69) gives the result

$$\left(\frac{A}{\sigma}\right)^2 = \frac{2H_0{}^2 W_1}{w_0 f_s} \qquad (4\text{-}71)$$

We note that $H_0{}^2 W_1$ is the average total signal power at the channel output and that $w_0 f_s$ is the average noise power in the channel output measured in a band of width equal to the signaling rate f_s. If we define

$$M_0 = \frac{H_0{}^2 W_1}{w_0 f_s} \qquad (4\text{-}72)$$

the minimum probability of error obtained by substituting Eqs. (4-71) and (4-72) in (4-42) is

$$P_e = \frac{1}{2} \operatorname{erfc} \sqrt{M_0} \qquad (4\text{-}73)$$

A classic result of detection theory[3] shows that Eq. (4-73) gives the minimum probability of error possible in the presence of gaussian noise when (1) the noise is *white*, that is, of constant density at all frequencies, (2) the bandwidth available for signaling is unlimited, and (3) the identification of a received binary symbol must be made from the sum of the signal and noise waves received during one signaling time slot.   The method usually prescribed for attaining the optimum performance consists of time-limited signaling and either a *correlation detector* or a *matched filter*.‡   The Nyquist method described here is actually superior because it uses only a limited band of frequencies and thereby enables other independent signals to be transmitted in the band of unused frequencies.

Equation (4-73) is a basic formula for the best possible performance of a data-transmission system when the channel is perturbed by additive white gaussian noise.   It is customary to express the signal-to-noise ratio in decibels.   By definition, 10 times the common logarithm of a power ratio expresses that ratio in decibels, abbreviated as db.   In Fig. 4-7, the minimum probability of error as calculated from Eq. (4-73) is plotted against M_0 in decibels.   This curve is often used as a reference for exhibiting error rates in a particular system.   No part of the curves for physical systems can be on the left side of the ideal curve.

The optimum relations for the simplified important case of a flat channel with additive white gaussian noise can be summarized as follows:

$$|Y_2(f)|^2 = \frac{f_s A Q(f)}{H_0{}^2 W_1} \tag{4-74}$$

$$|Y_1(f)G(f)|^2 = \frac{Q^2(f)}{H_0{}^2|Y_2(f)|^2} = \frac{W_1 Q(f)}{f_s A} \tag{4-75}$$

It is to be noted that $Y_1(f)$ and $G(f)$ play interchangeable roles.   Usually $G(f)$ would be determined by the telegraph switching process, and Eq. (4-75) would then govern the design of the sending filter.

4-6 ON–OFF SIGNALING

The bipolar telegraph signal with independent, equally likely choices between $+A$ and $-A$ in each signaling interval is optimum among binary systems with respect to minimum probability of error in transmission with fixed average signal power over a channel with additive white

‡ A correlation detector, in this case, integrates the product of the channel output and a copy of the positive noise-free signal wave over one signaling interval.   A positive value of the integral indicates that the symbol is $+1$, and a negative value indicates -1.   A matched filter is a filter with impulse response equal to a noise-free signal wave reversed in time.   The convolution formula shows that its response to the channel output duplicates the result of the correlation detector.

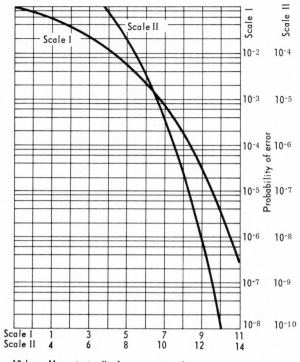

Fig. 4-7 Graph of Eq. (4-73), $P_e = \frac{1}{2} \text{erfc} \sqrt{M_0}$. Minimum error rate of binary channel with additive white gaussian noise.

gaussian noise. Other considerations such as simplicity of terminal apparatus may lead to choice of a system which is suboptimum from the standpoint of error rate. An example is *on-off telegraphy*, which requires only one polarity of current.

A general equation for an on-off telegraph signal can be written in the form

$$s_0(t) = \sum_{n=-N}^{N} (b_n + 1)g(t - nT) \tag{4-76}$$

in which the value of b_n can be either $+1$ or -1. The resulting value of $b_n + 1$ is then $+2$ or 0. If the system is designed to meet the Nyquist I requirement for suppression of intersymbol interference, the two possible signal samples at the output of the receiving amplifier are $2A$ and 0. The threshold indicator would then be set to register the "on" condition if the sample exceeds A and the "off" condition if the sample is less than A. This means that noise samples less than $-A$ falsify the "on" signal and that noise samples greater than A cause error in the "off" signal. These are the same conditions for error found in the bipolar binary case. To compare the two systems on a basis of average power required for identical error rates, we must compute the relative average power values at the channel input.

Equation (4-43) for the square of an individual trace of the eye pattern in the bipolar case can be modified to represent the on-off signal by replacing b_{k+l} by $b_{k+l} + 1$. Then for a message of infinite length,

$$\sum_{l=-\infty}^{\infty} \sum_{m=-\infty}^{\infty} (b_{k+l} + 1)(b_{k+m} + 1)g(t - lT)g(t - mT)$$

$$= \sum_{l=-\infty}^{\infty} \sum_{m=-\infty}^{\infty} b_{k+l}b_{k+m}\, g(t - lT)g(t - mT)$$

$$+ \sum_{l=-\infty}^{\infty} \sum_{m=-\infty}^{\infty} (b_{k+l} + b_{k+m} + 1)g(t - lT)g(t - mT) \quad (4\text{-}77)$$

The first series is identical with the one whose average value was previously found to be given by Eq. (4-45). In the second series, the terms in b_{k+l} and b_{k+m} can be paired with corresponding terms $b_{k'+l}$ and $b_{k'+m}$ in other traces to cancel the contributions to the average value. There remains the double series with coefficient unity, namely,

$$\sum_{l=-\infty}^{\infty} \sum_{m=-\infty}^{\infty} g(t - lT)g(t - mT) = \left[\sum_{l=-\infty}^{\infty} g(t - lT) \right]^2 \quad (4\text{-}78)$$

This series is independent of k, and hence its average value can be obtained by averaging over one trace from $-T/2$ to $T/2$. We calculate

$$\frac{1}{T} \sum_{l=-\infty}^{\infty} \sum_{m=-\infty}^{\infty} \int_{-T/2}^{T/2} g(t - lT)g(t - mT)\, dt$$

$$= \frac{1}{T} \sum_{l=-\infty}^{\infty} \sum_{m=-\infty}^{\infty} \int_{-lT-T/2}^{-lT+T/2} g(t')g[t' + (l - m)T]\, dt'$$

$$= \frac{1}{T} \sum_{n=-\infty}^{\infty} \sum_{l=-\infty}^{\infty} \int_{-lT-T/2}^{-lT+T/2} g(t)g(t - nT)\, dt$$

$$= \frac{1}{T} \sum_{n=-\infty}^{\infty} \int_{-\infty}^{\infty} g(t)g(t - nT)\, dt$$

$$= \frac{1}{T} \sum_{n=-\infty}^{\infty} \int_{-\infty}^{\infty} G(f)G^*(f)e^{j2\pi nfT}\, df = \frac{1}{T} \sum_{n=-\infty}^{\infty} \gamma(nT) \quad (4\text{-}79)$$

where

$$\gamma(t) = \int_{-\infty}^{\infty} |G(f)|^2 e^{j2\pi ft} \, df \qquad (4\text{-}80)$$

Now apply Poisson's formula from Sec. 1-5, that is,

$$\sum_{n=-\infty}^{\infty} x(nT) = \frac{1}{T} \sum_{n=-\infty}^{\infty} X\left(\frac{n}{T}\right) \qquad (4\text{-}81)$$

and obtain

$$\frac{1}{T} \sum_{n=-\infty}^{\infty} \gamma(nT) = \frac{1}{T^2} \sum_{n=-\infty}^{\infty} \left| G\left(\frac{n}{T}\right) \right|^2 \qquad (4\text{-}82)$$

Hence,

$$\text{av}\left[\sum_{l=-\infty}^{\infty} g(t-lT)\right]^2 = f_s^2 \sum_{n=-\infty}^{\infty} |G(nf_s)|^2 \qquad (4\text{-}83)$$

Adding the contribution of Eq. (4-83) to the result of Eq. (4-47), we have for the on-off case

$$\text{av } s_0^2(t) = f_s \int_{-\infty}^{\infty} |G(f)|^2 \, df + f_s^2 \sum_{n=-\infty}^{\infty} |G(nf_s)|^2 \qquad (4\text{-}84)$$

The average power is given by

$$W_{10} = f_s \int_{-\infty}^{\infty} |Y_1(f)G(f)|^2 \, df + f_s^2 \sum_{n=-\infty}^{\infty} |Y_1(nf_s)G(nf_s)|^2 \qquad (4\text{-}85)$$

The second series on the right of Eq. (4-85) represents an excess amount of average transmitted power which on-off binary signaling requires relative to that of the bipolar case. The excess power arises from discrete components in the signal wave at frequencies 0, $\pm f_s$, $\pm 2f_s$, $\ldots$. Actually, if we meet the Nyquist I requirement by limiting the band to frequencies less than f_s, the only discrete component which must be transmitted is the direct current, represented by $n = 0$ in the series. It is advantageous from the standpoint of conserving transmitted power to make $Y_1(0)G(0)$ as small as possible and thereby approach the optimum performance of bipolar signaling. However, we see from Eq. (4-27) that if we wish to preserve continuity of $Q(f)$ and also make $Q(f_s) = 0$, we must have

$$Q(0) = \frac{A}{f_s} \qquad (4\text{-}86)$$

Then from Eq. (4-3),

$$Y_1(0)G(0) = \frac{A}{f_s Y_2(0)H(0)} \qquad (4\text{-}87)$$

We deduce from Eq. (4-87) that we can make the transmitted direct current very small if $Y_2(0)$, the amplification of the receiving amplifier at zero frequency, is very large. This would mean inserting a notch circuit with very high but not infinite loss at $f = 0$ in the sending filter and a complementary narrow peak of gain in the receiving amplifier characteristic. If the effective bandwidth of the high-gain low-frequency region is very narrow, the increase in accepted noise is negligible. However, such a design is awkward from the practical standpoint. Since the principal merit of on-off signaling is simplicity, an elaborate pair of precisely matched circuits for d-c suppression and enhancement would tend to nullify any prospective advantage.

In the more typical on-off system, the transmission varies gradually in the region of zero frequency. The discontinuous approach to a theoretical optimum condition in which $Y_2(0)$ is very large compared with the remainder of $Y_2(f)$ is of little practical interest. In the special case in which $|H(f)| = H_0$ and $w(f) = w_0$, the optimum $Y_2(f)$ for $f \neq 0$ is given by Eq. (4-74). Substitution of the resulting relation (4-75) in (4-85) and application of (4-50) and (4-84) lead to

$$W_{10} = \frac{W_1}{A} \int_{-f_s}^{f_s} Q(f) \, df + f_s \frac{W_1}{A} Q(0) = 2W_1 \tag{4-88}$$

Equation (4-88) shows that for the case usually regarded as the binary standard of reference, on-off signaling with full d-c transmission requires twice as much average power as bipolar telegraphy for the same probability of error. In other words, the on-off system incurs a penalty of 3 db relative to ideal. On-off signaling is an example of the use of *orthogonal* signals; i.e., a choice is made in an interval $-T/2 < t < T/2$ between two signals $s_1(t)$ and $s_2(t)$ such that

$$\int_{-T/2}^{T/2} s_1(t)s_2(t) \, dt = 0 \tag{4-89}$$

In the on-off case, $s_1(t) = g(t)$ and $s_2(t) = 0$. Bipolar signaling makes use of *antipodal* binary signals, that is, $s_1(t)$ and $s_2(t)$ such that

$$\int_{-T/2}^{T/2} s_1(t)s_2(t) \, dt = -\int_{-T/2}^{T/2} s_1{}^2(t) \, dt = -\int_{-T/2}^{T/2} s_2{}^2(t) \, dt \tag{4-90}$$

The integral of the product $s_1(t)s_2(t)$ is a measure of the *correlation* of the two signals. The superiority of antipodal signaling over orthogonal signaling is consistent with the concept that functions with negative correlation are more unlike than functions with zero correlation.

4-7 MULTILEVEL TELEGRAPHY

We have seen how the signaling rate f_s can be matched to the bandwidth in order to avoid intersymbol interference. Convenient and economical bandwidths were found to lie between f_s and $2f_s$. With constant signaling rate and bandwidth, it is theoretically possible to increase the information rate indefinitely by allowing more possible signal values in each interval. To maintain a satisfactorily small error rate in the presence of noise, the average signal power must be increased as more signal levels are added. We shall explore these relations quantitatively.

We consider the case in which the signal values $a_1, a_2, \ldots, a_M$ are uniformly spaced two units apart. The separation of the adjacent possible sampled signal magnitudes at the receiving filter output is then $2A$ when the Nyquist I condition is satisfied, just as in the binary case. The decision thresholds are set halfway between adjacent levels, and a noise sample less than $-A$ or greater than $+A$ causes a lower or higher level, respectively, to be wrongfully selected. Exceptions occur at the highest and lowest levels, which can be in error on only one side.

The probability of correct reception at the interior signal levels can be equated to the probability that the noise sample is in the range $-A$ to A. When the highest signal level is transmitted, the decision is correct if the noise sample is between $-A$ and ∞, and when the lowest level is sent, a correct decision occurs if the noise sample is between $-\infty$ and A. If all transmitted signal levels are equally likely, P_c, the probability of correct detection of a symbol, can be written in terms of $P(v)$ defined by Eq. (2-32) for additive gaussian noise of rms value σ as

$$P_c = \frac{M-2}{M}\,[P(A) - P(-A)] + \frac{1}{M}\,[P(\infty) - P(-A)]$$
$$+ \frac{1}{M}\,[P(A) - P(-\infty)] = \frac{1}{M}\left[1 + (M-1)\,\mathrm{erf}\,\frac{A/\sigma}{\sqrt{2}}\right] \quad (4\text{-}91)$$

This equation holds for any selection of M uniformly spaced signal levels with separation $2A$. The probability of error is given by

$$P_e = 1 - P_c = \frac{M-1}{M}\,\mathrm{erfc}\,\frac{A/\sigma}{\sqrt{2}} \quad (4\text{-}92)$$

As in the binary case, the probability of error decreases monotonically with the ratio A/σ. Therefore, the same optimization procedure previously used to determine the best $Y_2(f)$ for a fixed amount of average signal power allowed as input to the channel is applicable to the multilevel case. A new calculation of the average signal power is required.

The most efficient use of signal power is obtained when the signal values $a_1, a_2, \ldots, a_M$ are symmetrically located with respect to zero. For $M = 2K + 2$ with K equal to zero or an integer, the choices are

$$a_m = -(2K+1), -(2K-1), \ldots, (2K-1), (2K+1) \quad (4\text{-}93)$$

while for $M = 2K + 1$, the choices are

$$a_m = -2K, -2(K-1), \ldots, 2(K-1), 2K \qquad (4\text{-}94)$$

The values of a_m from either (4-93) or (4-94) are assigned equal probability of choice for each b_{k+l} in Eq. (4-43) to find the average power. As in the binary case, we discard the terms $b_{k+l}b_{k+m}$ if $l \neq m$ since values of k can be paired to show zero contribution to the average square. The coefficients b_{k+m}^2 can be replaced by their average value. For the distribution of (4-93), with $M = 2K + 2$,

$$\text{av } b_{k+m}^2 = \frac{1}{K+1} \sum_{n=0}^{K} (2n+1)^2 = \frac{(2K+1)(2K+3)}{3} = \frac{M^2-1}{3}$$
$$(4\text{-}95)$$

while for (4-94), with $M = 2K + 1$,

$$\text{av } b_{k+m}^2 = \frac{1}{2K+1} \sum_{n=-K}^{K} (2n)^2 = \frac{4K(K+1)}{3} = \frac{M^2-1}{3} \qquad (4\text{-}96)$$

Both results are thus the same when expressed in terms of number of levels.

The average input power to the channel is therefore

$$W_M = \frac{M^2-1}{3} W_1 \qquad (4\text{-}97)$$

where W_1 is the bipolar value given by Eq. (4-48). From Eqs. (4-42), (4-92), and (4-97), the performance of the M-ary bipolar system relative to the binary system can be expressed as a probability of error $2(M-1)/M$ times as great when the average channel input power is $(M^2-1)/3$ times as great. The ratio $2(M-1)/M$ approaches 2 as M becomes large. A factor of 2, applied to error rate, is ordinarily not significant. For example, whether the error rate is 10^{-5} or 2×10^{-5} does not matter much; a small change in signal power would account for the difference. The factor $(M^2-1)/3$ applied to average signal power approaches $M^2/3$ as M becomes large, and corresponds to an increment of $(20 \log_{10} M - 4.8)$ db. A 16-level system would thus require a 19.3-db increment in average signal power to maintain approximately the same error rate as a binary system.

When a multilevel system is adapted to transmit binary data, we should keep in mind that the multilevel error rate just computed is in terms of errors per M-ary symbol and not errors per bit. If $M = 2^N$, binary words of length N bits would be coded as a single M-valued symbol. An error in a symbol can produce from 1 to N bits in error, depending on

Table 4-1   Gray code for binary representation of multilevel symbols

Level number	Gray code				Level number	Gray code			
1	0	0	0	0	9	1	1	0	0
2	0	0	0	1	10	1	1	0	1
3	0	0	1	1	11	1	1	1	1
4	0	0	1	0	12	1	1	1	0
5	0	1	1	0	13	1	0	1	0
6	0	1	1	1	14	1	0	1	1
7	0	1	0	1	15	1	0	0	1
8	0	1	0	0	16	1	0	0	0

which incorrect symbol is received and on what coding plan is used to go from binary to M-ary symbols.

If the probability of error is very low, almost all of the errors in an M-ary system are of the adjacent-level type. It becomes important, therefore, in translating from binary to M-ary to use a code in which adjacent-level errors produce few bit errors. In the Gray code, for example, two adjacent-level words differ only in one of the symbols, as shown in Table 4-1 for a 16-level system. For low error rates, the number of bits in error in a long message is approximately equal to the number of symbols in error. For N-bit words, the probability of a bit being in error is then approximately equal to $1/N$ times the probability that a symbol is in error.

PROBLEMS

4-1. In 1855 Kelvin analyzed the problem of signaling over a submarine cable and enunciated the KR law, which states that the maximum operating speed of a cable with shunt capacitance K and series resistance R is inversely proportional to KR. Relate this law to bandwidth of the cable. Assume that the transmittance function

$$H(f) = \exp\left(-l\sqrt{j2\pi frc}\right)$$

is valid for a cable of length l, series resistance r per unit of length, capacitance c per unit of length, negligible series inductance, and negligible shunt conductance. Define bandwidth in terms of any convenient reduction in transmission.

4-2. Give an example of a band-limited function which has nonzero components throughout a range from $f = 0$ to $f_s < |f| < 3f_s/2$ and satisfies Nyquist I.

4-3. What is $q(t)$ for a Nyquist I function with a linear rolloff between f_1 and $f_s - f_1$? How do the peaks decay with large $|t|$?

4-4. What is the maximum possible instantaneous magnitude attainable by an infinite sequence of synchronous binary signals which meet Nyquist I by a 100 percent linear rolloff?

4-5. Show how the minimum-bandwidth signal which satisfies Nyquist II can be constructed as the sum of two time-displaced sinc functions.

4-6. A bipolar binary telegraph signal wave is generated by sending a rectangular wave of $+1$ volt for the symbol 1 and -1 volt for the symbol 0. The channel is an RC circuit with

$$H(f) = \frac{1}{1 + jf/f_0}$$

The sending and receiving filters have uniform transmission at all frequencies. Construct traces of the eye pattern at a signaling speed of $4f_0$ bauds for the following data sequences:

    (a) All 1's

    (b) All 0's

    (c) Alternating 1's and 0's

    (d) A long sequence of 1's followed by a long sequence of 0's

    (e) A long sequence of 1's followed by a single zero and a long sequence of 1's

Show only enough traces to define the significant features of the eye pattern.

4-7. Prove that Eq. (4-39) is necessary as well as sufficient for satisfaction of Nyquist II.

4-8. A binary signaling system operates at 2.0 megabits/sec over a channel with $|H(f)| = 10^{-5}$ and a temperature of $290°K$. The average input power to the channel is 10^{-3} W. The receiving amplifier has a noise figure of 1.1 at all frequencies within its band. The system is designed to meet Nyquist's first criterion for suppression of intersymbol interference, and the filters are optimized for minimum error rate. What is the probability of error?

4-9. A binary telegraph transmitter delivers rectangular pulses of width T. What should $Y_1(f)$ be for minimum probability of error when the channel is flat with additive white gaussian noise?

4-10. Find the optimum $|Y_2(f)|$ when the channel consists of a cable with $H(f)$ as given in Prob. 4-1.

4-11. A quaternary transmission system is optimized for minimum error probability with the Nyquist I criterion met and with the four symbol values chosen as in Eq. (4-93). For all m and n, find the conditional decision probability $p(a_m|a_n)$ defined as the probability that the symbol a_m will be received when the symbol a_n is sent.

4-12. Show that if Nyquist I is satisfied by including both real and imaginary components of $Q(f)$ in Eq. (4-27), the probability of error is increased in the case of a flat channel with additive white gaussian noise and fixed average input power to the channel.

REFERENCES

1. Nyquist, H.: Certain Topics in Telegraph Transmission Theory, *Trans. AIEE*, vol. 47, pp. 617–644, April, 1928.
2. Gulstad, K.: Vibrating Cable Relay, *Elec. Rev.* (London), vol. 42, pp. 751–752, June, 3, 1898; pp. 792–794, June 10, 1898.
3. Bennett, W. R., and J. R. Davey: "Data Transmission," chap. 18, pp. 305–314, McGraw-Hill, New York, 1965.

5
Baseband Television Signals

In telegraphy and telephony we were able to express our primary data as a function of one variable, the time. In the case of telegraphy, successive choices of discrete magnitudes are made for successive discrete time intervals, while in telephony the original signal is defined by an instantaneous value of sound pressure varying continuously with time. In television we encounter a new situation in which more than one independent variable is required to describe the information which we desire to transmit. In black-and-white two-dimensional television transmission, the information consists of the brightness of the image, which may be expressed as a function of three independent variables x, y, and t, where x and y are the rectangular coordinates of the image and t is the time. Our electrical transmission systems exhibit a single quantity such as current or voltage as a function of only one variable, the time. We have, therefore, a problem which can be described in mathematical language as mapping a space into a space of a lower number of dimensions. Such mapping can be done but not continuously; i.e., adjacent parts of the signal wave cannot always represent adjacent parts of the television picture.   Some sort of a scanning process is required in which the values of brightness are given for x and y sequentially in time and the process repeated within a sufficiently short interval not to miss anything of value.

As in the case of telephony, the development of television has been closely integrated with the properties of the corresponding human sensory system involved.   In television it is the eye which plays the dominant role.   The phenomenon of persistence of vision determines the time rate at which the image field representing the picture must be reproduced in order to create the same sensation as a steady picture.   Here a matter of expediency in apparatus comes into play inasmuch as it is simpler to scan the picture repeatedly at this rate rather than to take advantage of the fact that the individual successive images do not differ much from each other.   The result is that at the scanning rates used we can get a fairly accurate idea of the spectrum by assuming that the image field does not vary with time, i.e., by treating it as a still picture.   To fix the scale in our minds, we note that in the United States 30 complete pictures are scanned per second with 525 horizontal scanning lines for each complete picture.

5-1 FOURIER–SERIES REPRESENTATION OF A TELEVISION SIGNAL

The theory of Fourier series can be used to calculate the spectrum resulting from repeated scanning of a still picture.   A convenient representation is obtained by assuming an array of fields periodically recurring in both the x and y dimensions as shown in Fig. 5-1.[1]   If the scanning aperture moves along the dashed line with slope proportional to the ratio of vertical and horizontal scanning velocities, the brightness of the field at points traversed by the line traces out the curve of electrical output versus time.   The insertion of the repeated infinite array of fields enables the infinite path along a straight line to provide the same mathematical result as quick flybacks from terminal edge to beginning would give if

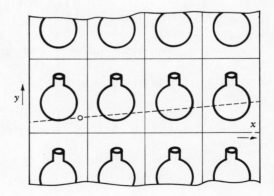

Fig. 5-1 Array of periodically recurring scanned fields.

only one field were drawn. The brightness function $B(x,y)$ is originally defined for all values of x and y comprised by the picture, say values of x from 0 to a and y from 0 to b. Introducing the doubly infinite array of similar pictures enables us to define $B(x,y)$ for all x and y as a doubly periodic function with period a in x and period b in y. The theory of Fourier series previously given for a single independent variable is easily generalized to any number of variables. For the case of two variables, we write

$$B(x,y) = \sum_{m=-\infty}^{\infty} \sum_{n=-\infty}^{\infty} c_{mn} e^{2\pi j(mx/a+ny/b)} \tag{5-1}$$

and determine the coefficient c_{mn} by a procedure similar to that used for the single-variable case, that is, by multiplying both sides by the conjugate exponential factor with a particular pair of values for m and n and integrating both sides with respect to both x and y throughout a period rectangle. The result is

$$c_{mn} = \frac{1}{ab} \int_0^a \int_0^b B(x,y) e^{-2\pi j(mx/a+ny/b)} \, dx \, dy \tag{5-2}$$

It is seen by increasing x by a and y by b in Eq. (5-1) that the function $B(x,y)$ defined by the double Fourier series has the proper periodicity in x and y.

If we assume that the scanning pickup is a geometrical point moving with horizontal component of velocity u and vertical component of velocity v, then

$$x = ut \qquad y = vt \tag{5-3}$$

The current flowing in the electric circuit may then be represented by

$$I(t) = k \sum_{m=-\infty}^{\infty} \sum_{n=-\infty}^{\infty} c_{mn} e^{2\pi j(mu/a+nv/b)t} \tag{5-4}$$

A line spectrum is thus obtained in which the frequencies are of the form $mu/a \pm nv/b$ with m and n taking on integer values. Now u/a is the horizontal velocity divided by the image width and is, therefore, the line-scanning frequency, which for commercial telecasting in the United States is 525×30 Hz = 15.75 kHz. Likewise v/b is the vertical velocity divided by the image height and is, therefore, the image repetition frequency, which is 30 Hz. The structure of the line spectrum is therefore a series of harmonics of 15.75 kHz (including the zeroth harmonic, or d-c) about each of which is clustered an array of satellite lines spaced 30 Hz apart.

The way in which the amplitudes of the line-scanning harmonics fall off with frequency is determined by the image detail parallel to the scanning direction. The widest frequency range is produced by a sharp vertical stripe which approximates an impulse function in the x direction. The minimum width of such a stripe which the system can resolve is determined by the range of frequencies transmitted, which in commercial telecasting is between 3 and 4 MHz. The rate at which the satellite amplitudes fall off in either direction from the central harmonic is determined by detail along the vertical direction. Since the vertical component of scanning velocity is only $\frac{1}{525}$ of the horizontal component, the important satellite components fall within a much narrower frequency range than the line-scanning harmonics. It is found in practice that centered midway between line-scanning harmonics there are very considerable gaps in which there is insignificant signal energy. Removal of these frequency ranges by filtering does not disturb the received picture.

5-2 THE APERTURE EFFECT

The assumption of point scanning is a first approximation. The so-called *aperture effect* resulting from the finite dimensions of the aperture is of basic importance in many communication problems and is worth examining in some detail. The aperture may be defined by a space transmission function $G(\xi, \eta)$, where ξ and η are rectangular coordinates defined with respect to an origin at the center of the aperture, and $G(\xi, \eta)$ gives the ratio of transmitted intensity to incident intensity for the aperture at point (ξ, η). For example, if the aperture were a rectangular hole of width w and height h, then $G(\xi, \eta)$ would be unity for ξ between $-w/2$ and $w/2$, and η between $-h/2$ and $h/2$. For coordinates outside this range, the value of $G(\xi, \eta)$ would be zero. The total illumination received through the aperture is obtained by integration, and the resulting electric current when the center of the aperture is at (x, y) must be of form

$$I = k \int_{-\infty}^{\infty} \int_{-\infty}^{\infty} G(\xi, \eta) \, B(x + \xi, \, y + \eta) \, d\xi \, d\eta \tag{5-5}$$

If we substitute the double-Fourier-series representation for $B(x, y)$, we find that

$$I = k \sum_{m=-\infty}^{\infty} \sum_{n=-\infty}^{\infty} c_{mn} \int_{-\infty}^{\infty} \int_{-\infty}^{\infty} e^{2\pi j[m(x+\xi)/a + n(y+\eta)/b]} \, G(\xi, \eta) \, d\xi \, d\eta$$

$$= k \sum_{m=-\infty}^{\infty} \sum_{n=-\infty}^{\infty} Y_{mn} c_{mn} e^{2\pi j(mx/a + ny/b)} \tag{5-6}$$

where

$$Y_{mn} = \int_{-\infty}^{\infty} \int_{-\infty}^{\infty} G(\xi, \eta) e^{2\pi j(m\xi/a + n\eta/b)} \, d\xi \, d\eta \tag{5-7}$$

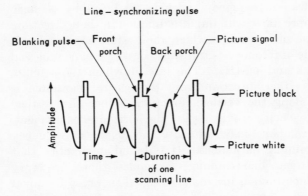

Fig. 5-2 Television signal wave.

That is, the aperture exerts a filter-like effect which may be calculated for each spectral frequency in terms of the dimensions of the aperture. We note that the filtering is a two-dimensional process applied to a spatial frequency pattern. The electrical current is, however, one-dimensional, and the aperture effect cannot be completely defined by a single response-vs.-frequency function but rather as a family of response-vs.-frequency functions centered about each harmonic of the scanning frequency.

The still-picture analysis is adequate for fields which change slowly with time. The effect of motion in the picture is to make the line structure diffuse giving a continuous instead of a line spectrum. The distribution of energy, however, remains concentrated near the same regions of the frequency scale.

Television is like telegraph in that phase as well as amplitude relations must be preserved over the principal parts of the spectrum, and also in that frequencies all the way down to zero must be transmitted. The actual d-c component determines the average illumination of the picture. The scanning process requires synchronism of the receiver with the transmitter. This is accomplished by sending, between line scans, a special pulse of standard height outside the bounds of the picture-signal amplitude range, as shown in Fig. 5-2. The presence of this standard pulse height also enables the receiver to employ circuits which do not transmit direct current. The d-c component can be reinserted where needed by closing a discharge circuit in series with a blocking condenser at the time the synchronizing pulse arrives, thereby forcing the condenser to take the reference potential established by the pulse.

5-3 COLOR TELEVISION AND OTHER VISUAL SIGNALS

Color television differs from black-and-white in that transmission of separate pictures in the three primary colors is required. This does not mean that we must be able to send and receive three independent pictures each equivalent to one black-and-white, for the three colors do not contain independent information and are not all equally important. Compatible color television is now being telecast in the United States without enlarging the bandwidth requirements standardized for black-and-white. Use is made of the relatively vacant spaces between harmonics of the line-scanning frequency in the black-and-white spectrum. Advantage is also taken of the fact that complete three-color information is needed only for the lower-frequency components of the television spectrum. Since the construction of the baseband color television signal requires modulation processes, the detailed treatment will be deferred until the necessary theory has been presented. (See Prob. 6-23.)

Our treatment of television signals is also applicable to telephotography and facsimile transmission. The latter problems are simpler in that only one field is sent and the time available is much longer.

PROBLEMS

5-1. Find the coefficient c_{mn} when the image consists of a white rectangle occupying the lower left-hand quarter of a black rectangular background. (See Fig. 5-3.)

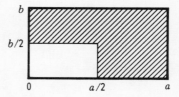

Fig. 5-3 Rectangular television image.

5-2. Find c_{mn} when the image is a white, horizontal, double fan-shaped pattern with angle $\theta°$ centrally located as shown in Fig. 5-4. The remainder of the rectangular field is black.

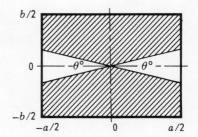

Fig. 5-4 Fan-shaped television image.

5-3. Evaluate the aperture effect for a rectangular aperture of width w and height h.

5-4. Evaluate the aperture effect when the scanning is performed by a uniform beam of circular cross section. Compare the result with that for a rectangular aperture.

Hint: Transform to polar coordinates. The following integrals may then be found useful:

$$\int_{\alpha}^{2\pi+\alpha} e^{jz\cos\phi}\, d\phi = 2\pi J_0(z) \qquad \int z J_0(z)\, dz = z J_1(z)$$

where $J_0(z)$ and $J_1(z)$ are Bessel functions of order 0 and 1, respectively. (See Appendix.)

5-5. Evaluate the aperture effect when the scanning beam is not bounded but varies in density as e^{-cr^2}, where r is the distance from the center and $c > 0$. The following integral may be useful:

$$\int_0^{\infty} z J_0(az) e^{-bz^2}\, dz = \frac{1}{2b} e^{-a^2/4b} \qquad b > 0$$

REFERENCE

1. Mertz, P., and F. Gray: A Theory of Scanning and Its Relation to the Characteristics of the Transmitted Signal in Telephotography and Television, *Bell System Tech. J.*, vol. 13, pp. 464–515, July, 1934.

6

Basic Principles of Modulation

The first four chapters have illustrated how baseband signals can be represented by sinusoidal components extending over a finite range of frequencies characteristic of the type of signal. Design of baseband transmission channels can be completely expressed in terms of the ability of the channel to respond to the appropriate frequencies. However, the design of communication systems would be most severely constrained if transmission of signals had to be performed exclusively at baseband frequencies throughout all parts of the system. The vast spectrum of frequencies which technology has made available for practical use in communication extends continuously from zero to many quadrillions of hertz. Transmission media making available large segments of this spectrum can be realized in the form of coaxial cables, radio beams, wave-guides, optical paths, and even simple pairs of wires. Effective utilization of the wideband resources of these media requires a shift of the range of baseband frequencies into other ranges for transmission and a corresponding shift back to the original range after reception. Band shifting not only offers a means of fitting a given baseband signal to the capabilities of a particular medium but also enables a plurality of baseband signals to share one wideband transmission channel.

6-1 DEFINITION OF MODULATION

A shift of the range of frequencies in a signal is accomplished by the process known as *modulation*, which has been defined by one appropriate standardization body[1] as "the process or result of the process whereby some characteristic of a wave is varied in accordance with another wave." There are, in fact, two reasons why modulation is important in signal transmission.   One is that the process is often an inherent defect leading to distortion and interference.   Our more immediate concern here, however, is with the second reason, which is that modulation can function as a controlled band-shifting process.

A simple block diagram in Fig. 6-1 illustrates the typical use of modulation in a signal-transmission system.   We assume that the band of frequencies passed by the medium does not coincide with the frequencies defining the baseband signal.   In the *modulator*, the baseband wave varies some characteristic of a *carrier wave* generated by a *carrier source*.   The *modulated wave* thus produced is defined by frequencies within the band of the transmission medium.   At the far end, the modulated wave acts on a carrier wave in a *demodulator*, which is a modulator designed to recover the baseband signal.   From the results of Chap. 1, it is clear that no linear time-invariant system can serve as a modulator since the response contains no frequencies not present in the original stimulus.   Modulation theory, therefore, is essentially a study of linear time-varying and nonlinear systems.

In the present chapter, we shall review the various kinds of modulation and define the terms customarily used in their description.   More detailed studies of the important modulation systems will be given in later chapters.

6-2 LINEAR MODULATION

In a *linear modulator*, the output is a linear time-varying function of the baseband signal wave.   In the simplest case, the modulated wave is proportional to the product of the baseband and carrier waves.   In an important class of modulation systems, the carrier source is an oscillator delivering a sine wave

$$c(t) = a_c \cos (\omega_c t + \theta_c) \tag{6-1}$$

If the baseband signal is $s(t)$, the output of a *productor*, or *product-type modulator*, is the *modulated wave*

$$\mu(t) = k_1 s(t) c(t) = k_1 a_c s(t) \cos (\omega_c t + \theta_c) \tag{6-2}$$

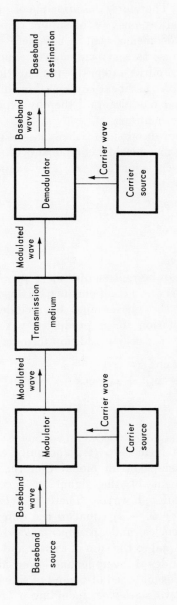

Fig. 6-1 Block diagram of carrier system for signal transmission.

The response $\mu(t)$ satisfies the condition for linearity in terms of the excitation function $s(t)$. Therefore, the principle of superposition can be used to calculate the total response as the sum of responses to individual components of $s(t)$. This means that a complete description can be obtained from the response to a typical single-frequency component of $s(t)$. Fourier-series and Fourier-integral representations can be used to express general signal waves as linear combinations of such components. The entire theory of linear modulators is thereby expressible in terms of elementary trigonometric relations.

We shall simplify our discussion without loss of essential generality by omitting phase angles in sinusoidal components of form $\cos(\omega t + \theta)$ if the functional dependence is on $\omega t + \theta$. For example, results for a single-frequency signal wave

$$s(t) = s_1 \cos(\omega_1 t + \theta_1) \tag{6-3}$$

can be obtained in terms of

$$s(t) = s_1 \cos \omega_1 t \tag{6-4}$$

In the final answer, $\omega_1 t$ can be replaced by $\omega_1 t + \theta_1$ when the phase is of interest. It is only in the case of components with dependent frequencies, e.g., ω_1 and $2\omega_1$, that the phase must be included throughout the solution. The basic equation for a productor with sinusoidal signal representation is then, by the cosine addition formula,

$$\begin{aligned}\mu(t) &= k_1 a_c s_1 \cos \omega_1 t \cos \omega_c t \\ &= \mu_1 s_1 \cos(\omega_c + \omega_1)t + \mu_1 s_1 \cos(\omega_c - \omega_1)t\end{aligned} \tag{6-5}$$

where

$$\mu_1 = \frac{k_1 a_c}{2} \tag{6-6}$$

Although simple in form, Eq. (6-5) actually expresses the most important basic relationships in all modulation theory. Note that a single-frequency component of the signal produces two sinusoidal components in the modulated wave. There is a *lower side-frequency* component with frequency $\omega_c - \omega_1$ equal to the difference between the carrier and signal frequencies, and an *upper side-frequency* component with frequency $\omega_c + \omega_1$ equal to the sum of carrier and signal frequencies. In a productor the amplitudes of the upper and lower side-frequency terms are equal. If the signal is composed of a band of sinusoidal components, the modulator delivers two *sidebands*, including a *lower sideband* composed of the lower side frequencies and an *upper sideband* composed of the upper side frequencies. The frequency relations are shown graphically in Fig. 6-2 for the case in which ω_c is greater than any frequency in the signal band. The upper sideband consists of the baseband components

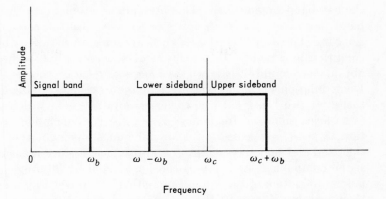

Fig. 6-2 Relation of signal and sidebands in linear modulation.

translated upward in frequency by the constant shift ω_c. The lower sideband is formed by translation and inversion of the baseband frequencies. By replacement of $\omega_c t$ by $\omega_c t + \theta_c$ and of $\omega_1 t$ by $\omega_1 t + \theta_1$, we establish that the phase angle of an upper-sideband component is the sum of the carrier and signal phases, while the phase of a lower-sideband component is the difference. Each sideband is linearly related to the baseband signal.

The baseband signal can be uniquely recovered from either sideband by a second modulation process with a carrier wave of the same frequency and phase as in the first modulator. It is instructive to derive this as a special case of the more general demodulation by a carrier of the same frequency but arbitrary phase difference ϕ. Assuming k_2 as the second productor constant, we obtain for an upper-sideband component

$$k_2 b_c \cos(\omega_c t + \phi) \, \mu_1 s_1 \cos(\omega_c + \omega_1)t$$
$$= \mu_2 s_1 \cos(\omega_1 t - \phi) + \mu_2 s_1 \cos[(2\omega_c + \omega_1)t + \phi] \quad (6\text{-}7)$$

where

$$\mu_2 = \frac{k_2 b_c \mu_1}{2} = \frac{k_1 k_2 a_c b_c}{4} \quad (6\text{-}8)$$

Similarly for a lower-sideband component

$$k_2 b_c \cos(\omega_c t + \phi) \, \mu_1 s_1 \cos(\omega_c - \omega_1)t$$
$$= \mu_2 s_1 \cos(\omega_1 t + \phi) + \mu_2 s_1 \cos[(2\omega_c - \omega_1)t + \phi] \quad (6\text{-}9)$$

The terms with frequencies $2\omega_c + \omega_1$ and $2\omega_c - \omega_1$ can be removed by low-pass filters if the carrier frequency is sufficiently elevated above the baseband frequencies. This presents no problem for the upper sideband since $2\omega_c + \omega_1 > \omega_1$ for any $\omega_1 > 0$. In the case of the lower sideband, however, $2\omega_c - \omega_1 > \omega_1$ if and only if $\omega_c > \omega_1$, which was the condition assumed in Fig. 6-2. If $\omega_c < \omega_1$ for some values of ω_1, we obtain the condition known as *sideband foldover* shown in Fig. 6-3. Demodulation of the lower sideband then becomes ambiguous because there are two baseband frequencies ω_1 and $2\omega_c - \omega_1$ which produce the same lower-sideband frequency $|\omega_c - \omega_1|$. We conclude that the condition $\omega_c > \omega_1$ is necessary for unambiguous demodulation of a lower sideband and that this condition is also sufficient since it ensures that the signal component in Eq. (6-9) can be selected by filtering. Distortionless reproduction of the signal from either the upper or lower sideband is then possible if $\phi = 0$, that is, if the demodulating and modulating carrier phases are equal.

The fact that either sideband contains all the signal information suggests that only one sideband need be transmitted, and hence that a carrier system can be operated with the same bandwidth as a baseband system. In a *single-sideband* (SSB) system, one sideband is removed from the modulator output. In the case of voice transmission, this can be done by a frequency-selective network without excessive difficulty because of the "energy gap" in the baseband between zero and a few hundred hertz. As shown in Fig. 6-4, the resulting vacant frequency interval between the two sidebands serves as a transition region between low and high loss in the SSB filter.

Telegraph and television signals, on the other hand, have spectra extending all the way to zero frequency, and the upper and lower sidebands, therefore, meet at the carrier frequency. To obtain a partial bandwidth reduction, *asymmetrical-sideband* (ASB) systems can be used. Equations (6-7) and (6-9) show that the contributions to signal from the upper and lower sidebands are equal when the amplitudes of the two side-

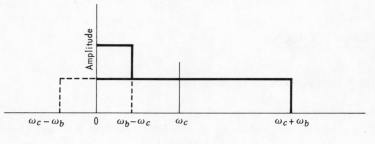

Fig. 6-3   Sideband foldover caused by a too low carrier frequency.

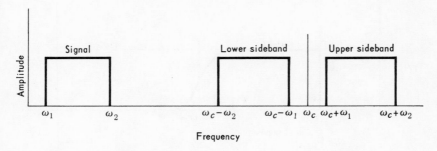

Fig. 6-4 Sideband produced by signal with low-frequency energy gap.

frequency components are equal.   In an ASB system, the upper and lower side frequencies are transmitted unequally.   This could result in a variation of gain versus signal frequency for the complete system.   In one particular species of ASB called *vestigial sideband* (VSB), the gain variation is avoided by adjusting the transmitted vestige of the unwanted sideband to compensate for the amount the filter removes from the desired sideband.   The transmittance function of a VSB filter, Fig. 6-5, satisfies the relation

$$Y(\omega_c - \omega) + Y(\omega_c + \omega) = 2Y(\omega_c) \tag{6-10}$$

This equation defines the same gradual transition which preserves freedom from intersymbol interference in telegraphy, as described in Chap. 4.

As shown by Eqs. (6-7) and (6-9), the effect of phase error in the demodulating carrier in SSB transmission is to insert a constant phase shift in all signal components.   In telephony this does not matter because the ear responds only to the amplitudes.   In fact, not only can the phase be wrong, but the frequency of the demodulating carrier can be in error by several hertz without the listener noticing any difference in quality.   In telegraph or television transmission, a constant phase shift in all components can be disastrous.

In a *double-sideband* (DSB) system the phase of the carrier affects not only the phase of individual components recovered from one sideband but also the phase angle between contributions from the two sidebands to the same baseband component.   From Eqs. (6-7) and (6-9), the recovered baseband wave of frequency ω_1 obtained by adding the demodulated DSB components is

$$\mu_2 s_1 \cos(\omega_1 t - \phi) + \mu_2 s_1 \cos(\omega_1 t + \phi) = 2\mu_2 s_1 \cos \phi \cos \omega_1 t \tag{6-11}$$

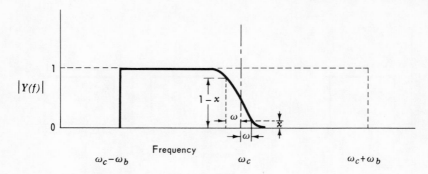

Fig. 6-5 Vestigial-sideband filter characteristic.

The net effect of the carrier-phase error is thus an amplitude reduction factor $\cos \phi$. When the error is $\pm 90°$, the resultant amplitude vanishes. This demonstrates that a two-channel DSB multiplex system can be realized with carriers phased 90° apart. Such a DSB system, which is called a quadrature-carrier multiplex, attains the same economical use of bandwidth as baseband and SSB transmission.

It has been assumed so far that the modulated wave is transmitted distortionlessly to the receiver. A linear phase shift can be compensated by appropriately retarding the phase of the demodulating carrier wave. In the general case of an intervening medium with transmittance function

$$Y(\omega) = A(\omega) \, e^{-jB(\omega)} \tag{6-12}$$

the recovered baseband component from the upper sideband of Eq. (6-7) is replaced by

$$s_+(t) = \mu_2 A(\omega_c + \omega_1) s_1 \cos [\omega_1 t - \phi - B(\omega_c + \omega_1)] \tag{6-13}$$

while the corresponding lower-sideband contribution of Eq. (6-9) becomes

$$s_-(t) = \mu_2 A(\omega_c - \omega_1) s_1 \cos [\omega_1 t + \phi + B(\omega_c - \omega_1)] \tag{6-14}$$

These results are obtained by modifying the terms $\cos(\omega_c + \omega_1)t$ and $\cos(\omega_c - \omega_1)t$ to take account of the amplitude and phase changes introduced by the medium.

In general, the total recovered baseband signal component is given by

$$\begin{aligned} s_b(t) &= s_+(t) + s_-(t) \\ &= \mu_2 s_1 \operatorname{Re} \{[Y(\omega_c + \omega_1)e^{-j\phi} + Y^*(\omega_c - \omega_1)e^{j\phi}]e^{j\omega_1 t}\} \end{aligned} \tag{6-15}$$

The average demodulated baseband signal power for a sine-wave signal component is accordingly

$$S_b = \frac{\mu_2{}^2 s_1{}^2}{2} \, |Y(\omega_c + \omega_1)e^{-j\phi} + Y^*(\omega_c - \omega_1)e^{j\phi}|^2 \tag{6-16}$$

These formulas hold for SSB, ASB, and DSB. For the SSB case, we have $s_b(t) = s_\pm(t)$ and

$$S_b = S_1 = \frac{\mu_2{}^2 s_1{}^2}{2} \, |Y(\omega_c \pm \omega_1)|^2 \tag{6-17}$$

with the upper and lower signs associated, respectively, with upper- and lower-sideband systems. For the distortionless DSB system with linear phase shift $B(\omega) = \tau\omega$, constant amplitude $A(\omega) = K$, and carrier phase $\phi = -\tau\omega_c$,

$$s_b(t) = 2\mu_2 K s_1 \cos \omega_1(t - \tau) = 2\mu_2 K s(t - \tau) \tag{6-18}$$

and

$$S_b = S_2 = 2\mu_2{}^2 K^2 s_1{}^2 \tag{6-19}$$

Note that the signal power received from the DSB system is four times as great as from the SSB case because the sideband contributions add in phase.

A transmission system employing linear modulation and demodulation has the same simplicity as a baseband system. The properties of the transmission medium can be converted into equivalent baseband properties by appropriate translation of the frequencies. Additive noise in the channel is linearly translated into the baseband at the receiver. A spectral density $w(f)$ in the channel produces a baseband spectral density $w_b(f)$ which in a DSB system is the sum of upper- and lower-sideband contributions; thus

$$w_b(f) = \left(\frac{k_2 b_c}{2}\right)^2 [w(f_c - f) + w(f_c + f)] \tag{6-20}$$

The mean total noise power received in a baseband extending from f_1 to f_2 is

$$N_2 = \left(\frac{k_2 b_c}{2}\right)^2 \int_{f_1}^{f_2} [w(f_c - f) + w(f_c + f)] \, df \tag{6-21}$$

For ASB and SSB systems, a receiving filter between the line and the demodulator would remove the noise from the sideband ranges containing no signal components. In particular, for an SSB system

$$N_1 = \left(\frac{k_2 b_c}{2}\right)^2 \int_{f_1}^{f_2} w(f_c \pm f) \, df \tag{6-22}$$

A practical case of interest is that of white gaussian noise, defined as gaussian noise with constant spectral density, that is, $w(f) = w_0$. The received noise-power values for SSB and DSB in a baseband of width $f_b = f_2 - f_1$ are

$$N_1 = \left(\frac{k_2 b_c}{2}\right)^2 w_0 f_b \tag{6-23}$$

$$N_2 = 2N_1 \tag{6-24}$$

The received noise power in the DSB system is twice that for the SSB system. The multiplying factor of 2, applied to power, is characteristic of equal components with random phase. We recall that the signal components recovered from the two sidebands of an ideal DSB system are in phase and produce a total mean power four times as great as that from one sideband.

We compare the output signal-to-noise ratios in the ideal SSB and DSB systems by assuming $Y(\omega_c \pm \omega_1) = K$ in Eqs. (6-16) and (6-17) and by introducing as a reference the mean transmitted signal power W_s. In the SSB case, selection of one component in Eq. (6-5) gives

$$W_s = W_1 = \frac{\mu_1^2 s_1^2}{2} \tag{6-25}$$

while in the DSB case, transmission of the two components of Eq. (6-5) requires average power twice as great, or

$$W_s = W_2 = \mu_1^2 s_1^2 \tag{6-26}$$

Then for ideal SSB, Eqs. (6-8), (6-17), (6-23), and (6-25) give

$$\frac{S_1}{N_1} = \frac{K^2 W_1}{w_0 f_b} \tag{6-27}$$

For ideal DSB, Eqs. (6-8), (6-19), (6-24), and (6-26) give

$$\frac{S_2}{N_2} = \frac{K^2 W_2}{w_0 f_b} \tag{6-28}$$

The same signal-to-noise ratios are thus obtained for the same mean transmitted power. The DSB system admits twice as much noise power but produces four times as much recovered signal power by expending twice as much transmitted power.

The demodulating procedure just described is known under the three different names of *homodyne*, *synchronous*, and *coherent detection*. Usage of the last two terms is in accord with their familiar meanings. The word *homodyne* signifies a locally supplied carrier with the same frequency as that applied at the transmitting modulator. *Homodyning* is distinguished from *heterodyning*, in which a different carrier frequency is used to translate the modulated wave to still another frequency range. In a heterodyne receiver, the incoming *radio-frequency* (r-f) wave is translated to an *intermediate-frequency* (i-f) range suitable for amplification before demodulation to baseband. In a receiver which selects channels on the basis of their frequency occupancies, the heterodyning carrier-frequency oscillator, often called the beating oscillator, is the tuning control which determines what part of the incoming spectrum is moved into the band of the i-f amplifier.

6-3 AMPLITUDE MODULATION

While linear modulation and demodulation systems are not only pleasingly tractable for analysis but are also outstanding in economy of bandwidth and signal power, they have a serious practical disadvantage. They require apparatus of high precision to supply synchronous carrier at the receiver. From the standpoint of simple and rugged circuitry, there are two nonlinear modulation methods which excel the linear scheme. These are *amplitude modulation* (AM) and *frequency modulation* (FM).

Amplitude modulation is defined as a process in which the amplitude of a carrier wave varies linearly with the baseband signal. It might seem wrong to call such a process nonlinear, but the failure to satisfy the definition of linearity inevitably follows from the definition of *amplitude* of an oscillatory wave as a *positive-valued* quantity. A purely amplitude-modulated wave can be written as

$$\mu(t) = a(t) \cos \omega_c t \qquad (6\text{-}29)$$

with $a(t) \geq 0$. If $a(t)$ were to change sign, a positive amplitude could be retained only by inserting a phase change of π rad, which would mean that the wave would acquire both amplitude and phase modulation.

To make $a(t)$ proportional to the baseband signal would not satisfy the general condition for linearity since all signals in which changes of sign occur would be excluded. More general inclusion is obtained by setting

$$a(t) = a_0 + s(t) \qquad (6\text{-}30)$$

where $s(t) \geq -a_0$. By making a_0 sufficiently large we could include any specified range of signal values. But the response wave

$$\mu(t) = [a_0 + s(t)] \cos \omega_c t \qquad (6\text{-}31)$$

fails to meet the definition of a linear system with $s(t)$ as input. For if $\mu_1(t)$ is the response to $s_1(t)$ and $\mu_2(t)$ is the response to $s_2(t)$, the response to $s_1(t) + s_2(t)$ is not $\mu_1(t) + \mu_2(t)$.

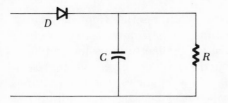

Fig. 6-6   Envelope detector.

It is true that the departure from linearity in AM is of a mild sort and that most of the mathematical procedures applicable to linear modulation can be retained.   We need only keep in mind that there is an unmodulated carrier wave $a_0 \cos (\omega_c t + \theta_c)$ not related to the signal. Although the unmodulated carrier component contains no signal information, its presence at the receiver can be of great practical value.   We have seen that a significant difficulty in realization of a linear modulation system is the local carrier supply at the receiver.   In an AM system the carrier accompanies the received signal, and no local carrier is needed for the demodulation process.   The term *double-sideband transmitted carrier* (DSBTC) is sometimes used to distinguish the case in which unmodulated carrier is present from the linear DSB case, which is also called *double-sideband suppressed carrier* (DSBSC).   A DSBTC system does not necessarily include enough carrier to qualify as AM.

A narrow-band AM wave, i.e., one in which the width of the baseband is small compared with the carrier frequency, can be demodulated very simply by an *envelope detector*.   An envelope detector of series type is shown in Fig. 6-6.   The diode D has low resistance to current flow in the direction shown by the arrow and a high resistance when the current is in the opposite direction.   The shape of the applied AM voltage wave is shown in Fig. 6-7.   When the voltage builds up in the conducting direction of D, the capacitor C charges rapidly and follows the applied voltage up to the positive peak.   As the voltage decreases from the peak, the capacitor discharges slowly through the high resistance R.   The result is that a back-bias voltage nearly balancing the positive peaks of the applied voltage is maintained on the capacitor and hence across R, which forms the load resistance.   The output voltage of the detector is very nearly the envelope of the AM wave as shown by the solid upper line of Fig. 6-7.

An approximate mathematical study of the envelope detector can be performed by considering the unmodulated sine wave

$$c(t) = a_c \cos \omega_c t \tag{6-32}$$

as the applied voltage.   Let $i_d(t)$ represent the input current, which is also the current in the diode.   Because of the nonlinearity of the diode,

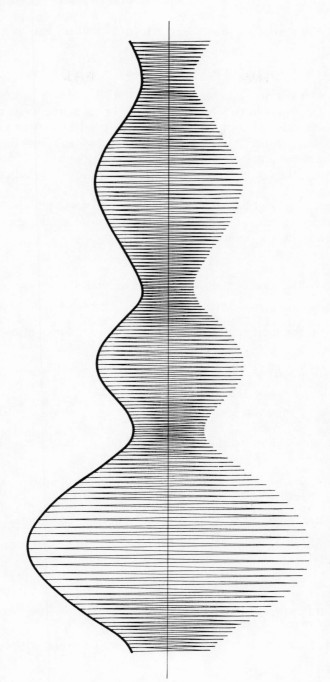

Fig. 6-7 Response of envelope detector to an AM wave.

harmonics of the carrier frequency occur in $i_d(t)$, and we can write, in general,

$$i_d(t) = i_0 + i_1 \cos (\omega_c t + \alpha_1) + i_2 \cos (2\omega_c t + \alpha_2) + \cdots \qquad (6\text{-}33)$$

The current $i_d(t)$ divides between the capacitor C and the resistor R. If the carrier-frequency impedance $(j\omega_c C)^{-1}$ of the capacitor has a much smaller absolute value than the resistance R, a good approximation is obtained by assuming that only the d-c component i_0 of $i_d(t)$ flows through R and that the remaining components of $i_d(t)$ flow through C. It follows that the output voltage, which is the voltage across R, is very nearly equal to $i_0 R$.

To calculate i_0, we observe that the voltage across the diode is well approximated by $a_c \cos \omega_c t - i_0 R$. Let the response of the diode be defined by the functional relationship

$$i = F(v) \qquad (6\text{-}34)$$

where v is the voltage across and i the current through the diode. Then,

$$i_d(t) \approx F(a_c \cos \omega_c t - i_0 R) \qquad (6\text{-}35)$$

The function on the right can be expanded in a Fourier series in $x = \omega_c t$; thus

$$F(a_c \cos x - i_0 R) = \frac{a_0}{2} + \sum_{n=1}^{\infty} a_n \cos nx \qquad (6\text{-}36)$$

$$a_n = \frac{1}{\pi} \int_{-\pi}^{\pi} F(a_c \cos x - i_0 R) \cos nx \, dx \qquad (6\text{-}37)$$

Equating the series (6-36) to the approximately equivalent series (6-33), we deduce that

$$i_0 \approx \frac{a_0}{2} = \frac{1}{2\pi} \int_{-\pi}^{\pi} F(a_c \cos x - i_0 R) \, dx \qquad (6\text{-}38)$$

which implicitly determines i_0 under the assumed conditions. The output voltage v_2 of the detector is given by

$$v_2 \approx i_0 R \qquad (6\text{-}39)$$

and satisfies the implicit relationship

$$v_2 \approx \frac{R}{2\pi} \int_{-\pi}^{\pi} F(a_c \cos x - v_2) \, dx \qquad (6\text{-}40)$$

Suppose, for example, that D is an ideal linear rectifier with

$$F(v) =. \begin{cases} \dfrac{v}{r} & v > 0 \\ 0 & v < 0 \end{cases} \qquad (6\text{-}41)$$

Then,

$$\int_{-\pi}^{\pi} F(a_c \cos x - v_2) \, dx = \frac{2}{r} \int_0^{\arccos (v_2/a_c)} (a_c \cos x - v_2) \, dx$$

$$= \frac{2}{r} \left[(a_c{}^2 - v_2{}^2)^{1/2} - v_2 \arccos \frac{v^2}{a_c} \right] \quad (6\text{-}42)$$

Treating Eq. (6-40) as an equality and representing the ratio of d-c output to input envelope by

$$\rho = \frac{v_2}{a_c} \quad (6\text{-}43)$$

we obtain the relation

$$\pi \frac{r}{R} = [\rho^{-2} - 1]^{1/2} - \arccos \rho \quad (6\text{-}44)$$

This equation can be used to calculate r/R as a function of ρ. The result of the computation can be used inversely to define ρ as a function of r/R, the ratio of the forward resistance of the rectifier to the load resistance. Figure 6-8 shows the curve thereby obtained. It appears that when r/R approaches zero, the value of ρ approaches unity and, therefore, the envelope detector actually delivers the envelope. The limiting condition occurs when the rectifier is an ideal switch, which is closed when the voltage across it is positive and open when the voltage is negative. The existence of the limit can be verified from Eq. (6-44) by noting that the right-hand side approaches zero as ρ approaches unity.

The analysis based on constant amplitude of the applied voltage can be extended to the case in which a_c is a slowly varying positive-valued function of time. The coefficients $i_0, i_1, i_2, \ldots$ in Eq. (6-33) are then slowly varying functions of time, and the division of current components between C and R remains the same. We conclude that the envelope detector can be used to recover the function $a(t)$ from an amplitude-

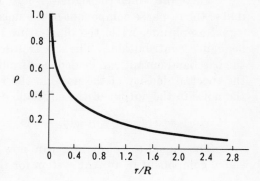

Fig. 6-8 Response of envelope detector as function of ratio of forward diode resistance to load resistance.

modulated wave $a(t) \cos \omega_c t$, provided that $a(t)$ is a positive-valued function composed of frequencies small compared with the carrier frequency ω_c. By reversing the diode, we can equally well recover a negative amplitude function. But if the values of $a(t)$ change in sign, the envelope detector gives the distorted response $|a(t)|$ instead of $a(t)$.

The simplicity of the envelope detector makes amplitude modulation attractive when the cost of the receiver is a critical consideration. A familiar example is that of radio broadcasting, in which the number of receivers is very large compared with the number of transmitters. A saving in the complexity of the receiver is, in effect, magnified by a large factor. An attempt to conserve bandwidth by changing over to SSB with a more expensive receiver would be prohibitively costly.

Since an AM system includes nonlinear operations, the r-f noise spectrum does not translate directly to baseband as in the case of linear modulation. We require a calculation of the effect of noise on the envelope of the received AM wave. A model for this computation has already been described in Chap. 2. From Eq. (2-78) as there given, the formula for the envelope $E(t)$ can be written

$$E^2(t) = [a(t) + x(t)]^2 + y^2(t) \tag{6-45}$$

where $x(t)$ and $y(t)$ are the in-phase and quadrature components of the noise as defined in Eqs. (2-59) and (2-60). The calculation can be simplified in the practically important case in which the noise is relatively weak compared with the signal, and hence $|x(t)|$ and $|y(t)|$ are small relative to $a(t)$. Then the binomial theorem can be used to obtain a first-order approximation; thus

$$E(t) = a(t) \left[1 + \frac{2x(t)}{a(t)} + \frac{x^2(t) + y^2(t)}{a^2(t)} \right]^{1/2}$$
$$\approx a(t) \left[1 + \frac{x(t)}{a(t)} \right] = a(t) + x(t) \tag{6-46}$$

Therefore, when the signal-to-noise ratio is considerably better than unity, the in-phase component of the noise adds directly to the recovered signal amplitude, while the quadrature component of the noise gives a negligible contribution. The spectral density of the noise appearing in the baseband output can be deduced from Eq. (2-69). If $w(f)$ represents the spectral density of the noise in the r-f band, the spectral density of the noise in the output of the envelope detector is

$$w_b(f) = w(f_c + f) + w(f_c - f) \tag{6-47}$$

The signal-to-noise ratio can now be calculated for a sine-wave signal component in an AM system for the low-noise case. We consider the simplified but important case of distortionless transmission and white gaussian noise. Let

$$a(t) = a_0 + s_1 \cos \omega_1 t \tag{6-48}$$

with $s_1 \geq a_c \geq 0$. Then the response of the envelope detector is

$$E(t) \approx a_0 + s_1 \cos \omega_1 t + x(t) \tag{6-49}$$

The term a_0 is a d-c bias unrelated to the baseband signal. The mean received signal power in a 1-ohm circuit is

$$S_a = \frac{s_1{}^2}{2} \tag{6-50}$$

and the mean received noise power is

$$N_a = \int_{f_1}^{f_2} [w(f_c + f) + w(f_c - f)]\, df = 2w_0 f_b \tag{6-51}$$

The mean power in the AM wave can be calculated from the trigonometric expansion

$$
\begin{aligned}
\mu(t) &= (a_0 + s_1 \cos \omega_1 t) \cos \omega_c t \\
&= a_0 \cos \omega_c t + \frac{s_1}{2} \cos (\omega_c + \omega_1)t + \frac{s_1}{2} \cos (\omega_c - \omega_1)t
\end{aligned}
\tag{6-52}
$$

The mean-square value of this three-frequency wave is

$$W_\mu = \frac{a_0{}^2}{2} + \frac{(s_1/2)^2}{2} + \frac{(s_1/2)^2}{2} = \frac{a_0{}^2}{2} + \frac{s_1{}^2}{4} \tag{6-53}$$

It is customary to define an *index of modulation* μ_i for AM by the ratio

$$\mu_i = \frac{s_1}{a_0} \tag{6-54}$$

The value of μ_i lies between zero and unity. In terms of the modulation index,

$$S_a = \frac{a_0{}^2 \mu_i{}^2}{2} \tag{6-55}$$

and

$$W_\mu = \frac{a_0{}^2}{2} \left(1 + \frac{\mu_i{}^2}{2}\right) \tag{6-56}$$

If the channel has a constant transmittance K throughout the DSB range, the mean power W_a supplied at the sending end is related to W_μ by

$$W_\mu = K^2 W_a \tag{6-57}$$

Hence the signal-to-noise ratio in the baseband output circuit becomes

$$\frac{S_a}{N_a} = \frac{a_0{}^2\mu_i{}^2}{4w_0f_b} = \frac{K^2W_a\mu_i{}^2}{(2 + \mu_i{}^2)w_0f_b} \tag{6-58}$$

For *100 percent modulation*, $\mu_i = 1$, and

$$\frac{S_a}{N_a} = \frac{K^2W_a}{3w_0f_b} \tag{6-59}$$

Comparison of this result with Eqs. (6-27) and (6-28) shows that the signal-to-noise ratio for AM is at best only one-third of that attained by SSB and DSB with the same mean transmitted power. This 4.8-db penalty arises because of the power wasted in transmitting the unmodulated carrier. A compensation for this disadvantage is the elimination of the carrier-recovery problem. Whether or not the compensation is adequate depends on the application.

6-4 FREQUENCY MODULATION

The advantage of detection without a local carrier supply is not confined to amplitude modulation. If the frequency of a carrier wave is varied linearly with the baseband signal, the variations can be measured at the receiver without the presence of a local reference carrier. The term *frequency* can be defined as the number of oscillations per second. If the frequency is variable, a more precise definition can be framed in terms of a representation of the carrier wave in the form

$$c(t) = a(t) \cos \phi(t) \tag{6-60}$$

where $a(t)$ is a positive-valued amplitude function and $\phi(t)$ represents the phase angle. A complete oscillation occurs when $\phi(t)$ changes by 2π rad. If $\phi(t)$ increases monotonically with time, the average frequency f_T in hertz over an interval from t to $t + T$ is given by

$$f_T = \frac{\phi(t + T) - \phi(t)}{2\pi T} \tag{6-61}$$

The *instantaneous frequency* f_i is then defined by

$$f_i = \lim_{\Delta t \to 0} f_{\Delta t} = \lim_{\Delta t \to 0} \frac{\phi(t + \Delta t) - \phi(t)}{2\pi \Delta t} = \frac{\phi'(t)}{2\pi} \tag{6-62}$$

or in radians per second by

$$\omega_i = \phi'(t) \tag{6-63}$$

This definition is in accord with the concept of $c(t)$ as a rotating vector with length $a(t)$ and phase $\phi(t)$. The angular velocity of such a vector is $\phi'(t)$, customarily written as $\dot{\phi}$. In the case of a constant frequency, $\phi(t) = \omega_c t + \theta_c$ and $\dot{\phi} = \omega_c$.

Frequency modulation (FM) is defined as a process in which the time derivative of the phase of the carrier wave varies linearly with the baseband signal. If we write

$$\phi'(t) = \omega_c + ks(t) \tag{6-64}$$

it follows that

$$\phi(t) = \omega_c t + k \int_{t_0}^{t} s(t)\, dt \tag{6-65}$$

where t_0 is an arbitrary reference time. In pure FM, the amplitude of the carrier wave is constant, and the expression for the frequency-modulated wave is

$$\mu(t) = a_c \cos\left[\omega_c t + k \int_{t_0}^{t} s(t)\, dt \right] \tag{6-66}$$

It is clear that $\mu(t)$ is a nonlinear function of $s(t)$ and hence that FM is a nonlinear modulation process.

The term *phase modulation* (PM) is defined as the process in which the carrier phase varies linearly with the baseband signal. In PM, we have

$$\mu(t) = a_c \cos\left[\omega_c t + ks(t)\right] \tag{6-67}$$

Comparing (6-67) with (6-66) shows that an FM wave is a PM wave in which the signal has been integrated before modulation and that a PM wave is an FM wave in which the signal has been differentiated before modulation. Since both differentiation and integration are linear processes, FM and PM can be regarded as essentially the same. The terms *angle modulation* and *exponential modulation* are sometimes used to include both. A practical distinction between FM and PM is customarily made in terms of the particular linear signal preemphasis employed at the transmitter.

A *frequency demodulator* or *frequency detector* can be simply realized by a device which counts the zero crossings of the FM wave. This can be done, for example, by generating a standard narrow pulse at each axis crossing and passing the pulse train through a low-pass filter. The low-frequency component of the pulse train reproduces the baseband signal. Another procedure, shown in Fig. 6-9, begins with an amplitude limiter, which clips the wave to very nearly the zero axis. The resulting rectangular wave is rounded off by a bandpass filter which suppresses

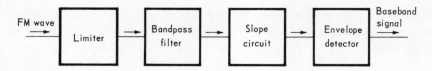

Fig. 6-9 Block diagram of frequency detector.

harmonics of the carrier frequency. A slope circuit, which has steady-state amplitude response varying linearly with frequency, then produces a hybrid-modulated wave in which both amplitude and frequency vary with the baseband signal. An envelope detector recovers the amplitude variations and hence reproduces the signal.

A frequency detector is, in general, simpler than a phase detector, which would require a reference carrier phase. In telegraph systems, however, a method known as *differential phase detection,* in which the carrier phase of the previous signaling interval furnishes a reference, is found attractive in many applications. We note that a frequency detector can be realized by differentiating the output of a phase detector and that a phase detector can be realized by integrating the output of a frequency detector.

Angle-modulation systems exhibit more extensive nonlinear phenomena than encountered in amplitude modulation. In the latter the nonlinearity arises from the presence of an unmodulated carrier component not related to the signal. The frequency of this component is within or near the band transmitted, and since no other new frequencies are introduced, the nonlinearity does not widen the band appreciably over that of the linear DSB case. An angle-modulated wave, on the other hand, definitely contains other frequencies than those of the upper and lower sidebands of linear modulation.

The band widening in angle modulation can be illustrated by the case of a single-frequency baseband component

$$s(t) = s_1 \cos \omega_1 t \tag{6-68}$$

Then with $t_0 = 0$,

$$\int_{t_0}^{t} s(t)\, dt = \frac{s_1}{\omega_1} \sin \omega_1 t \tag{6-69}$$

and setting $\mu_1 = k s_1/\omega_1$, we obtain for the FM wave

$$\mu(t) = a_c \cos(\omega_c + \mu_1 \sin \omega_1 t)$$

$$= a_c \sum_{n=-\infty}^{\infty} J_n(\mu_1) \cos(\omega_c + n\omega_1)t \tag{6-70}$$

Thus instead of a single pair of sideband components, there is an infinite number of sidebands, and an infinite bandwidth is required for perfect transmission.‡

Perfect transmission is, however, not a requirement of communication systems. We therefore investigate the conditions under which an approximate representation of Eq. (6-70) can be obtained with a finite number of sideband components. The Bessel function $J_n(\mu_1)$ has the property that its value rapidly becomes negligible when $|n|$ increases beyond μ_1. For good transmission when μ_1 is large, the bandwidth must be of the order of $2\mu_1\omega_1$. If μ_1 is small, the bandwidth must be at least $2\omega_1$ since there can be no signal information if no sidebands are transmitted. These conditions are encompassed in the requirement

$$\omega_r = 2(\mu_1\omega_1 + \omega_b) \tag{6-71}$$

where ω_r is the r-f bandwidth and ω_b is the highest baseband signal frequency in radians per second. We note that the peak-to-peak variation in the instantaneous frequency is given by

$$\omega_m = (\omega_c + \mu_1\omega_1) - (\omega_c - \mu_1\omega_1) = 2\mu_1\omega_1 \tag{6-72}$$

Therefore, Eq. (6-71) can be rewritten as

$$\omega_r = \omega_m + 2\omega_b \tag{6-73}$$

We thus obtain an approximate rule calling for a bandwidth equal to peak-to-peak frequency deviation plus twice the baseband width. For large values of the *frequency modulation index* μ_1, the rule does not give a sharply critical value, but only a sort of knee on the curve of performance versus bandwidth. For small values of μ_1, the insertion of twice the baseband width in the rule is of crucial importance since the term ω_m approaches zero. It is perhaps difficult to believe that FM systems have been seriously proposed in which a bandwidth narrower than that of the signal could be made sufficient by restricting the carrier-frequency deviation to a narrow range. This concept ranks with the equally faulty one of an AM system in which the carrier amplitude is varied without producing sidebands.

The increased transmission bandwidth necessary when wide-swing FM is used can be exploited to improve the signal-to-noise ratio in the output of the frequency detector. To demonstrate this, we examine the effect of additive noise on the instantaneous frequency of the FM wave.

‡ The coefficient $J_n(\mu_1)$ is an nth order Bessel function of argument μ_1. A summary of the properties of Bessel functions is given in the Appendix.

From the model used in Chap. 2, and in particular from Eq. (2-82), we can write

$$a_c \cos [\omega_c t + \theta(t)] + v(t) = E(t) \cos [\omega_c t + \theta(t) + \Phi(t)] \tag{6-74}$$

where

$$\Phi(t) = \arctan \frac{y(t)}{a_c + x(t)} \tag{6-75}$$

with $x(t)$ and $y(t)$ defined by Eqs. (2-59) and (2-60).

If $x(t)$ and $y(t)$ are small compared with a_c, we can use the first-order approximation of Eq. (6-75),

$$\Phi(t) \approx \frac{y(t)}{a_c} \tag{6-76}$$

Then

$$\dot{\Phi} \approx \frac{\dot{y}}{a_c} \tag{6-77}$$

The response of a perfect frequency detector to the sum of the FM wave and noise is found by differentiating the phase of the right-hand side of Eq. (6-74) and is

$$\omega_i = \omega_c + \dot{\theta} + \dot{\Phi}$$
$$\approx \omega_c + \dot{\theta} + \frac{\dot{y}}{a_c} \tag{6-78}$$

In the case of a sinusoidal baseband component as in Eq. (6-70),

$$\dot{\theta} = \mu_1 \omega_1 \cos \omega_1 t \tag{6-79}$$

Hence the mean-square detected signal is given by

$$S_f = \frac{(\mu_1 \omega_1)^2}{2} \qquad (\text{rad/sec})^2 \tag{6-80}$$

It is simpler at this point to calculate the ratio of mean-square signal to the mean-square noise in the absence of baseband signal. In calculating the noise, we can then set $\dot{\theta} = 0$ in Eq. (6-78) and recall from (2-70) that $w_y(f) = w_x(f)$. Since the wave $u(t) = \dot{y}/a_c$ is generated from y by the transmission function $H(f) = j2\pi f/a_c$, we apply Eq. (2-57) to the result of Eq. (6-47) and get

$$w_u(f) = \frac{4\pi^2 f^2}{a_c^2} [w(f_c + f) + w(f_c - f)] \tag{6-81}$$

The mean-square total noise in the baseband output is

$$N_f = \frac{4\pi^2}{a_c^2} \int_{f_1}^{f_2} f^2 [w(f_c + f) + w(f_c - f)] \, df \tag{6-82}$$

In the case of white noise with $w(f) = w_0$, Eq. (6-82) reduces to

$$N_f = \frac{8\pi^2 w_0}{3a_c^2} (f_2^3 - f_1^3) \qquad (\text{rad/sec})^2 \tag{6-83}$$

If $f_1 = 0$,

$$N_f = \frac{8\pi^2 w_0 f_b^3}{3a_c^2} \qquad (\text{rad/sec})^2 \tag{6-84}$$

and

$$\frac{S_f}{N_f} = \frac{3a_c^2}{4w_0 f_b} \left(\frac{\mu_1 f_1}{f_b}\right)^2 \tag{6-85}$$

In the same notation as used for the AM and linear modulation systems,

$$\frac{a_c^2}{2} = K^2 W_f \tag{6-86}$$

where W_f is the mean carrier power from the transmitter.   Then

$$\frac{S_f}{N_f} = \frac{3K^2 W_f}{2w_0 f_b} \left(\frac{\mu_1 f_1}{f_b}\right)^2 \tag{6-87}$$

The quantity $\mu_1 f_1$ represents the maximum frequency deviation from f_c. Although N_f has been calculated for the case of no frequency modulation, the same result is valid when the frequency is varied.   The intuitive explanation for this is that the noise accepted by the frequency detector arises from difference-frequency components between the carrier and the band of noise components extending from f_b below to f_b above the carrier frequency.   If the noise is white, a change in the carrier frequency does not change the amount of accepted mean noise power.

Comparison of Eq. (6-87) with Eqs. (6-27) and (6-28) for linear modulation indicates that FM is capable of multiplying the signal-to-noise ratio by a factor $3(\mu_1 f_1/f_b)^2/2$ for the same average transmitted power.   From (6-73), setting $\omega_r = 2\pi f_r$ and $\omega_m = 2\pi(2\mu_1 f_1)$, we obtain

$$\frac{\mu_1 f_1}{f_b} = \frac{f_r - 2f_b}{2f_b} \tag{6-88}$$

As f_r is made large relative to f_1, the ratio approaches $f_r/2f_b$, which is the *bandwidth-expansion ratio*.   Provided that the approximations continue to hold, we can thus improve the signal-to-noise ratio by a factor proportional to the square of the bandwidth-expansion ratio.   The intuitive explanation is that the received signal amplitude is proportional to the maximum frequency deviation and hence proportional to r-f bandwidth. The accepted noise power, on the other hand, depends only on the baseband width and does not change with the frequency deviation.

However, the signal-to-noise ratio cannot be improved indefinitely by increase in bandwidth, because the approximation made in the calculation requires that the mean total r-f noise power must be small compared with the mean carrier power. As the r-f bandwidth is increased, the total noise which must be accepted at the *input* to the frequency detector increases, and the approximation must eventually fail. The r-f signal-to-noise ratio at which the approximate theory fails is called the *improvement threshold* and is of the order of 10 db. Improvement in baseband signal-to-noise ratio is possible by widening the frequency excursion if and only if the r-f signal-to-noise ratio is above the improvement threshold.

6-5 PULSE MODULATION

The methods of modulation discussed so far are all of the *continuous-wave* or CW type, which means that the carrier wave does not vanish over any time interval of duration greater than zero. The other important category is *pulse modulation*, in which the carrier wave is equal to zero a finite part of the time. It might seem that some of the signal wave would then be lost, but it will be shown that the gaps can be accurately bridged if the signal does not change too rapidly. A hint of this possibility is furnished by product modulation of a sinusoidal carrier. Here the carrier wave actually goes through the value zero periodically and is small in the neighborhood of the zero crossings. The corresponding nulls in the response of the modulator do not disturb the representation of the signal if the signal frequencies are not too high.

In *pulse-amplitude modulation* (PAM), the heights of regularly spaced pulses are proportional to the signal ordinates. We can regard the carrier as a periodic pulse train $g(t)$, which can be represented by the general Fourier series

$$g(t) = \frac{g_0}{2} + \sum_{n=1}^{\infty} g_n \cos(n\omega_0 t + \theta_n) \tag{6-89}$$

where the spacing between pulses is $T = 1/f_0 = 2\pi/\omega_0$. In *linear pulse modulation*, the signal $s(t)$ is multiplied by $g(t)$ to produce the pulse-modulated wave

$$\mu(t) = s(t)g(t) \tag{6-90}$$

As in the CW case, we may wish to add a bias s_0 to $s(t)$ to prevent sign changes. The resulting modulation is then nonlinear because of the presence of an unmodulated pulse train $s_0 g(t)$ in the output.

We observe that representation of the signal by a sinusoidal component $s_1 \cos \omega_1 t$ is just as effective as in the treatment of CW modulation. We obtain

$$2\mu(t) = 2s_1 g(t) \cos \omega_1 t$$

$$= g_0 s_1 \cos \omega_1 t + \sum_{n=1}^{\infty} g_n s_1 \cos [(n\omega_0 + \omega_1)t + \theta_n]$$

$$+ \sum_{n=1}^{\infty} g_n s_1 \cos [(n\omega_0 - \omega_1)t + \theta_n] \quad (6\text{-}91)$$

Instead of a single pair of sidebands as in linear CW modulation, there is a pair of sidebands associated with each harmonic of the pulse repetition frequency. In addition, there is an unshifted signal band represented by the term $g_0 s_1 \cos \omega_1 t$. Since $g_0/2$ is the average value of the original pulse train, the signal exists in the output except in the special case of a pulse train with no d-c component. If $\omega_0 > \omega_1$, the lowest frequency represented in the sideband components is $\omega_0 - \omega_1$. A low-pass filter can be provided to select the signal band from the PAM output if

$$\omega_0 - \omega_1 > \omega_1 \qquad \text{or} \qquad \omega_0 > 2\omega_1 \qquad (6\text{-}92)$$

This is the condition for prevention of sideband overlap and is a basic requirement for pulse-modulation systems. As illustrated in Prob. 6-30, exceptions occur when the baseband is displaced from zero frequency. The necessary requirement is that the pulse rate must exceed twice the signal bandwidth.

The Fourier series of Eq. (6-89) can represent a general periodic wave not necessarily composed of pulses. A pulsed structure is determined by particular sets of amplitude coefficients g_n and phase angles θ_n. For example, if $g(t)$ is a train of rectangular pulses of height h and width τ with the origin of time at the midpoint of a pulse,

$$g_n = \frac{\omega_0}{\pi} \int_{-\tau/2}^{\tau/2} h \cos n\omega_0 t \, dt = \frac{2h}{n\pi} \sin \frac{n\omega_0 \tau}{2} \qquad (6\text{-}93)$$

In the limit as τ goes to zero,

$$g_n \rightarrow \frac{2h}{n\pi} \frac{n\omega_0 \tau}{2} = 2hf_0\tau \qquad (6\text{-}94)$$

and

$$\mu(t) \rightarrow s_1 h f_0 \tau [\cos \omega_1 t + \cos (\omega_0 + \omega_1)t + \cos (\omega_0 - \omega_1)t$$
$$+ \cos (2\omega_0 + \omega_1)t + \cos (2\omega_0 - \omega_1)t + \cdots] \qquad (6\text{-}95)$$

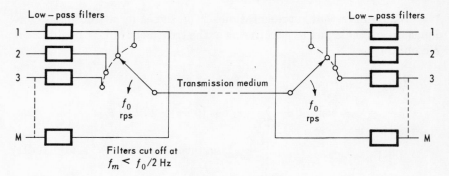

Fig. 6-10   Time-division multiplex system.

Equation (6-95) represents the case of *instantaneous sampling* and shows that a band-limited signal can be uniquely reproduced from regularly spaced samples taken at a rate exceeding twice the highest signal frequency.[2]   The reproduction is obtained by applying the samples as weighted impulses to a filter which passes the signal band uniformly and suppresses all higher frequencies, i.e., an ideal low-pass filter with cutoff f_m satisfying $f_1 < f_m < f_0/2$.

The two principal applications of pulse modulation are (1) time-division multiplex transmission and (2) digital transmission of analog signals.   In *time-division multiplex* (TDM), independent signals are assigned mutually exclusive time slots, and if the pulses occupying these slots do not overlap each other appreciably in time, the signals can be received without interfering with each other.   Schematically, we can represent a TDM system, as shown in Fig. 6-10, with synchronized rotating switches connecting the individual channels successively to the transmission line.   Actually, high-speed electronic switches would be used to provide the sampling rates necessary in all but very narrow-band communication channels.

The switching process can be represented by conductance functions designated as $g_m(t)$ for the mth channel.   The complete TDM wave in the common transmission medium is

$$\mu(t) = \sum_{m=1}^{M} \mu_m(t) g_m(t) \tag{6-96}$$

for an M-channel system.   If $g_1(t)$ is identified with $g(t)$ as defined by Eq. (6-89),

$$g_m(t) = g\left[t - \frac{(m-1)T}{M} \right] \tag{6-97}$$

Assuming unity as the transmittance of the line, we demodulate the signal in the kth channel by forming the product

$$
\begin{aligned}
g_k(t)\mu(t) &= \sum_{m=1}^{M} \mu_m(t) g_m(t) g_k(t) \\
&= \sum_{m=1}^{M} \mu_m(t) g\left[t - \frac{(m-1)T}{M}\right] g\left[t - \frac{(k-1)T}{M}\right]
\end{aligned}
\qquad (6\text{-}98)
$$

In an ideal TDM the switching functions do not overlap, and, therefore,

$$
g\left(t - \frac{mT}{M}\right) g\left(t - \frac{kT}{M}\right) = 0 \qquad k \neq m \qquad (6\text{-}99)
$$

When this condition is satisfied,

$$
g_k(t)\mu(t) = \mu_k(t) g^2\left[t - \frac{(k-1)T}{M}\right] \qquad (6\text{-}100)
$$

Since $g(t)$ is periodic in t with period T, $g^2(t)$ is also periodic with the same period. Therefore, we can write

$$
g^2(t) = \frac{\gamma_0}{2} + \sum_{n=1}^{\infty} \gamma_n \cos\left(n\omega_0 t + \theta_n\right) \qquad (6\text{-}101)
$$

It follows that the response of an ideal low-pass filter to $2g_k(t)\mu(t)$ is $\gamma_0 \mu_k(t)$ as in Eq. (6-91).

TDM has an advantage over *frequency-division multiplex* (FDM) as practiced with CW modulation systems in that no bandpass filters are required. The electronic switches which are used instead of the bandpass filters are typically smaller in size and lower in cost. However, these considerations are usually outweighed by the disadvantage of requiring nearly distortionless transmission in the common medium. The function $g(t)$ in Eq. (6-89) can be made to simulate switching action only by careful control of the amplitude and phase relations of the harmonics of the repetition frequency. These amplitude and phase relations must be preserved throughout the important sidebands generated by the switching. A linear phase shift with frequency can be compensated by a corresponding time shift in the demodulating switches, but otherwise both amplitude and phase variations with frequency in the line can easily lead to intolerable interchannel interference. The requirement on phase linearity is particularly vexatious, since in an FDM system the phase characteristic of the medium has no effect whatsoever on channel selectivity.

The fact that the approach to infinitesimal contact time in PAM leads to a good approximation to instantaneous sampling is important in the realization of nonlinear pulse-modulation methods. Once the instantaneous samples have been obtained, the actual numerical values can be transmitted in a variety of ways. In *pulse-duration modulation* (PDM) the pulse durations are made proportional to the samples, and in *pulse-position modulation* (PPM) very narrow pulses are deviated from uniformly spaced reference positions by amounts proportional to the samples. These are inherently wideband methods and offer means similar but inferior to FM for trading excess bandwidth for improved signal-to-noise ratio.

By far the most powerful use of pulse modulation is based on digitalizing the samples and sending the resulting discrete numbers as telegraph signals. The nonlinear pulse-modulation system thus realized is called *pulse-code modulation* or PCM. The accuracy with which the samples need to be represented depends on the type of baseband signal. The errors made in rounding off the sampled values to the nearest permitted discrete number appear as so-called *quantizing noise* in the output of the channel. The steps between numbers can be made sufficiently small to reduce the quantizing noise to an arbitrarily low level.

When the number of quantizing steps in the signal range is large and the size of each step is small, the amount of quantizing error in the samples is uniformly distributed throughout a range extending from a negative half-step to a positive half-step. If E_0 is the height of a step, the average squared error is

$$\epsilon^2 = \frac{1}{E_0} \int_{-E_0/2}^{E_0/2} x^2 \, dx = \frac{E_0{}^2}{12} \tag{6-102}$$

The full-load signal of a PCM system utilizes all the quantizing steps provided. If there are M equal steps, the full-load sine-wave signal has amplitude $ME_0/2$ and mean-square value $M^2E_0{}^2/8$. Therefore, the signal-to-noise ratio for a full-load sine wave is

$$\frac{S}{N} = \frac{M^2E_0{}^2/8}{\epsilon^2} = \frac{3M^2}{2} \tag{6-103}$$

Instead of sending the values of the quantized samples by M-level telegraphy, we can code the M levels in terms of pulses with fewer levels. In particular, if $M = 2^m$ we can use binary telegraphy with m binary pulses representing each M-level sample. In terms of the number of pulses per sample,

$$\frac{S}{N} = 3 \cdot 2^{2m-1} \tag{6-104}$$

We have seen that a baseband of width f_b Hz requires at least $2f_b$ samples/sec. If m binary pulses are used to represent each sample, the minimum pulse rate is $2mf_b$ pulses/sec. From the results of Chap. 4, the bandwidth f_p required to transmit this number of pulses per second is given by

$$f_p = kmf_b \qquad (6\text{-}105)$$

where the value of k is between 1 and 2. Hence, the signal-to-noise ratio of Eq. (6-104) can also be written

$$\frac{S}{N} = \frac{3}{2} \cdot 4^{f_p/(kf_b)} \qquad (6\text{-}106)$$

In other words, a PCM system is capable of improving the signal-to-noise ratio exponentially with the bandwidth-expansion ratio. This is potentially much better than FM, in which the improvement as shown by Eqs. (6-87) and (6-88) follows a square law.

We have assumed that the quantizing noise constitutes all of the noise in a PCM system. This assumption can be realized by the use of regenerative repeaters in the transmission medium. A binary regenerative repeater observes the received wave from a section of the line at each sampling instant and decides which of the two pulse values is present. A correctly shaped and timed noise-free pulse of that value is then sent over the next section of line. If no errors are made, the only noise in the analog output of a PCM system is the quantizing noise. Actually in the case of gaussian noise, there is a finite although small probability that the noise magnitudes can exceed any value no matter how large. Therefore, even the best regenerative repeater must make errors occasionally when the channel contains additive gaussian noise. The error rate can be made arbitrarily small by appropriately increasing the pulse amplitudes.

It was pointed out in Chap. 3 that the effective signal-to-noise ratio for telephone signals can be improved by companding. The quantizing noise in a PCM voice channel can be reduced in this way. Since the companding is applied to instantaneous samples, no bandwidth penalty is incurred. The effect is identical with the use of unequal quantizing steps in the analog-to-digital converter. Weak signals are provided with steps close together, and large signal magnitudes are represented by coarser steps. Experiments have shown that with the most effective companding characteristics, satisfactory telephone quality can be obtained with 128 steps, which are representable by seven binary pulses. If companding were not used, 10 binary pulses giving 1024 steps would be needed. For a nominal 4-kHz band, the minimum sampling rate is 8 kHz, and the minimum bandwidth required for a 7-bit PCM channel is between 28 and 56 kHz. Although this may seem to be a gross waste of bandwidth, it must be kept in mind that the 56 kHz can be supplied by a very noisy channel which is useless for analog transmission.

PCM can be combined with TDM to transmit a large number of channels over a noisy wave-distorting medium. The severe requirements on amplitude constancy and phase linearity, which militate against TDM systems based on linear pulse modulation, are much relaxed in PCM. Interchannel interference becomes translated to intersymbol interference, which is damaging only when errors are made. By the use of short sections equipped with regenerative repeaters, we can keep the error rate low.

6-6 CONCLUDING REMARKS

In this chapter we have discussed the significant facts concerning modulation without getting involved in advanced mathematics. The basic results have been shown to be understandable in terms of operations on sine waves, and for this reason little more than elementary trigonometry has been needed. In the remaining chapters, we shall delve more deeply into the theory of signal processing and will make use of more sophisticated concepts where they seem appropriate. Our intent, however, is not to go beyond an introductory text which will prepare the reader to study more advanced and comprehensive treatments.

References 3 to 8 include material parallel with and complementary to the present chapter.

PROBLEMS

6-1. Suppose a productor is followed by an ideal high-pass filter which has zero transmittance for frequencies below $\omega_c - \omega_k$ and unit transmittance for higher frequencies. An ASB wave is generated by the productor and filter with carrier frequency at ω_c. Assume that the transmitting medium is distortionless and that homodyne demodulation with carrier phase error ϕ is used at the receiver. How does the response of the ASB system vary with signal frequency?

6-2. In Prob. 6-1, what would be the design requirements on a VSB filter to be inserted between the medium and the receiver to produce a uniform response versus frequency for the ASB system? Assume $\phi = 0$.

6-3. (a) An incoming signal which occupies the range of frequencies from 995 to 1005 kHz is multiplied by the output of a local oscillator tuned at 550 kHz. What modulation products are produced and what are their frequency ranges?

(b) If the input signal of (a) is in the range 1495 to 1505 kHz instead of that previously given, where do the modulation products fall on the frequency scale? What change would be necessary in the frequency of the local oscillator to keep one of the modulation products in the same band as before?

(c) What range of tuning must be provided in the local oscillator to enable any narrow-band signal with midband frequency in the range from 500 to 1600 kHz to be shifted to a fixed frequency band centered at 450 kHz?

6-4. Suppose nonlinear resistors are available in which the current i and voltage v are related by

$$i = g_1 v + g_2 v^2$$

How can you use these to obtain a productor? An amplitude modulator?

6-5. Repeat Prob. 6-4 for nonlinear resistors in which

$$i = g_1 v + g_3 v^3$$

6-6. Calculate the output of the on-off switch-type modulator in Fig. 6-11 for a single-frequency baseband input. Assume that the resistance from collector to emitter of

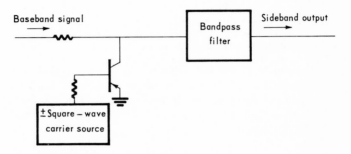

Fig. 6-11 On-off switch-type modulator.

the transistor is R_1 when the base voltage is positive and R_2 when the base voltage is negative. What filtering must be supplied and what frequency restrictions must be imposed to make this modulator serve as an ideal productor?

6-7. Repeat Prob. 6-6 for the reversing switch-type modulator of Fig. 6-12 on the assumption that the two transistors are identical.

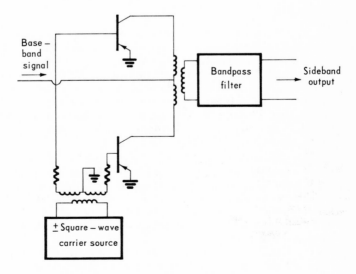

Fig. 6-12 Reversing switch-type modulator.

6-8. Assume that a band of frequencies from 300 to 3500 Hz is adequate for a voice channel. If a signal wave occupying this band modulates the amplitude of a 100-kHz carrier, what frequencies are present in the AM wave? Suppose it is desired to select the lower sideband of the modulator output when the carrier has the frequency f_c Hz. The selection is to be performed by a filter with its passband placed as low as possible in frequency without distortion from overlapping components. What value of f_c enables this minimum condition to be met if (a) the modulator permits voice-frequency as well as sideband components to appear in the output and if (b) the modulator is balanced to suppress voice-frequency components in the output?

6-9. What are the answers to Prob. 6-8 if the upper sideband is selected?

6-10. A baseband signal is divided equally between two paths. One path leads to the signal input of a productor to which a sinusoidal carrier wave is applied. The other path encounters a phase-shifting network which retards the phase of all sinusoidal signal components by a fixed angle θ without changing the amplitudes. The output of the phase shifter is the input to a second productor with carrier wave retarded in phase by an angle ϕ with respect to the carrier input to the first productor. The sideband outputs of the two productors are then added or subtracted. Find the relations which θ and ϕ must satisfy in order to deliver a single-sideband output. Show under what conditions the lower and upper sidebands are obtained. Why does single-sideband production fail for a d-c component of the signal?

6-11. Construct an analog of the system in Prob. 6-10 to demodulate one sideband only of a "twin-carrier multiplex" wave, in which independent signals form the upper and lower sidebands on the same carrier.

6-12. Suppose the telegraph pulse

$$s(t) = \frac{1}{f_b} \int_0^{f_b} \cos \frac{\pi f}{2f_b} \cos 2\pi ft \, df$$

is multiplied by the carrier wave $a_c \cos \omega_c t$ with $\omega_c = 2\pi f_c$ and $f_c > f_b$. A high-pass filter with an even transmittance function defined by

$$Y(f) = \begin{cases} 0 & 0 < f < f_c - f_1 \\ \dfrac{1}{2}\left(1 + \dfrac{f - f_c}{f_1}\right) & f_c - f_1 < f < f_c + f_1 \\ 1 & f_c + f_1 < f < f_c + f_b \\ 0 & f_c + f_b < f \end{cases}$$

with $0 < f_1 < f_b$ is inserted between the productor output and the input to a transmission line. Assume a distortionless transmission line, a homodyne receiver with no carrier phase error, and a low-pass filter with cutoff at $2f_c - f_b$ in the baseband output circuit. Which, if any, of Nyquist's criteria for distortionless telegraph transmission does the system satisfy at a signaling speed of $2f_b$ bauds?

6-13. Generalize Eqs. (4-74) and (4-75), which give conditions for optimum filtering in a baseband telegraph system, to apply to the case of a linear DSB telegraph system. Use Fig. 6-1 as the model and consider the four filters which can be inserted in the path between baseband source and baseband destination.

6-14. Show that if the diode D in Fig. 6-6 has the current-voltage relationship of an ideal crystal, namely,

$$i = i_s(e^{bv} - 1) \qquad b > 0$$

the output of the detector approaches equality with the amplitude of the modulated input wave as b approaches infinity.

   Hints:

$$\int_0^\pi e^{z \cos x}\, dx = \pi I_0(z) \qquad \text{where } I_0(z) = J_0(jz)$$

For large z, $I_0(z) \sim e^z/(2\pi z)^{1/2}$.

6-15. Discuss the dual of the envelope detector in which a current source drives a diode in parallel with a series combination of inductance and resistance.

6-16. Evaluate the response of a full-wave linear rectifier defined by

$$i = k|v|$$

to an AM wave. Show under what circumstances the baseband signal can be recovered without distortion.

6-17. Assume that overmodulation takes place in an AM transmitter and that the resulting transmitted wave for a sinusoidal signal component is

$$v(t) = (s_0 + s_1 \cos \omega_1 t) \cos \omega_c t$$

with $\omega_c \gg \omega_1$ and $0 < s_0 < s_1$. Express the response of an ideal envelope detector to $v(t)$ as a Fourier series. What is the ratio of second-harmonic amplitude to fundamental amplitude in the baseband output?

6-18. Express the signal-to-noise ratio, Eq. (6-59), of an AM system in terms of mean unmodulated carrier power at the transmitter.

6-19. A sinusoidal test signal with frequency of 1 kHz is used to produce 50 percent amplitude modulation of a 1000-kHz carrier wave. When the AM wave is received, it is accompanied by additive interference consisting of a sine wave at 1002 kHz with amplitude equal to 1 percent of that of the unmodulated carrier component. What interfering wave would be obtained in the output of an envelope detector and what would be the ratio of the amplitude of the detected test signal to that of the detected interference? Use the linear approximation of the envelope which is valid when the interference is small relative to the carrier amplitude.

6-20. Suppose in Prob. 6-19 the interference consisted of 10 sine waves with the amplitude of each equal to 0.1 percent of the amplitude of the unmodulated carrier component and with frequencies 997.0, 997.7, 998.4, 999.1, 999.7, 1000.4, 1001.1, 1001.8, 1002.5, and 1003.3 kHz. What interfering waves would be detected and what would be the ratio of their amplitudes to that of the detected test signal? What would be the ratio of mean-square test signal to mean-square total interference in the detector output? Express in decibels. (The signal-to-interference ratio in decibels is equal to 10 times the logarithm of the ratio of average signal power to average noise power.)

6-21. In Prob. 6-20, replace the interfering sine waves by random noise uniformly distributed in frequency throughout a range from 996.5 to 1003.5 kHz with the average noise power in a band of width 1 Hz given as 75 db below the average unmodulated carrier power. What db signal-to-noise ratio is obtained in the detector output?

6-22. Suppose in Prob. 6-19 the interference comes from an adjacent AM channel in which a carrier frequency of 1010 kHz is 100 percent modulated by a sine wave of 1 kHz. The two AM waves arrive at the receiver input with equal unmodulated carrier amplitudes, but between the receiver input and the detector input there is a chain of tuned circuits which has the following values of relative response in decibels versus frequency:

Frequency, kHz	Relative gain, db
999	−1.0
1000	0.0
1001	−1.0
1009	−19.0
1010	−20.0
1011	−22.0

What are the frequencies of the interfering components? What is the ratio, expressed in decibels, of the average detected test-signal power to the average detected power of each interfering component? What requirements in terms of loss versus frequency would be needed in a low-pass filter following the detector in order to reduce the average power in each interfering component to a value at least 40 db below the power in the test signal?

6-23. The National Television System Committee (NTSC) specifications[9] approved by the U.S. Federal Communications Commission, December 17, 1953, for compatible color television broadcasting include the following:

A. The baseband color signal consists of:

(1) A luminescence signal with band from zero to 4.2 MHz.

(2) Two subcarrier chrominance signals obtained by suppressed-carrier amplitude modulation of quadrature carriers at 3.579545 MHz, which is halfway between the 227th and 228th harmonics of the line-scanning frequency of 15,734 Hz. The baseband of one chrominance signal extends from zero to 1.3 MHz and the baseband of the other extends from zero to 0.6 MHz.

(3) A frequency-modulated sound carrier at 4.5 MHz with maximum frequency deviation of ±25 kHz.

(4) Synchronizing pulses in the time interval between adjacent line scans.

B. The bandwidth of the broadcast channel is 6.0 MHz, the carrier frequency is 1.25 MHz above the lower bound of the channel band, and ASB modulation with transmitted carrier is used. A VSB low-pass filter follows the demodulator.

Questions:

(a) What sources of interference and distortion would you expect to be significant in the reception of the NTSC signal? How or why can the end result be made acceptable to the viewer? Considering that the same channel bandwidth is assigned for color TV as for black-and-white, would you expect black-and-white receivers to give the same performance on colorcasts as formerly obtainable on monochrome transmission?

(b) Suppose the NTSC baseband color signal can be satisfactorily quantized in 128 levels. How many pulses per second would be adequate for binary PCM transmission and how much bandwidth would be needed?

6-24. Beginners in a study of FM are sometimes tempted to define an FM wave by substituting $\omega_c = k_0 + k_1 s(t)$ in Eq. (6-1). Discuss the wave thereby defined when $s(t)$ is sinusoidal.

6-25. The phase-modulated wave

$$\mu(t) = a_c \cos (\omega_c t + \phi \cos \omega_1 t) \qquad \omega_c \gg \omega_1$$

is transmitted through an ideal bandpass filter which has unit transmittance for all frequencies between $\omega_c - 1.5\omega_1$ and $\omega_c + 1.5\omega_1$ rad/sec and has zero transmittance for all other positive frequencies. Express the envelope, phase, and instantaneous frequency of the output wave as functions of time.

6-26. Consider a phase modulator constructed by adding the response of a productor to unmodulated carrier shifted in phase by $\pi/2$ rad. What is the phase of the output wave when the signal is sinusoidal? Over what range of phase variation can linearity of phase versus signal input be maintained within 1 percent? What modification can be made to obtain FM with instantaneous frequency linearly related to signal input?

6-27. The modulated wave of Prob. 6-26 is applied as input to a square-law device with output voltage v_2 related to input voltage v_1 by

$$v_2 = a v_1{}^2$$

Show how an FM wave can be obtained from the output with a greater frequency swing for a given departure from linearity than available at the input.

6-28. An FM wave

$$\mu_1(t) = a_c \cos \left(\omega_c t + \frac{\omega_d}{\omega_1} \sin \omega_1 t \right) \qquad \omega_c \gg \omega_1$$

is added to a delayed replica of itself to form the resultant wave

$$\mu_2(t) = \mu_1(t) + k\mu_1(t - \tau)$$

Assume that the delay τ is sufficiently small to make the approximations $\sin \omega_1\tau \approx \omega_1\tau$ and $\cos \omega_1\tau \approx 1$ valid.

    (a) What is the envelope of $\mu_2(t)$?
    (b) Evaluate the envelope when $\omega_c\tau = \pi/2$ and $\sin \omega_d\tau \approx \omega_d\tau$.
    (c) What change would be made in the answer to (b) if $k\mu_1(t - \tau)$ were subtracted from $\mu_1(t)$?
    (d) What are the approximate results of (b) and (c) if $2k\tau\omega_d \ll 1$?
    (e) Use the results (a) through (d) to design a frequency detector giving a response proportional to the instantaneous frequency deviation of the input wave.

6-29. Suppose a signal is multiplied by a periodic train of pulses in which the sign of alternate pulses is reversed. What sidebands are produced? What is the condition for no sideband overlap? How can the signal be recovered?

6-30. Show that a baseband signal containing no frequencies outside the range f_1 to $2f_1$ Hz can be recovered without distortion from $2f_1$ samples/sec.

6-31. Instead of allowing the output of a pulse modulator to follow the signal variations throughout the duration of the pulse, we can measure instantaneous samples and multiply the pulse $g(t - nT)$ by the nth sample value. Find a transmittance function of a linear system to which the modulated impulse train of Eq. (6-95) can be applied to produce this result. What effect would this have on the recovered baseband signal? Compare with the aperture effect discussed in Chap. 5.

6-32. Suppose that quantization of samples in 2^m equal steps gives satisfactory signal quality. The signal is transmitted by binary PCM over an N-link system. Digital-to-analog conversion is performed at the output of each link, and the resulting analog signal is sampled and coded at the input to the succeeding link. Assume that the quantizing errors in successive links are independent and are uniformly distributed throughout the quantizing interval. How many binary pulses per sample should be provided?

REFERENCES

1. "IRE Dictionary of Electronics Terms and Symbols," The Institute of Radio Engineers, Inc. (now Institute of Electrical and Electronics Engineers, Inc.), New York, N.Y., 1961, p. 92.
2. Bennett, W. R.: Time-division Multiplex Systems, *Bell System Tech. J.*, vol. 20, pp. 199–221, April, 1941.
3. Black, H. S.: "Modulation Theory," D. Van Nostrand, Princeton, N.J., 1953.
4. Schwartz, M.: "Information Transmission, Modulation, and Noise," McGraw-Hill, New York, 1959.
5. Downing, J. J.: "Modulation Systems and Noise," Prentice-Hall, Englewood Cliffs, N.J., 1964.
6. Schwartz, M., W. R. Bennett, and S. Stein: "Communication Systems and Techniques," McGraw-Hill, New York, 1966.
7. Carlson, A. B.: "Communication Systems," McGraw-Hill, New York, 1968.
8. McMullen, C. W.: "Communication Theory Principles," Macmillan, New York, 1968.
9. NTSC Signal Specifications, *Proc. IRE*, vol. 42, pp. 17–19, January, 1954.

7
Linear Operations on Signals and Sidebands

This chapter deals with the problems encountered in the production and utilization of sidebands linearly related to signals. As described in the previous chapter, a device with response equal to the product of two inputs is sufficient for these purposes. Although such devices exist in nature, e.g., the electric motor and the Hall-effect multiplier, their applications to signal transmission and reception have not been extensive. The most important practical method of generating sidebands linearly is by a first-order perturbation of a highly nonlinear process. Typically, a carrier wave of large amplitude drives a system through a nonlinear range and produces a response which in the absence of signal can be expressed as a Fourier series containing frequencies which are multiples of the carrier frequency. The superposition of a relatively small signal produces terms which to a first approximation are products of the signal and harmonics of the carrier. In the usual case many more sidebands are generated than desired. Efficient generation and selection of the wanted components constitute a part of the subject matter of the present chapter.

7-1 THE PROBLEM OF EFFICIENT SIDEBAND PRODUCTION

Isolation of particular sidebands can be accomplished by three principal methods, which can be classified as (1) amplitude selectivity, (2) frequency selectivity, and (3) phase selectivity. In the first method, the modulator is so designed that the unwanted sidebands are relatively weak. This procedure is ineffective in selecting a single sideband because the upper and lower sidebands are inherently of equal strength in linear modulation processes. The second method employs filters and is highly effective in all cases in which the desired and undesired sidebands occupy mutually exclusive frequency ranges. Adequate selection of a single sideband can be accomplished in this way provided we do not ask for the impossible operation of a knife-edge separation at the carrier frequency.

The third method combines the outputs of two or more modulators in which there are phase shifts between signal inputs and between carrier inputs. The simplest phase shift is one of π rad, which is a mere polarity reversal. Such a phase shift can actually produce cancellation of some unwanted sidebands which overlap the frequency range of the desired ones. It cannot isolate a single sideband, because a polarity reversal of either signal or carrier reverses the polarity of both the upper and lower sidebands. Single-sideband selection is possible, however, when phase shifts of $\pi/2$ rad are applied to both signal and carrier. The wave produced by shifting the phases of all components of a signal wave by 90° is therefore of great importance in modulation theory. The function of time produced in this way is known as the *Hilbert transform* of the signal.

We shall find it useful to devote a considerable preliminary effort to develop the properties and applications of the Hilbert transform. After this treatment the design of modulators from nonlinear resistances and reactances will be analyzed.

7-2 THE HILBERT TRANSFORM AND ITS RELATION TO SIDEBANDS

We define the wave obtained by *retarding* the phases of all sinusoidal components of a signal $s(t)$ by $\pi/2$ rad as the Hilbert transform $\hat{s}(t)$ of the signal. A second Hilbert transformation produces a phase shift of π rad, which is equivalent to a polarity reversal. In our notation, if we represent the number of successive transforms by a superscript on the left, we obtain

$$^2\hat{s}(t) = -s(t) \qquad ^3\hat{s}(t) = -\hat{s}(t) \qquad \text{and} \qquad ^4\hat{s}(t) = s(t) \qquad (7\text{-}1)$$

The Hilbert transform thus resembles the operator j in that two operations reverse the sign and four operations restore the original function.

Odd numbers of transformations produce an entirely different series of functions, which we shall study in detail. Phase shift of a zero-frequency term is meaningless, and the Hilbert transform of a constant is accordingly defined as zero. The rules on successive transforms do not hold in this singular case.

Orderly presentation of linear modulation theory is greatly facilitated by efficient mathematical notation. Complex representation of signals, carriers, and sidebands can be used to reduce the drudgery of computations. However, the fact that we deal with linear time-varying systems in which frequency shifts occur requires some extensions of the more familiar applications of complex algebra as encountered in time-invariant systems.

We first note that if all mathematical operations are to be permissible on a complex representation of real waveforms, the conjugate of every complex term must be included as an additive term. A convenient model is the exponential integral representation

$$s(t) = \int_{-\infty}^{\infty} S(f)e^{j2\pi ft}\,df \tag{7-2}$$

with $S(-f) = S^*(f)$ to ensure reality of $s(t)$.

We recall from Chap. 1 that when the signal wave $s(t)$ is applied as input to a linear time-invariant system with transmittance function $H(f)$, the response is

$$r(t) = \int_{-\infty}^{\infty} H(f)S(f)e^{j2\pi ft}\,df \tag{7-3}$$

and that for real systems $H(-f) = H^*(f)$. The Hilbert transform of $s(t)$ is defined in terms of a phase retardation of $\pi/2$ rad for real components with positive frequencies. In the complex representation this phase shift is accomplished by multiplication of $S(f)$ by $e^{-j\pi/2} = -j$ when $f > 0$ and by $e^{j\pi/2} = j$ when $f < 0$. In other words, the Hilbert transform is the response of a linear time-invariant system with $H(f) = -j\,\mathrm{sgn}\,f$, where $\mathrm{sgn}\,f$, which is equal to $|f|/f$, is the function introduced in Prob. 1-5 of Chap. 1. The singular case in which $f = 0$ will be covered by defining $\mathrm{sgn}\,0 = 0$. The mathematical formula is then

$$\hat{s}(t) = -j\int_{-\infty}^{\infty} \mathrm{sgn}\,f\,S(f)e^{j\pi2ft}\,df \tag{7-4}$$

The case of discrete frequencies can be included by use of δ functions as components of the integrand. In particular, if $s(t)$ is a sine wave specified by

$$s(t) = a_1 \cos\left(2\pi f_1 t + \theta_1\right) \tag{7-5}$$

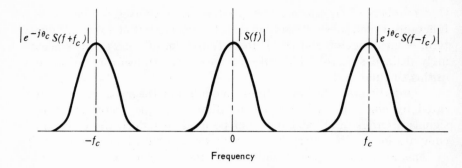

Fig. 7-1   Spectral representation of signal and sidebands.

with a_1, f_1, and θ_1 real, we write

$$2S(f) = a_1 e^{j\theta_1} \delta(f - f_1) + a_1 e^{-j\theta_1} \delta(f + f_1) \tag{7-6}$$

We readily verify that in this case

$$\hat{s}(t) = a_1 \sin (2\pi f_1 t + \theta_1) \tag{7-7}$$

The response of a productor to a general signal wave $\hat{s}(t)$ and the sinusoidal carrier wave,

$$c(t) = a_c \cos (2\pi f_c t + \theta_c) \qquad f_c > 0 \tag{7-8}$$

is

$$m(t) = k_1 s(t) c(t) = \int_{-\infty}^{\infty} M(f) e^{j2\pi ft}\, df \tag{7-9}$$

where

$$2M(f) = k_1 a_c\, S(f) * [e^{j\theta_c} \delta(f - f_c) + e^{-j\theta_c} \delta(f + f_c)]$$
$$= k_1 a_c [e^{j\theta_c} S(f - f_c) + e^{-j\theta_c} S(f + f_c)] \tag{7-10}$$

Figure 7-1 illustrates the frequency shifts which Eq. (7-10) implies. The upper sideband is represented in duplicate by the frequencies above $f = f_c$ and those below $f = -f_c$. Likewise the lower sideband is represented by the frequencies between 0 and f_c and those between $-f_c$ and 0. Writing $m_u(t)$ and $m_l(t)$ for the upper and lower sidebands, respectively, we obtain

$$\frac{2m_u(t)}{k_1 a_c} = e^{j\theta_c} \int_{f_c}^{\infty} S(f - f_c) e^{j2\pi ft}\, df + e^{-j\theta_c} \int_{-\infty}^{-f_c} S(f + f_c) e^{j2\pi ft}\, df \tag{7-11}$$

and

$$\frac{2m_l(t)}{k_1 a_c} = e^{j\theta_c} \int_{0}^{f_c} S(f - f_c) e^{j2\pi ft}\, df + e^{-j\theta_c} \int_{-f_c}^{0} S(f + f_c) e^{j2\pi ft}\, df \tag{7-12}$$

We have assumed that $S(f) = 0$ for $|f| > f_c$ throughout in order to avoid sideband foldover and consequent ambiguities. In Eq. (7-11), the upper limit of the first integral and the lower limit of the second integral could be replaced by $2f_c$ and $-2f_c$, respectively.

A compact representation of sidebands as functions of time is furnished by considering the *analytic signal* $z(t)$ defined by

$$z(t) = s(t) + j\hat{s}(t) \tag{7-13}$$

The reasons underlying the choice of the name will be explained later. The analytic signal is not a real signal, and its Fourier transform $Z(f)$ is exempt from the condition of conjugate values for positive and negative values of f. In fact,

$$Z(f) = S(f) + j(-j \operatorname{sgn} f)S(f) = (1 + \operatorname{sgn} f)S(f)$$
$$= \begin{Bmatrix} 0 & f < 0 \\ 2S(f) & f > 0 \end{Bmatrix} = 2u(f)S(f) \tag{7-14}$$

where $u(f)$ is the unit step function previously defined in Prob. 1-4 of Chap. 1. Thus the Fourier transform of the complex function $z(t)$ vanishes for all *negative* frequencies, and we can write

$$z(t) = 2 \int_0^\infty S(f)e^{j2\pi ft}\, df \tag{7-15}$$

The conjugate $z^*(t)$ of the analytic signal satisfies the relations

$$z^*(t) = s(t) - j\hat{s}(t) = 2 \int_0^\infty S^*(f)e^{-j2\pi ft}\, df$$
$$= 2 \int_{-\infty}^0 S(f)e^{j2\pi ft}\, df \tag{7-16}$$

The Fourier transform of $z^*(t)$ thus vanishes for all *positive* frequencies. Adding and subtracting $z(t)$ and $z^*(t)$ give the relations

$$z(t) + z^*(t) = 2s(t) \tag{7-17}$$
$$z(t) - z^*(t) = 2j\hat{s}(t) \tag{7-18}$$

The one-sidedness of the Fourier transform of the analytic signal can be used to construct sideband representations. The function $w(t)$ defined by

$$w(t) = e^{j(\omega_c t + \theta_c)}z(t) = 2e^{j\theta_c} \int_0^\infty S(f)e^{j2\pi(f+f_c)t}\, df$$
$$= 2e^{j\theta_c} \int_{f_c}^\infty S(f - f_c)e^{j2\pi ft}\, df \tag{7-19}$$

contains no components of frequency less than f_c. It can be made to represent a real upper sideband on the carrier frequency f_c by adding the conjugate term.

$$w^*(t) = e^{-j(\omega_c t + \theta_c)} z^*(t) = 2e^{-j\theta_c} \int_{-\infty}^{0} S(f) e^{j2\pi(f-f_c)t}\, df$$
$$= 2e^{-j\theta_c} \int_{-\infty}^{-f_c} S(f + f_c) e^{j2\pi ft}\, df \tag{7-20}$$

Comparison with Eq. (7-11) shows that the Fourier transform of $w(t) + w^*(t)$ is equal to $4M_u(f)/(k_1 a_c)$. We conclude that the upper sideband $m_u(t)$ from the productor can be expressed by

$$\frac{4m_u(t)}{k_1 a_c} = w(t) + w^*(t) = z(t) e^{j(\omega_c t + \theta_c)} + z^*(t) e^{-j(\omega_c t + \theta_c)}$$
$$= [s(t) + j\hat{s}(t)] e^{j(\omega_c t + \theta_c)} + [s(t) - j\hat{s}(t)] e^{-j(\omega_c t + \theta_c)}$$

or

$$\frac{2m_u(t)}{k_1 a_c} = s(t) \cos(\omega_c t + \theta_c) - \hat{s}(t) \sin(\omega_c t + \theta_c) \tag{7-21}$$

Since

$$m(t) = m_u(t) + m_l(t) \tag{7-22}$$

we deduce that

$$m_l(t) = k_1 a_c\, s(t) \cos(\omega_c t + \theta_c) - m_u(t) \tag{7-23}$$

or

$$\frac{2m_l(t)}{k_1 a_c} = s(t) \cos(\omega_c t + \theta_c) + \hat{s}(t) \sin(\omega_c t + \theta_c) \tag{7-24}$$

Equations (7-21) and (7-24) are canonical representations of upper and lower sidebands modulated on a carrier of frequency ω_c and phase θ_c. The equations illustrate how the sidebands can be isolated by subtracting or adding the outputs of product modulators in which phase shifts of $\pi/2$ rad are inserted between signal inputs and between carrier inputs. The equations also give a convenient means of calculating the result of demodulation of the sidebands by a productor with carrier of arbitrary phase.

We define a low-pass signal $s_l(t)$ as one whose Fourier transform $S_l(f)$ vanishes for $|f| > f_c$. Similarly, a high-pass signal $s_h(t)$ is defined as one for which the Fourier transform $S_h(f)$ vanishes for $|f| < f_c$. It follows from these definitions that

$$s_l(t) = \int_{-f_c}^{f_c} S_l(f) e^{j2\pi ft}\, df \tag{7-25}$$

and

$$s_h(t) = \left[\int_{-\infty}^{-f_c} + \int_{f_c}^{\infty} \right] S_h(f) e^{j2\pi ft}\, df \tag{7-26}$$

Then from Eqs. (7-13) through (7-16),

$$z_h(t) = s_h(t) + j\hat{s}_h(t) = 2 \int_{f_c}^{\infty} S_h(f) e^{j2\pi ft}\, df \tag{7-27}$$

and

$$z_h^*(t) = s_h(t) - j\hat{s}_h(t) = 2 \int_{-\infty}^{-f_c} S_h(f)e^{j2\pi ft}\, df \qquad (7\text{-}28)$$

Let

$$p(t) = s_l(t)s_h(t) \qquad (7\text{-}29)$$

Then from (7-17),

$$2p(t) = s_l(t)z_h(t) + s_l(t)z_h^*(t) \qquad (7\text{-}30)$$

Equating Fourier transforms gives

$$2P(f) = S_l(f) * Z_h(f) + S_l(f) * Z_h^\dagger(f) \qquad (7\text{-}31)$$

where the Fourier transform of $z_h^*(t)$ is designated by $Z_h^\dagger(f)$, which is *not* equal to $Z_h^*(f)$. From Eq. (7-27), $Z_h(f)$ vanishes for $f < f_c$, and from Eq. (7-28), $Z_h^\dagger(f)$ vanishes for $f > -f_c$. Since $S_l(f)$ vanishes for $|f| > f_c$, the convolution of $S_l(f)$ and $Z_h(f)$ vanishes for all negative frequencies, and the convolution of $S_l(f)$ and $Z_h^\dagger(f)$ vanishes for all positive frequencies. It follows that

$$-2j \operatorname{sgn} f\, P(f) = -jS_l(f) * Z_h(f) + jS_l(f) * Z_h^\dagger(f) \qquad (7\text{-}32)$$

Equating inverse Fourier transforms of the two sides and applying (7-18) demonstrate the important result

$$\begin{aligned}
\hat{p}(t) &= \frac{-js_l(t)z_h(t)}{2} + \frac{js_l(t)z_h^*(t)}{2} \\
&= \frac{-js_l(t)[z_h(t) - z_h^*(t)]}{2} \\
&= s_l(t)\hat{s}_h(t) \qquad (7\text{-}33)
\end{aligned}$$

Stated in words, the rule for calculating the Hilbert transform of the product of nonoverlapping low-pass and high-pass signals is to multiply the low-pass signal by the Hilbert transform of the high-pass signal.

In the special case of the product $s(t) \cos(\omega_c t + \theta_c)$ with $S(f) = 0$ for $|f| > f_c$, the rule tells us that the Hilbert transform is $s(t) \sin(\omega_c t + \theta_c)$. If $S(f) = 0$ for $|f| < f_c$, the Hilbert transform is $\hat{s}(t) \cos(\omega_c t + \theta_c)$. Applying the rule to the upper and lower sidebands of Eqs. (7-21) and (7-24), we find

$$\frac{2\hat{m}_u(t)}{k_1 a_c} = s(t) \sin(\omega_c t + \theta_c) + \hat{s}(t) \cos(\omega_c t + \theta_c) \qquad (7\text{-}34)$$

and

$$\frac{2\hat{m}_l(t)}{k_1 a_c} = s(t) \sin(\omega_c t + \theta_c) - \hat{s}(t) \cos(\omega_c t + \theta_c) \qquad (7\text{-}35)$$

By solving Eqs. (7-21) and (7-34) for $s(t)$ and $\hat{s}(t)$, we obtain

$$\frac{k_1 a_c \, s(t)}{2} = m_u(t) \cos (\omega_c t + \theta_c) + \hat{m}_u(t) \sin (\omega_c t + \theta_c) \tag{7-36}$$

and

$$\frac{k_1 a_c \, \hat{s}(t)}{2} = \hat{m}_u(t) \cos (\omega_c t + \theta_c) - m_u(t) \sin (\omega_c t + \theta_c) \tag{7-37}$$

The corresponding equations in terms of the lower sideband obtained from Eqs. (7-24) and (7-35) are

$$\frac{k_1 a_c \, s(t)}{2} = m_l(t) \cos (\omega_c t + \theta_c) + \hat{m}_l(t) \sin (\omega_c t + \theta_c) \tag{7-38}$$

and

$$\frac{k_1 a_c \, \hat{s}(t)}{2} = m_l(t) \sin (\omega_c t + \theta_c) - \hat{m}_l(t) \cos (\omega_c t + \theta_c) \tag{7-39}$$

Equation (7-36) shows how to find the signal wave $s(t)$ which produces an upper sideband $m_u(t)$ on a carrier wave of frequency ω_c and phase θ_c. Likewise, Eq. (7-38) shows how to find the signal wave $s(t)$ which produces a lower sideband $m_l(t)$ on a carrier wave of frequency ω_c and phase θ_c. These formulas not only indicate the method for calculating the signals but also show how the signals can be detected by paired demodulators with specified phase shifts between inputs.

The Hilbert transform can be used to solve another problem which we have previously encountered—that of expressing an arbitrary band-limited wave in terms of in-phase and quadrature modulation of an arbitrary sinusoidal carrier wave. Suppose we are given the wave $v(t)$, band-limited to frequencies of absolute value between ω_1 and ω_2. We wish to express $v(t)$ in the form

$$v(t) = s_r(t) \cos (\omega_c t + \theta_c) + s_q(t) \sin (\omega_c t + \theta_c) \tag{7-40}$$

where ω_c can be any frequency not less than $\omega_2/2$, θ_c can be any phase angle, and $s_r(t)$ and $s_q(t)$ are band-limited to frequencies of absolute value less than ω_c. The restrictions are imposed to avoid sideband foldover. Then

$$\hat{v}(t) = s_r(t) \sin (\omega_c t + \theta_c) - s_q(t) \cos (\omega_c t + \theta_c) \tag{7-41}$$

Equations (7-40) and (7-41) are linear in $s_r(t)$ and $s_q(t)$ and have the solution:

$$\begin{aligned} s_r(t) &= v(t) \cos (\omega_c t + \theta_c) + \hat{v}(t) \sin (\omega_c t + \theta_c) \\ s_q(t) &= v(t) \sin (\omega_c t + \theta_c) - \hat{v}(t) \cos (\omega_c t + \theta_c) \end{aligned} \tag{7-42}$$

Note that $s_q(t)$ is *not* the Hilbert transform of $s_r(t)$ since $v(t)$ can contain frequencies greater than ω_c. As in the SSB representation, the DSB solution (7-42) shows how in-phase and quadrature signals can be recovered by balanced demodulators as an alternative to filtering the output of one demodulator. The equations in fact do more than that— they show how to calculate the response of envelope, phase, and frequency detectors to the wave $v(t)$ when $v(t)$ is a narrow-band wave, that is, $\omega_2 - \omega_1 \ll \omega_c$. To do this, write (7-40) in the equivalent form

$$v(t) = \rho(t) \cos [\omega_c t + \theta_c + \phi(t)] \qquad (7\text{-}43)$$

where

$$\rho^2(t) = s_r{}^2(t) + s_q{}^2(t) \qquad (7\text{-}44)$$

and

$$\tan \phi(t) = \frac{-s_q(t)}{s_r(t)} \qquad (7\text{-}45)$$

Then on substituting the values of $s_r(t)$ and $s_q(t)$ from (7-42), we find

$$\rho(t) = [v^2(t) + \hat{v}^2(t)]^{1/2} \qquad (7\text{-}46)$$

$$\phi(t) = \arctan \frac{\hat{v}(t)}{v(t)} - \omega_c t - \theta_c \qquad (7\text{-}47)$$

$$\dot{\phi}(t) = \frac{v(t)\dot{\hat{v}}(t) - \hat{v}(t)\dot{v}(t)}{v^2(t) + \hat{v}^2(t)} - \omega_c \qquad (7\text{-}48)$$

The solutions embodied in (7-46)–(7-48) have physical meaning as detector outputs only if $\rho(t)$, $\phi(t)$, and $\dot{\phi}(t)$ are sufficiently slowly varying functions of time relative to $\cos (\omega_c t + \theta_c)$ to enable their isolation by filtering. This is the reason the narrow-band requirement on $v(t)$ is physically necessary. We can, however, use these equations as a basis for a purely mathematical definition of the envelope, phase, and frequency of an arbitrary signal wave $s(t)$ without specifying any carrier frequency ω_c. These are:

$$\text{Envelope of } s(t) = e(t) = |z(t)| = [s^2(t) + \hat{s}^2(t)]^{1/2} \qquad (7\text{-}49)$$

$$\text{Phase of } s(t) = \theta(t) = \text{ph } z(t) = \arctan \frac{\hat{s}(t)}{s(t)} \qquad (7\text{-}50)$$

$$\text{Frequency of } s(t) = \dot{\theta}(t) = \frac{d}{dt} \text{ph } z(t) = \frac{s(t)\dot{\hat{s}}(t) - \hat{s}(t)\dot{s}(t)}{s^2(t) + \hat{s}^2(t)} \qquad (7\text{-}51)$$

The envelope, phase, and frequency thus defined coincide with the corresponding physically observable functions of narrow-band waves for arbitrary choice of a carrier within the band. To obtain the phase and frequency *deviations* in the narrow-band case, we subtract $\omega_c t + \theta_c$ and ω_c, respectively, from θ and $\dot{\theta}$.

The canonical representations of upper and lower sidebands produced by a signal $s(t)$ on a carrier of frequency ω_c and phase θ_c, Eqs. (7-21) and (7-24), show that the envelope of an SSB wave is given by $e(t)$, the absolute value of the analytic signal. We should not expect the envelope of an SSB wave to represent the signal itself. The SSB envelope is important, however, because it determines a range of magnitudes which an SSB transmission system must be able to handle.

So far we have calculated the Hilbert transform by shifting the phase of the components in the Fourier-integral representation of the signal. To express $\hat{s}(t)$ directly in terms of $s(t)$, we make use of the convolution theorem and find

$$\hat{s}(t) = s(t) * h(t) \tag{7-52}$$

where $h(t)$ is the inverse Fourier transform of $-j \operatorname{sgn} f$. From the known integral

$$\int_{-\infty}^{\infty} \frac{\sin 2\pi ft}{t} \, dt = \pi \operatorname{sgn} f \tag{7-53}$$

we deduce that

$$P \int_{-\infty}^{\infty} \frac{e^{-j2\pi ft}}{\pi t} \, dt = -j \operatorname{sgn} f \tag{7-54}$$

where P stands for the Cauchy principal value of an integral with a singularity in the integrand. For a singularity at $t = t_0$, P represents the limit as ϵ goes to zero of the sum of the integrals from $-\infty$ to $t_0 - \epsilon$ and $t_0 + \epsilon$ to ∞. In Eq. (7-54), $t_0 = 0$. From the uniqueness of the Fourier transform,

$$h(t) = \frac{1}{\pi t} \tag{7-55}$$

$$\hat{s}(t) = \frac{1}{\pi} P \int_{-\infty}^{\infty} \frac{s(\lambda)}{t - \lambda} \, d\lambda \tag{7-56}$$

Equation (7-56) furnishes another model for the Hilbert transform—the output when the signal is applied to a network with impulse response $h(t) = 1/(\pi t)$. This impulse response, like the transmittance function $H(f) = -j \operatorname{sgn} f$, is not physically realizable. We can, however, approximate the impulse response $h(t - \tau)$ when τ is very large. This is equivalent to approximating the transmittance function $H(f)e^{-j2\pi\tau f}$. What is actually done to realize a single-sideband modulator with satisfactory accuracy is to insert a delay network with transmittance function $e^{-j2\pi\tau f}$ in one signal input branch and to insert in the other branch a network which approximates $-j \operatorname{sgn} f \, e^{-j2\pi\tau f}$ over the band containing the essential signal components. In other words, the attenuation of the two networks should be equal and constant over the signal band, while the phase-vs.-frequency curves should be parallel straight lines with ordinates differing by $\pi/2$ rad and with the intercept of the first network equal to zero or a multiple of π. In this way the signal inputs to the two modulators can be made approximately equal to $s(t - \tau)$ and $\hat{s}(t - \tau)$.

As an example, let us apply the formula (7-56) to calculate the Hilbert transform of a rectangular signal wave. Let

$$s(t) = \begin{cases} 0 & t < 0 \\ A & 0 < t < T \\ 0 & T < t \end{cases} \tag{7-57}$$

Then

$$\hat{s}(t) = \frac{A}{\pi} P \int_0^T \frac{d\lambda}{t - \lambda} \tag{7-58}$$

When $t < 0$, the singularity in the integrand is below the range of integration and the significant values of $t - \lambda$ are negative. We then find

$$\hat{s}(t) = -\frac{A}{\pi} \log (\lambda - t) \Big|_0^T = -\frac{A}{\pi} \log \frac{t - T}{t}$$

When $t > T$, the singularity is above the range of integration and the significant values of $t - \lambda$ are positive. The corresponding result is

$$\hat{s}(t) = -\frac{A}{\pi} \log (t - \lambda) \Big|_0^T = -\frac{A}{\pi} \log \frac{t - T}{t}$$

When $0 < t < T$, we write

$$\begin{aligned} \hat{s}(t) &= \frac{A}{\pi} \lim_{\epsilon \to 0} \left[\int_0^{t-\epsilon} \frac{d\lambda}{t - \lambda} + \int_{t+\epsilon}^T \frac{d\lambda}{t - \lambda} \right] \\ &= \frac{A}{\pi} \lim_{\epsilon \to 0} \left[-\log (t - \lambda) \Big|_0^{t-\epsilon} - \log (\lambda - t) \Big|_{t+\epsilon}^T \right] \\ &= \frac{A}{\pi} \lim_{\epsilon \to 0} \left[-\log \epsilon + \log t - \log (T - t) - \log \epsilon \right] \\ &= -\frac{A}{\pi} \log \frac{T - t}{t} \end{aligned}$$

The three cases can be combined in the single formula

$$\hat{s}(t) = -\frac{A}{\pi} \log \left| \frac{t - T}{t} \right| \tag{7-59}$$

Graphs of $s(t)$ and $\hat{s}(t)$ for the rectangular signal are shown in Fig. 7-2. These results can be used to calculate the envelope of a single-

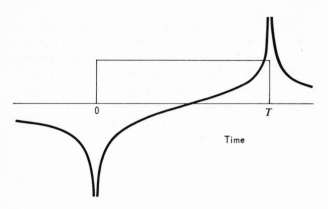

Time

Fig. 7-2 Rectangular signal and its Hilbert transform.

sideband wave for such an idealized elementary signal. Figure 7-3 shows the resulting SSB wave for the limiting case in which T is infinite. The graph applies, for example, to the case of a sudden change in brightness in a television signal. Transmission of television by single sideband produces a wave of this nature. The high peaks are customarily referred to as "horns" and the rounding off of the step is called "smear."

7-3 THE HILBERT TRANSFORM IN THE THEORY
OF FUNCTIONS OF A COMPLEX VARIABLE

The definition of an analytic signal was given in Sec. 7-2 without explaining the reason for the use of the term. The source of this nomenclature is the important role which the Hilbert transform plays in the theory of analytic functions of a complex variable. We begin with Cauchy's integral formula which states that if the function $w(z)$ is analytic within

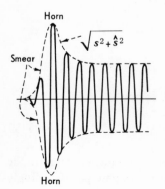

Fig. 7-3 Envelope of SSB wave resulting from signal step.

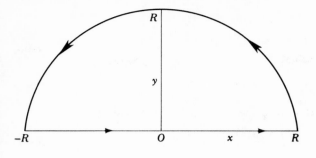

Fig. 7-4 The contour C.

and on a simple closed contour C in the complex plane of the variable $z = x + jy$, the following results hold for integrals around the contour in a counterclockwise direction:

1. If ζ is any point inside the contour C,

$$\int_C \frac{w(z)\, dz}{z - \zeta} = 2\pi j\, w(\zeta) \tag{7-60}$$

2. If ζ is any point outside the contour C,

$$\int_C \frac{w(z)\, dz}{z - \zeta} = 0 \tag{7-61}$$

3. If ζ is any point on the contour C,

$$P \int_C \frac{w(z)\, dz}{z - \zeta} = \pi j\, w(\zeta) \tag{7-62}$$

Assume C consists of the closed semicircle in the upper half of the z plane, as in Fig. 7-4, with diameter coincident with the real axis from $-R$ to R, and let ζ be a point x on the diameter. Then from (7-62)

$$w(x) = \frac{1}{\pi j} P \int_{-R}^{R} \frac{w(\lambda)\, d\lambda}{\lambda - x} + \frac{1}{\pi j} \int_{C'} \frac{w(z)\, dz}{z - x} \tag{7-63}$$

where C' is the semicircular arc. The complex variable z has been replaced by the real variable λ in the first integral because the path of integration is along the real axis. A deduction concerning Hilbert transforms can be made for the class of functions $w(z)$ for which

$$\lim_{R \to \infty} \int_{C'} \frac{w(z)\, dz}{z - x} = 0 \tag{7-64}$$

For if (7-64) is true, we obtain from (7-63)

$$w(x) = \frac{1}{\pi j} P \int_{-\infty}^{\infty} \frac{w(\lambda) \, d\lambda}{\lambda - x} \tag{7-65}$$

Let

$$w(x) = u(x) + jv(x) \tag{7-66}$$

where $u(x)$ and $v(x)$ are real. Then if Eq. (7-65) is valid,

$$u(x) + jv(x) = \frac{1}{\pi j} P \int_{-\infty}^{\infty} \frac{u(\lambda) + jv(\lambda)}{\lambda - x} \, d\lambda \tag{7-67}$$

Equating reals and imaginaries separately, we see that

$$\begin{aligned} u(x) &= -\hat{v}(x) \\ v(x) &= \hat{u}(x) \end{aligned} \tag{7-68}$$

The conclusion under the circumstances set forth is that along the real axis the imaginary part of an analytic function of a complex variable is equal to the Hilbert transform of the real part. In using this theorem one must be careful to verify that the analytic function satisfies Eq. (7-64).

A sufficient condition for validity of Eq. (7-64) is that $|w(z)|$ approaches zero uniformly for all values of z on the semicircle as R goes to infinity. This means that given any $\epsilon > 0$, a value R_0 independent of z can be found such that $|w(z)| < \epsilon$ for all values of z on semicircles of radius exceeding R_0. Since the absolute value of the integral along C' cannot exceed the product of the path length πR and the maximum absolute value of the integrand on the path, the integral must be bounded in absolute value by $\pi R \epsilon / |Re^{j\theta} - x|$, $0 \le \theta \le \pi$, $R > R_0$, and must approach zero as R goes to infinity.

Equation (7-64) also holds under somewhat less stringent conditions. For example, Jordan's lemma[1] shows that if $k > 0$ and $Q(z)$ approaches zero uniformly on C' as R goes to infinity,

$$\lim_{R \to \infty} \int_{C'} e^{jkz} Q(z) \, dz = 0 \tag{7-69}$$

In particular we can set $Q(z) = 1/(z - x)$ and deduce that the function $w(z) = e^{jkz}$, which does not approach zero uniformly for all points of C' as $|z|$ goes to infinity, nevertheless does satisfy (7-64). Hence the analytic function e^{jkz}, which has real part $\cos kx$ and imaginary part $\sin kx$ on the real axis, satisfies sufficient conditions to prove the already known fact that $\sin kx$ is the Hilbert transform of $\cos kx$.

An example in which the imaginary part of $w(x)$ is not the Hilbert transform of the real part is furnished by

$$w(z) = e^{jk \sin \omega z} \qquad k \text{ real} \tag{7-70}$$

which is an analytic function of z in the *finite* upper half plane. Setting $z = Re^{j\theta}$, we calculate

$$w(z) = e^{jk \sin (\omega R \cos \theta + j\omega R \sin \theta)}$$
$$= e^{-k \cos (\omega R \cos \theta) \sinh (\omega R \sin \theta)} e^{jk \sin (\omega R \cos \theta) \cosh (\omega R \sin \theta)} \quad (7\text{-}71)$$

The value of sinh $(\omega R \sin \theta)$ cannot be negative for $0 \leq \theta \leq \pi$, but the value of cos $(\omega R \cos \theta)$ changes sign as C' is traversed when R is large. Hence $|w(z)|$ not only fails to converge to zero but actually grows without limit in some parts of C' as R goes to infinity. We conclude that the imaginary part of $w(x)$ is not the Hilbert transform of the real part; that is, sin $(k \sin \omega x)$ is not the Hilbert transform of cos $(k \sin \omega x)$.

We can make the physical meaning of the preceding example clearer by considering the Fourier-series expansion

$$w(t) = e^{jk \sin \omega t} = \sum_{n=-\infty}^{\infty} J_n(k)e^{jn\omega t}$$
$$= \sum_{n=-\infty}^{\infty} J_n(k) \cos n\omega t + j \sum_{n=-\infty}^{\infty} J_n(k) \sin n\omega t \quad (7\text{-}72)$$

Let

$$s(t) = \sum_{n=-\infty}^{\infty} J_n(k) \cos n\omega t$$
$$= J_0(k) + \sum_{n=1}^{\infty} [J_n(k) + J_{-n}(k)] \cos n\omega t \quad (7\text{-}73)$$

Then

$$\hat{s}(t) = \sum_{n=1}^{\infty} [J_n(k) + J_{-n}(k)] \sin n\omega t$$
$$= \sum_{n=1}^{\infty} J_n(k) \sin n\omega t - \sum_{n=-\infty}^{-1} J_n(k) \sin n\omega t$$
$$= \sum_{n=-\infty}^{\infty} \text{sgn } n\, J_n(k) \sin n\omega t \quad (7\text{-}74)$$

which is evidently not equal to the imaginary part of $w(t)$.

If we consider the function

$$w(t) = e^{j(\omega_c t + k \sin \omega t)}$$
$$= \sum_{n=-\infty}^{\infty} J_n(k)e^{j(\omega_c + n\omega)t}$$
$$= \sum_{n=-\infty}^{\infty} J_n(k) \cos (\omega_c + n\omega)t + j \sum_{n=-\infty}^{\infty} J_n(k) \sin (\omega_c + n\omega)t$$
$$(7\text{-}75)$$

with

$$s(t) = \sum_{n=-\infty}^{\infty} J_n(k) \cos (\omega_c + n\omega)t \qquad \text{and} \qquad \omega_c > 0 \qquad (7\text{-}76)$$

we calculate

$$\hat{s}(t) = \sum_{n=-\infty}^{\infty} J_n(k) \, \text{sgn} \, (\omega_c + n\omega) \sin (\omega_c + n\omega)t \qquad (7\text{-}77)$$

The Hilbert transform in this case differs from the imaginary part of $w(t)$ only in the sign of terms in which $\omega_c + n\omega$ is negative. In the narrow-band case in which ω_c is large compared with $k\omega$, the exceptional terms are negligibly small and the analytic signal is approximately equal to $w(t)$.

The foregoing theory furnishes a convenient method of calculating many Hilbert transforms. If we can identify $s(x)$ as the real part of an analytic function $w(x)$ with x real, and if $w(z)$ with $z = x + jy$ satisfies (7-64), then $\hat{s}(x)$ is given by the imaginary part of $w(x)$. Similarly, if we can identify $s(x)$ as the imaginary part of an analytic function $w(x)$ with x real and with $w(z)$ satisfying (7-64), then $\hat{s}(x)$ is equal to the negative of the real part of $w(x)$. As an example, consider the function

$$s(x) = \text{sinc} \, f_0 x = \frac{\sin \pi f_0 x}{\pi f_0 x} = \text{Im} \, w(x) \qquad (7\text{-}78)$$

with

$$w(x) = \frac{e^{j\pi f_0 x} - 1}{\pi f_0 x} \qquad (7\text{-}79)$$

The function

$$w(z) = \frac{e^{j\pi f_0 z} - 1}{\pi f_0 z} \qquad (7\text{-}80)$$

is an analytic function of z which satisfies (7-64) if $f_0 > 0$. Hence,

$$\hat{s}(x) = - \, \text{Re} \, w(x) = \frac{1 - \cos \pi f_0 x}{\pi f_0 x} \qquad (7\text{-}81)$$

7-4 LINEAR MODULATION BY VARISTORS

A varistor is a two-terminal device in which the relationship between instantaneous current and voltage is time-invariant and nonlinear. Semiconducting materials such as germanium and silicon are typical ingredients of varistors. One example of a varistor characteristic is the equation for current i versus voltage v for an ideal crystal, namely,

$$i = i_0(e^{qv/kT} - 1) \qquad (7\text{-}82)$$

In this equation, i_0 is the saturation current, T is the temperature in degrees Kelvin, $q = 1.59 \times 10^{-19}$ coulomb is the electric charge, and k is Boltzmann's constant. The current increases rapidly as the voltage is increased positively, but if the applied voltage is negative, the current is limited by the asymptotic value $i = -i_0$, which is typically very small in absolute value. Such a crystal produces a d-c component of current in response to an alternating voltage and therefore can be used as a rectifying element. A variety of nonlinear relations between current and voltage can be realized by combining rectifying elements in various ways.

A varistor can be used as a "curvature modulator" by applying the sum of signal and carrier voltages to the varistor terminals. The current is then a nonlinear function of the sum and accordingly contains various modulation products involving the signal and carrier. An example of a nonlinear function which produces sidebands linearly related to the signal is furnished by a simple square-law variation. This comes about because the square of the sum of two components contains a term proportional to the product of the components. The square-law device also produces terms proportional to the square of the signal and to the square of the carrier wave. Since these terms do not change sign when the polarity of signal or carrier is reversed, they can be suppressed by balanced modulators without losing the sidebands. The appropriate procedure is to subtract the outputs of two identical square-law modulators with inputs identical except for a polarity difference between either the two signal or two carrier inputs.

We note that if the square law were replaced by a cube law, there would be one component of the output varying as the product of the signal and the square of the carrier wave. Therefore, a cube-law modulator can be used to generate linear sidebands on the second harmonic of the input carrier frequency. In general, an nth-power variation could serve as a linear modulator in which the $(n - 1)$st harmonic of the input carrier frequency becomes the carrier frequency of the modulated output wave. Many other modulation products would also be generated in these high-order modulators, and successful operation would require satisfactory reduction of the unwanted terms by some combination of amplitude disparity, frequency selectivity, and phase balance.

In actual varistors a square law, cube law, or, in general, an nth-power law of variation cannot be realized over an indefinitely wide range, and in fact can only be approximated over a quite limited range. Restraining the range of signal plus carrier to an approximately parabolic arc of a varistor curve would typically result in the production of weak sidebands. A more effective utilization of the nonlinear characteristic of the varistor is obtained when the input carrier wave is large enough to drive the varistor through most of the available nonlinear range and the added signal wave is sufficiently small to produce an approximately linear perturbation of the highly nonlinear response to the carrier.

The theory of the large-carrier, small-signal approach can be developed by considering varistor characteristics capable of Taylor's series expansion in power series about any point. If the part of the characteristic in the neighborhood of $v = v_0$ can be represented by

$$i = g(v_0) + \frac{g'(v_0)}{1!} (v - v_0) + \frac{g''(v_0)}{2!} (v - v_0)^2 + \cdots \tag{7-83}$$

then for sufficiently small $|v - v_0|$,

$$i \approx g(v_0) + g'(v_0)(v - v_0) \tag{7-84}$$

Then, if we set

$$v = v_c \cos \omega_c t + v_1 \cos \omega_1 t$$

and $\tag{7-85}$

$$v_0 = v_c \cos \omega_c t$$

we obtain

$$i \approx g(v_c \cos \omega_c t) + g'(v_c \cos \omega_c t)v_1 \cos \omega_1 t \tag{7-86}$$

The functions $g(v_c \cos \omega_c t)$ and $g'(v_c \cos \omega_c t)$ are then expanded in Fourier series, thus:

$$g(v_c \cos \omega_c t) = g_0 + 2 \sum_{m=1}^{\infty} g_m \cos m\omega_c t$$

$$g'(v_c \cos \omega_c t) = g_0' + 2 \sum_{m=1}^{\infty} g_m' \cos m\omega_c t \tag{7-87}$$

Representing $\omega_c t$ by x, we note that both $g(v_c \cos x)$ and $g'(v_c \cos x)$ are even functions of x and hence that the equations for the Fourier coefficients become

$$g_m = \frac{1}{\pi} \int_0^\pi g(v_c \cos x) \cos mx \, dx = \int_{-v_c}^{v_c} \frac{g(v) \cos [m \arccos (v/v_c)]}{\pi (v_c^2 - v^2)^{1/2}} \, dv \tag{7-88}$$

$$g_m' = \frac{1}{\pi} \int_0^\pi g'(v_c \cos x) \cos mx \, dx = \int_{-v_c}^{v_c} \frac{g'(v) \cos [m \arccos (v/v_c)]}{\pi (v_c^2 - v^2)^{1/2}} \, dv$$

It follows that

$$i \approx g_0 + 2 \sum_{m=1}^{\infty} g_m \cos m\omega_c t + g_0' v_1 \cos \omega_1 t$$

$$+ v_1 \sum_{m=1}^{\infty} g_m'[\cos (m\omega_c + \omega_1)t + \cos (m\omega_c - \omega_1)t] \tag{7-89}$$

Linear upper and lower sidebands thus appear on every harmonic of ω_c.

Linear sideband production obtained in this way requires constraint of the signal variation to a linear part of an operating range centered at the instantaneous carrier value.   This may not always be possible if the varistor curve contains a sudden break.   In fact, in idealized varistor characteristics such as pure rectifiers, it is often convenient to consider points at which the response function or its derivative is discontinuous and no linear range exists.   At such points, of course, the Taylor's series representation is not possible.   In the usual case of interest there are at most only a few such points, and it seems intuitively plausible that their influence on the linearity of the modulator could be made negligible. It will be noted that the existence of a finite number of discontinuities in either g or g' does not disturb calculations of Fourier coefficients.   The treatment can, in fact, be made rigorous by invoking the theory of double Fourier series.[2]

Consider the function $g(v_c \cos x + v_1 \cos y)$ of the two independent real variables x and y.   Results obtained for this general function are applicable to the case in which x and y are dependent and, in particular, to the special case in which $x = \omega_c t$ and $y = \omega_1 t$, and g represents the response of the modulator.   The general function is periodic in x and y with periods 2π in each and has a simple representation as a double Fourier series:

$$g(v_c \cos x + v_1 \cos y) = \sum_{m=0}^{\infty} \sum_{n=0}^{\infty} a_{mn} \cos mx \cos ny \qquad (7\text{-}90)$$

where

$$a_{mn} = \frac{\epsilon_m \epsilon_n}{4\pi^2} \int_{-\pi}^{\pi} \int_{-\pi}^{\pi} g(v_c \cos x + v_1 \cos y) \cos mx \cos ny \, dx \, dy$$

$$(7\text{-}91)$$

and ϵ_m is Neumann's discontinuous factor equal to 2 when $m \neq 0$ and 1 when $m = 0$.   Since the integrand is an even function of both x and y, the lower limits can be changed to 0 if the value of the integral is multiplied by 4.   It is seen that first-order sidebands on frequency $m\omega_c$ are represented by the term $a_{m1} \cos m\omega_c t \cos \omega_1 t$.   Evidently a_{m1} is a function of the two independent variables v_c and v_1 and can be written as

$$a_{m1} = \alpha(v_c, v_1) \qquad (7\text{-}92)$$

where the function α is defined by the double integral.   It is evident from the integrand that

$$\alpha(v_c, 0) = 0 \qquad (7\text{-}93)$$

since the integration in y, which can be performed separately in this case, reduces to the integral of a sine wave over a complete period.   Now if

v_c is held constant, we obtain a function of a single variable,

$$\alpha_1(v_1) = \alpha(v_c, v_1) \qquad \alpha_1(0) = 0 \tag{7-94}$$

If $\alpha_1(v_1)$ can be represented by a Maclaurin's series, we can write

$$\alpha_1(v_1) = \frac{\alpha_1'(v_1)}{1!} v_1 + \frac{\alpha_1''(v_1)}{2!} v_1{}^2 + \cdots \tag{7-95}$$

Then

$$\alpha_1(v_1) \approx \alpha_1'(v_1) v_1 \tag{7-96}$$

if v_1 is confined to the linear range of $\alpha(v_c, v_1)$ considered as a function of v_1 only.

The advantage of the double-Fourier-series solution is that the validity of the power-series expansion in terms of signal needs to be examined only for the coefficient of interest at a fixed value of carrier amplitude. This expansion can typically be expressed in terms of powers of v_1/v_c, and the range of linearity thus readily determined.

As an example, consider the ideal hard limiter defined by

$$g(v) = \begin{cases} A & v > 0 \\ -A & v < 0 \end{cases} \tag{7-97}$$

This function is discontinuous at $v = 0$. The function $g(v_c \cos x + v_1 \cos y)$ consists of positive and negative plateaus separated by branches of the curve $v_c \cos x + v_1 \cos y = 0$. Let $k = v_1/v_c$ and assume $0 \leq k \leq 1$. As indicated by Fig. 7-5, the value of the general first-order sideband coefficient becomes:

$$\begin{aligned} a_{m1} &= \frac{4A}{\pi^2} \int_0^\pi \cos y \, dy \left[\int_0^{\arccos(-k \cos y)} - \int_{\arccos(-k \cos y)}^\pi \right] \cos mx \, dx \\ &= \frac{8A}{m\pi^2} \int_0^\pi \sin[m \arccos(-k \cos y)] \cos y \, dy \end{aligned} \tag{7-98}$$

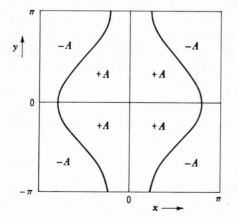

Fig. 7-5 Map showing the values of $g(x,y)$, Eq. (7-97), in a period square of the xy plane. The boundaries between $g(x,y) = +1$ and $g(x,y) = -1$ are branches of the curve $\cos x + k \cos y = 0$.

This integral vanishes when m is an odd number.   The lowest frequency which can be used for sideband production is $2\omega_c$, corresponding to $m = 2$. We calculate

$$a_{21} = -\frac{8kA}{\pi^2} \int_0^\pi (1 - k^2 \cos^2 y)^{\frac{1}{2}} \cos^2 y \, dy \tag{7-99}$$

This is an elliptic integral which can be evaluated in terms of a finite combination of tabulated functions. However, it is sufficient for illustrative purposes to calculate the first few terms of a power-series expansion in k.   Let $k^2 = z$ and define

$$u(z) = \int_0^\pi (1 - z \cos^2 y)^{\frac{1}{2}} \cos^2 y \, dy \tag{7-100}$$

Then

$$a_{21} = -\frac{8kA}{\pi^2} u(z) \tag{7-101}$$

and

$$u(z) = u(0) + \frac{u'(0)}{1!} z + \frac{u''(0)}{2!} z^2 + \cdots \tag{7-102}$$

We calculate

$$u(0) = \int_0^\pi \cos^2 y \, dy = \frac{\pi}{2}$$

$$u'(z) = -\frac{1}{2} \int_0^\pi (1 - z \cos^2 y)^{-\frac{1}{2}} \cos^4 y \, dy \tag{7-103}$$

$$u'(0) = -\frac{1}{2} \int_0^\pi \cos^4 y \, dy = -\frac{3\pi}{16} \qquad \text{etc.}$$

In this way it is found that

$$a_{21} = -\frac{4kA}{\pi} \left(1 - \frac{3}{8} k^2 - \frac{5}{64} k^4 - \cdots \right) \tag{7-104}$$

Thus the highly nonlinear response function characterizing a hard limiter is capable of linear sideband production when the ratio of signal-to-carrier amplitude is kept sufficiently small.   Equation (7-104) shows that a_{21} varies linearly with v_1 if v_1/v_c is small compared with $(\frac{8}{3})^{\frac{1}{2}} = 1.633$. In the limit,

$$a_{21} \approx -\frac{4A}{\pi v_c} v_1 \tag{7-105}$$

It appears that an increase in the amplitude of the carrier applied to the hard limiter acts as a linearizing agent.   The ratio of sideband to signal amplitude actually decreases as the carrier is made larger.   These are characteristic properties of varistor modulators.   We can prove a general theorem concerning the impossibility of utilizing the carrier input power to increase the sideband output power beyond the amount of power supplied by the signal itself. Consider a passive varistor with the single-valued current-vs.-voltage response function $i = g(v)$. Passivity will be defined here by requiring that $g(0) = 0$ and that $g(v)$ is a monotonically nondecreasing function of v. The latter condition is imposed to exclude negative resistance at any operating point. The mathematical statement is that if $\Delta v > 0$, $g(v + \Delta v) \geq g(v)$.

When a sinusoidal carrier wave of frequency ω_c and a sinusoidal signal wave of frequency ω_1 are applied to a passive varistor, the nonlinearity causes the appearance of modulation products with frequencies $m\omega_c \pm n\omega_1$, where m and n take on all integer values and zero. Let v_a represent the sum of all voltage components with frequencies of form $m\omega_c$, and let v_b represent the remaining components of v. The frequencies represented in v_b are of form $m\omega_c \pm n\omega_1$, where n takes on all integer values but is never zero. The value of m can be zero or any integer. We write

$$v = v_a + v_b$$
$$i = g(v) = g(v_a + v_b) \tag{7-106}$$

Consider the mathematically defined current

$$i_a = g(v_a) \tag{7-107}$$

Since v_a contains no components related to the signal frequency ω_1, neither does i_a. Therefore, i_a and v_b contain no frequencies in common, and the product $v_b i_a$ consists of the sum of sinusoidal components with nonzero frequencies. Therefore, the long-time average value of $v_b i_a$ approaches zero. The average power absorbed by the varistor at frequencies related to the signal is

$$
\begin{aligned}
w_1 &= \text{av } (v_b i) = \text{av } [v_b(i - i_a) + v_b i_a] \\
&= \text{av } [v_b(i - i_a)] + \text{av } (v_b i_a) = \text{av } [v_b(i - i_a)] \\
&= \text{av } \{v_b[g(v_a + v_b) - g(v_a)]\}
\end{aligned}
\tag{7-108}
$$

If $v_b \geq 0$, $g(v_a + v_b) - g(v_a) \geq 0$, while if $v_b < 0$, $g(v_a + v_b) - g(v_a) \leq 0$. In either case the product of v_b and $g(v_a + v_b) - g(v_a)$ cannot be negative, and hence

$$w_1 \geq 0 \tag{7-109}$$

A positive sign of w_1 means that the varistor exhibits a net absorption of power at the signal-related frequencies. The average power can be negative at some of these frequencies, but there must be enough positive power at the others to keep the sum positive.

The set of signal and sideband components thus constitutes a closed system in the sense that average power delivered at any signal-related frequency cannot exceed that supplied at other signal-related frequencies. In the case of a modulator, the average output power in the sidebands cannot exceed the average signal power supplied, while in the case of a demodulator, the average signal output power cannot exceed the average sideband power supplied. In this respect, passive varistors differ from passive nonlinear reactors. We shall see in the next section that varactor modulators can make use of carrier power to deliver more output power in the sidebands than is supplied from the signal source.

We illustrate by solving a simplified example of a varistor modulation circuit. A computational complexity which arises in typical cases is the presence of many modulation products in addition to the carrier and signal terms in both the current in and voltage across the varistor. Idealized circuit design can suppress the nonessential products in either the current or voltage but not both. Consider the circuit shown in Fig. 7-6 in which the signal and carrier sources are in series with the varistor and the sideband output. Assume that the varistor characteristic $i = g(v)$ is an odd function. Then linear sidebands do not exist on the frequency ω_c of the carrier source, but can be produced on the frequency $2\omega_c$.

Assume that an upper sideband on $2\omega_c$ is to be generated. We specify that the voltage v across the varistor contains only the signal frequency ω_1, the carrier source frequency ω_c, and the sideband frequency $2\omega_c + \omega_1$. This condition can be obtained by insertion of stiff antiresonant circuits across each source and load as shown. The idealized equivalent circuit of the signal source is then a current generator with shunt admittance equal to a pure conductance G_1 at frequency ω_1 and equal to zero at all frequencies involving ω_c. The carrier source has shunt admittance equal to a pure conductance G_c at ω_c and equal to zero at all the modulation product frequencies. The sideband output admit-

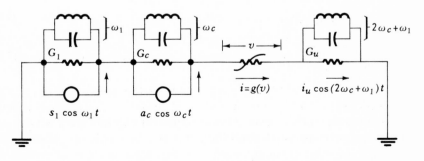

Fig. 7-6 Single-sideband varistor modulator with low impedance outside band.

tance is G_u at frequency $2\omega_c + \omega_1$ and is zero at all other modulation product frequencies. It follows that v can contain only the three specified frequencies since components at other frequencies are short-circuited.

Let

$$v = v_c \cos x + v_1 \cos y + v_u \cos (2x + y) \tag{7-110}$$

where $x = \omega_c t$ and $y = \omega_1 t$. Then

$$
\begin{aligned}
i &\approx g(v_c \cos x) + g'(v_c \cos x)[v_1 \cos y + v_u \cos (2x + y)] \\
&= g_0 + 2 \sum_{m=1}^{\infty} g_m \cos mx \\
&\quad + (g_0' + 2 \sum_{m=1}^{\infty} g_m' \cos mx)[v_1 \cos y + v_u \cos (2x + y)] \\
&= 2g_1 \cos x + g_0' v_1 \cos y + g_0' v_u \cos (2x + y) \\
&\quad + g_2' v_u \cos y + g_2' v_1 \cos (2x + y) \\
&\quad + \text{terms of frequencies other than } \omega_c, \, \omega_1, \text{ and } 2\omega_c + \omega_1 \tag{7-111}
\end{aligned}
$$

Kirchhoff's second law gives for the carrier input circuit

$$a_c \cos \omega_c t - G_c v_c \cos \omega_c t = 2g_1 \cos \omega_c t$$

from which

$$G_c v_c + \frac{1}{\pi} \int_{-\pi}^{\pi} g(v_c \cos x) \cos x \, dx \approx a_c \tag{7-112}$$

This relation enables an approximate calculation of a_c as a function of v_c, and the result can be inverted to obtain v_c versus a_c, neglecting v_c/a_c relative to unity. The corresponding equations for the signal and sideband circuits give

$$
\begin{aligned}
s_1 - G_1 v_1 &= g_0' v_1 + g_2' v_u \\
i_u &= -G_u v_u = g_0' v_u + g_2' v_1
\end{aligned}
$$

which can be rewritten as

$$
\begin{aligned}
(G_1 + g_0') v_1 + g_2' v_u &= s_1 \\
g_2' v_1 + (G_u + g_0') v_u &= 0
\end{aligned} \tag{7-113}
$$

Equations (7-113) are recognizable as the solution of the two-node network of Fig. 7-7. The maximum transfer of power from source to load is known to be obtained by matching the terminating conductances to the iterative conductance of the Π-network, i.e., by setting

$$G_1 = G_u = (g_0'^2 - g_2'^2)^{1/2} \tag{7-114}$$

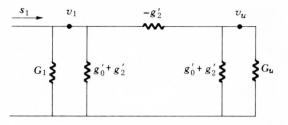

Fig. 7-7 Equivalent linear circuit of single-sideband modulator.

The conversion power gain, which is defined as the ratio of sideband output power to available signal power, is then

$$\Gamma_c = \frac{v_u{}^2 G_u}{s_1{}^2/(4G_1)} = g_2'^2 [g_0' + (g_0'^2 - g_2'^2)^{1/2}]^{-2} \tag{7-115}$$

The maximum value of unity is approached when g_0' approaches equality with g_2'. However, no power can actually be delivered in the limiting case since the terminating conductances approach zero. As illustrated in Prob. 7-13, the maximum gain is approached when the slope of the varistor response approaches a δ function.

7-5 LINEAR MODULATION BY VARACTORS

A varactor is a nonlinear element which stores but does not dissipate energy. Examples are the ideal nonlinear inductor and the ideal nonlinear capacitor. These elements are defined by a single-valued nonlinear relationship between magnetic flux ϕ and current i in the case of the inductor and between charge q and voltage v in the case of the capacitor. The two kinds of elements are duals of each other, and a solution of a circuit containing one kind can be applied to an analogous circuit containing the other by interchanges of ϕ and q, and i and v. It will be sufficient, therefore, to restrict our treatment to one kind, which we shall take as the nonlinear capacitor.

Let w represent the instantaneous value of power delivered to a nonlinear capacitor in which $v = \eta(q)$. Then since $i = dq/dt$, it follows that $w = vi = v\, dq/dt$, and the time average of w is given by

$$\text{av } w = \text{av}\left(v \frac{dq}{dt}\right) = \lim_{T \to \infty} \frac{1}{T} \int_{t_1}^{t_1+T} v \frac{dq}{dt}\, dt$$

$$= \lim_{T \to \infty} \frac{1}{T} \int_{q(t_1)}^{q(t_1+T)} \eta(q)\, dq \tag{7-116}$$

Since $\eta(q)$ is single-valued, the area accumulated by integration over any arc of the curve $\eta(q)$ is canceled when this arc is retraced in the reverse direction. The value of the integral at any time cannot exceed the area under the curve representing the maximum monotonic change in q. For finite impressed waves the area under one traversal is finite, and a division by a value of T approaching infinity gives in the limit a value of zero for the average power. Over an infinite time the nonlinear reactor returns as much power to as received from the external circuit.

Assume a nonlinear capacitor connected to an external network containing generators at the frequencies ω_c and ω_1. The nonlinear element then produces components with frequencies $m\omega_c \pm n\omega_1$, where m and n can have all integer values. If the external network is of unlimited generality, the various frequencies can occur in both the voltage and charge expressed as functions of time. Also, the relative phases of these components are not restricted to any simple set of values. The most general representation of the components of voltage and charge is expressed by

$$v = \sum_{m=0}^{\infty} \sum_{n=-\infty}^{\infty} [a_{mn} \cos (m\omega_c + n\omega_1)t + b_{mn} \sin (m\omega_c + n\omega_1)t]$$

(7-117)

$$q = \sum_{m=0}^{\infty} \sum_{n=-\infty}^{\infty} [c_{mn} \cos (m\omega_c + n\omega_1)t + d_{mn} \sin (m\omega_c + n\omega_1)t]$$

(7-118)

The only constraint on the coefficients a_{mn}, b_{mn}, c_{mn}, and d_{mn} is that embodied by the functional relationship $v = \eta(q)$. This constraint enables a very important property of varactor modulators to be deduced.

First, we consider the function $q(x,y)$ defined by

$$q(x,y) = \sum_{m=0}^{\infty} \sum_{n=-\infty}^{\infty} [c_{mn} \cos (mx + ny) + d_{mn} \sin (mx + ny)]$$

(7-119)

where x and y are independent variables. We note that $q(x,y)$ is periodic in both x and y with period 2π in each. It follows that the function

$$v(x,y) = \eta[q(x,y)]$$

(7-120)

is also doubly periodic in x and y with the period 2π. Furthermore, the function $v(x,y)$ satisfies a sufficient set of conditions to enable its expansion in a double Fourier series in x and y of form

$$v(x,y) = \sum_{m=1}^{\infty} \sum_{n=-\infty}^{\infty} [a_{mn} \cos (mx + ny) + b_{mn} \sin (mx + ny)]$$

(7-121)

where a_{mn} and b_{mn} can be calculated in terms of c_{mn} and d_{mn} by rules previously given. When this calculation has been completed, the results can be applied to the special case in which $x = \omega_c t$ and $y = \omega_1 t$. The current $i(t)$ can then be found by differentiating $q(\omega_c t, \omega_1 t)$ as given by Eq. (7-119). The result is

$$i(t) = \frac{dq}{dt} = \sum_{m=0}^{\infty} \sum_{n=-\infty}^{\infty} [-c_{mn}(m\omega_c + n\omega_1) \sin (m\omega_c + n\omega_1)t$$
$$+ d_{mn}(m\omega_c + n\omega_1) \cos (m\omega_c + n\omega_1)t] \quad (7\text{-}122)$$

We can adjust the values of c_{mn} and d_{mn} defining the charge at will by suitable choice of the source generators and external impedances. The values of a_{mn} and b_{mn} are then completely determined and are independent of the choice of ω_c and ω_1. From Eq. (7-122) the amplitude of a component of current at any of the frequencies represented is proportional to the frequency of that component. Let the resultant components of v, q, and i with frequency $m\omega_c + n\omega_1$ be represented by v_{mn}, q_{mn}, and i_{mn}, respectively. Then

$$v_{mn} = a_{mn} \cos (m\omega_c + n\omega_1)t + b_{mn} \sin (m\omega_c + n\omega_1)t$$
$$q_{mn} = c_{mn} \cos (m\omega_c + n\omega_1)t + d_{mn} \sin (m\omega_c + n\omega_1)t \quad (7\text{-}123)$$
$$i_{mn} = (m\omega_c + n\omega_1)[-c_{mn} \sin (m\omega_c + n\omega_1)t + d_{mn} \cos (m\omega_c + n\omega_1)t]$$
$$= -(m\omega_c + n\omega_1)\hat{q}_{mn}$$

The product of voltage and current components at the same frequency is

$$p_{mn} = v_{mn}i_{mn} = -(m\omega_c + n\omega_1)v_{mn}\hat{q}_{mn} \quad (7\text{-}124)$$

where the amplitudes of v_{mn} and $\hat{q}_{mn}$ are independent of ω_c and ω_1.

The average power over a long interval of time must reduce to the sum of products of voltage and current at the same frequency, since products of components at different frequencies are sums of sinusoidal functions of time which approach zero average value. Hence the average power can be written in the form

$$\text{av } w = \sum_{m=0}^{\infty} \sum_{n=-\infty}^{\infty} \text{av } p_{mn} = - \sum_{m=0}^{\infty} \sum_{n=-\infty}^{\infty} (m\omega_c + n\omega_1) \text{ av } (v_{mn}\hat{q}_{mn})$$
$$= \sum_{m=0}^{\infty} \sum_{n=-\infty}^{\infty} k_{mn}(m\omega_c + n\omega_1) \quad (7\text{-}125)$$

where $k_{mn} = -\text{av } (v_{mn}\hat{q}_{mn})$ does not depend on ω_c and ω_1.

But we have previously proved that av $w = 0$. Hence Eq. (7-125) leads to

$$\omega_c \sum_{m=0}^{\infty} \sum_{n=-\infty}^{\infty} mk_{mn} + \omega_1 \sum_{m=0}^{\infty} \sum_{n=-\infty}^{\infty} nk_{mn} = 0 \quad (7\text{-}126)$$

Since ω_c and ω_1 are linearly independent frequencies, the coefficients must vanish separately, and

$$\sum_{m=0}^{\infty} \sum_{n=-\infty}^{\infty} m k_{mn} = 0$$
$$\sum_{m=0}^{\infty} \sum_{n=-\infty}^{\infty} n k_{mn} = 0 \tag{7-127}$$

Let w_{mn} represent the average power delivered to the varactor at frequency $m\omega_c + n\omega_1$. Then, from (7-124)

$$w_{mn} = \text{av } p_{mn} = -(m\omega_c + n\omega_1)\,\text{av}\,(v_{mn}\hat{q}_{mn}) = (m\omega_c + n\omega_1)k_{mn}$$

or

$$k_{mn} = \frac{w_{mn}}{m\omega_c + n\omega_1} \tag{7-128}$$

Substitution of (7-128) into (7-127) gives

$$\sum_{m=0}^{\infty} \sum_{n=-\infty}^{\infty} \frac{m w_{mn}}{m\omega_c + n\omega_1} = 0$$
$$\sum_{m=0}^{\infty} \sum_{n=-\infty}^{\infty} \frac{n w_{mn}}{m\omega_c + n\omega_1} = 0 \tag{7-129}$$

These equations, which are commonly known now as the Manley-Rowe relations, were discovered by J. M. Manley.[3-5] They show under what conditions power gain can be obtained in a varactor modulator or demodulator. For example, if the associated circuit were so designed that the only nonzero components of voltage across the varactor were of frequencies ω_c, ω_1, and $m\omega_c + \omega_1$, the values of w_{mn} would be zero except for w_{10}, w_{01}, and w_{m1}. Equations (7-129) would become

$$\frac{w_{10}}{\omega_c} + \frac{m w_{m1}}{m\omega_c + \omega_1} = 0$$
$$\frac{w_{01}}{\omega_1} + \frac{w_{m1}}{m\omega_c + \omega_1} = 0 \tag{7-130}$$

from which

$$w_{m1} = -\left(1 + \frac{\omega_1}{m\omega_c}\right)w_{10} = -\left(1 + \frac{m\omega_c}{\omega_1}\right)w_{01} \tag{7-131}$$

If power is supplied at the frequencies ω_c and ω_1, the values of w_{10} and w_{01} in Eq. (7-131) are positive. The resulting negative value of w_{m1} indicates that the varactor delivers power at the sideband frequency $m\omega_c + \omega_1$. If ω_c represents the carrier frequency and ω_1 the signal frequency and if $m\omega_c \gg \omega_1$, the sideband power w_{m1} is much larger in magnitude than the signal power w_{01}, and a large conversion gain from signal to sideband results. Such a modulator is called an "up converter." A "down converter," in which, for example, the varactor demodulates the sideband frequency $m\omega_c + \omega_1$ to recover the signal frequency ω_1, would obey the relation

$$w_{01} = -\frac{\omega_1}{m\omega_c + \omega_1} w_{m1} \tag{7-132}$$

It is seen that the condition $m\omega_c \gg \omega_1$ in a down converter leads to a large conversion loss.

If the external circuit is designed to receive power at the lower-sideband frequency $m\omega_c - \omega_1$ instead of the upper, the Manley-Rowe equations become

$$\begin{aligned} \frac{w_{10}}{\omega_c} + \frac{m w_{m,-1}}{m\omega_c - \omega_1} &= 0 \\ \frac{w_{01}}{\omega_1} - \frac{w_{m,-1}}{m\omega_c - \omega_1} &= 0 \end{aligned} \tag{7-133}$$

It follows that

$$w_{m,-1} = -\left(1 - \frac{\omega_1}{m\omega_c}\right) w_{10} = \left(\frac{m\omega_c}{\omega_1} - 1\right) w_{01} \tag{7-134}$$

The fact that the sign of the power at sideband and signal frequencies is the same shows that the varactor can deliver power at both these frequencies while absorbing power at the carrier frequency. This means that the varactor can exhibit a negative resistance at the frequency ω_1. and can thereby serve either as an amplifier of signal without conversion or as an oscillator generating an intrinsic frequency at which resonance occurs. In either case, the carrier source acts as the power supply. The carrier frequency is often called the "pump" frequency, and the essential but not directly used difference frequency $m\omega_c - \omega_1$ is called the "idler" frequency. Physically, the signal component is regenerated by modulation of the mth harmonic of ω_c by the idler frequency.

As an example of a varactor modulator, consider Fig. 7-8 in which the varistor of Fig. 7-6 is replaced by a nonlinear capacitor. It is convenient to base the analysis on the function $q = \gamma(v)$, which is the inverse of the function η previously introduced. Phase angles must be included in the solution because of the presence of both resistive and reactive elements. We assume that in the absence of signal, $v = v_0 \cos(\omega_c t + \theta_0)$. Voltages at other frequencies are short-circuited. Then,

$$q = \gamma[v_0 \cos(\omega_c t + \theta_0)] = q_0 + 2 \sum_{n=1}^{\infty} q_n \cos n(\omega_c t + \theta_0) \tag{7-135}$$

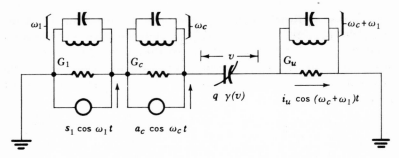

Fig. 7-8 Single-sideband varactor modulator with low impedance outside band.

where

$$q_n = \frac{1}{2\pi} \int_{-\pi}^{\pi} \gamma(v_0 \cos x) \cos nx \, dx \tag{7-136}$$

and

$$i = \frac{dq}{dt} = -2 \sum_{n=1}^{\infty} n\omega_c q_n \sin n(\omega_c t + \theta_0) \tag{7-137}$$

Kirchhoff's second law applied at the input-carrier node gives

$$i = a_c \cos \omega_c t - G_c v \tag{7-138}$$

Hence,

$$-2\omega_c q_1 \sin (\omega_c t + \theta_0) = a_c \cos \omega_c t - G_c v_0 \cos (\omega_c t + \theta_0) \tag{7-139}$$

from which

$$\begin{aligned} G_c v_0 \cos (\omega_c t + \theta_0) &- 2\omega_c q_1 \sin (\omega_c t + \theta_0) \\ &= a_c \cos (\omega_c t + \theta_0 - \theta_0) \\ &= a_c \cos \theta_0 \cos (\omega_c t + \theta_0) + a_c \sin \theta_0 \sin (\omega_c t + \theta_0) \end{aligned} \tag{7-140}$$

Equating coefficients of cosine and sine terms separately gives

$$G_c v_0 = a_c \cos \theta_0 \qquad 2\omega_c q_1 = -a_c \sin \theta_0 \tag{7-141}$$

from which

$$(G_c v_0)^2 + \frac{\omega_c^2}{\pi^2} \left[\int_{-\pi}^{\pi} \gamma(v_0 \cos x) \cos x \, dx \right]^2 = a_c^2 \tag{7-142}$$

From Eq. (7-142), we can calculate a_c as a function of v_0, and inversion of this result gives v_0 as a function of a_c. The value of θ_0 can then be found from (7-141), and q_n can be computed for all n from (7-136).

When the carrier solution in the absence of signal has been determined, the signal and sideband relations can be found by a linear first-order perturbation. The linearity of the first-order approximation enables complex representation of the components to be used. The applicable theorem is that in a real linear system the response to the real part of a complex excitation is equal to the real part of the response to the complex excitation. We write for the case in which a small signal is applied and a small response occurs at the upper-sideband frequency $\omega_c + \omega_1$

$$v = v_0 \cos (\omega_c t + \theta_0) + v_1 e^{j\omega_1 t} + v_u e^{j(\omega_c + \omega_1)t} \qquad (7\text{-}143)$$

where v, v_1, and v_u are now complex. The solution when only the real part of v is present will then be the real part of the solution for complex v. We assume that the varactor characteristic is capable of producing even-order modulation; that is, $\gamma(v)$ is not an odd function of v. We calculate

$$q \approx \gamma[v_0 \cos (\omega_c t + \theta_0)] + \gamma'[v_0 \cos (\omega_c t + \theta_0)][v_1 e^{j\omega_1 t} + v_u e^{j(\omega_c + \omega_1)t}]$$

$$= q_0 + 2 \sum_{n=1}^{\infty} q_n \cos n(\omega_c t + \theta_0)$$

$$+ \left[q_0' + 2 \sum_{n=1}^{\infty} q_n' \cos n(\omega_c t + \theta_0) \right] \left[v_1 e^{j\omega_1 t} + v_u e^{j(\omega_c + \omega_1)t} \right] \qquad (7\text{-}144)$$

where

$$q_n' = \frac{1}{2\pi} \int_{-\pi}^{\pi} \gamma'(v_0 \cos x) \cos nx \, dx \qquad (7\text{-}145)$$

The components of q at the signal frequency ω_1 and upper-sideband frequency $\omega_c + \omega_1$ are then included in

$$q_{1,s} \approx q_0' v_1 e^{j\omega_1 t} + q_0' v_u e^{j(\omega_c + \omega_1)t} + q_1' v_1 e^{j\theta_0} e^{j(\omega_c + \omega_1)t} + q_1' v_u e^{-j\theta_0} e^{j\omega_1 t} \qquad (7\text{-}146)$$

The corresponding components of current in the varactor are

$$i_{1,s} = \frac{dq_{1,s}}{dt} \approx j\omega_1 (q_0' v_1 + q_1' v_u e^{-j\theta_0}) e^{j\omega_1 t}$$

$$+ j(\omega_c + \omega_1)(q_0' v_u + q_1' v_1 e^{j\theta_0}) e^{j(\omega_c + \omega_1)t} \qquad (7\text{-}147)$$

The network equations then are

$$\begin{aligned} (G_1 + j\omega_1 q_0') v_1 + j\omega_1 q_1' e^{-j\theta_0} v_u &= s_1 \\ j(\omega_c + \omega_1) q_1' e^{j\theta_0} v_1 + [G_u + j(\omega_c + \omega_1) q_0'] v_u &= 0 \end{aligned} \qquad (7\text{-}148)$$

Solving for v_u, we find

$$q_1'^2 \left| \frac{s_1}{v_u} \right|^2 = \frac{G_1^2 + \omega_1^2 (q_0')^2}{(\omega_c + \omega_1)^2} G_u^2 + \frac{2G_1 G_u \omega_1 (q_1')^2}{\omega_c + \omega_1}$$

$$+ \omega_1^2 [(q_1')^2 - (q_0')^2]^2 + G_1^2 (q_0')^2 \qquad (7\text{-}149)$$

If $\omega_c \gg \omega_1$, the relation becomes

$$\left| \frac{v_u}{s_1} \right|^2 \sim \frac{(q_1'/q_0')^2}{G_1^2 + \omega_1^2 [(q_1')^2 - (q_0')^2]^2/(q_0')^2} \qquad (7\text{-}150)$$

In the interesting case in which $q'_1 = \pm q'_0$, we find for the conversion gain

$$\Gamma_c = \frac{|v_u|^2 G_u}{|s_1|^2/(4G_1)} = \frac{4G_u}{G_1} = \frac{4R_1}{R_u} \tag{7-151}$$

It appears that the conversion gain could be increased indefinitely by increasing the ratio of resistances of the signal and sideband circuits. A practical limit occurs in that the larger the internal resistance of the signal source is made, the more difficult it becomes to realize an antiresonant circuit with maximum impedance high compared to $1/G_1$.

In the case of production of a lower sideband, we replace (7-143) by

$$v = v_0 \cos(\omega_c t + \theta_0) + v_1 e^{-j\omega_1 t} + v_l e^{j(\omega_c - \omega_1)t} \tag{7-152}$$

It follows that

$$q_{1,s} \approx q'_0 v_1 e^{-j\omega_1 t} + q'_0 v_l e^{j(\omega_c-\omega_1)t} + q'_1 v_1 e^{j\theta_0} e^{j(\omega_c-\omega_1)t}$$
$$+ q'_1 v_l e^{-j\theta_0} e^{-j\omega_1 t} \tag{7-153}$$

and

$$i_{1,s} \approx -j\omega_1 (q'_0 v_1 + q'_1 v_l e^{-j\theta_0}) e^{-j\omega_1 t}$$
$$+ j(\omega_c - \omega_1)(q'_0 v_l + q'_1 v_1 e^{j\theta_0}) e^{j(\omega_c-\omega_1)t} \tag{7-154}$$

We assume that the driving current from the signal generator is $s_1 e^{-j\omega_1 t}$, that the sideband load conductance is G_l instead of G_u, and that the tuned circuit shunting the load is antiresonant at the frequency $\omega_c - \omega_1$. The network equations then become

$$\begin{aligned}(G_1 - j\omega_1 q'_0)v_1 - j\omega_1 q'_1 e^{-j\theta_0}v_l &= s_1 \\ j(\omega_c - \omega_1)q'_1 e^{j\theta_0}v_1 + [G_l + j(\omega_c - \omega_1)q'_0]v_l &= 0\end{aligned} \tag{7-155}$$

An interesting feature exhibited by these equations is the sign of the conductance G_s facing the generator. By calculation

$$G_s = \mathrm{Re}\left(\frac{s_1}{v_1}\right)_{G_1=0} = -\frac{\omega_1(\omega_c - \omega_1)(q'_1)^2 G_l}{G_l^2 + (\omega_c - \omega_1)^2 (q'_0)^2} \tag{7-156}$$

The driving-point conductance of the system is thus seen to be negative if $\omega_c > \omega_1$. If the value of this negative conductance is more than sufficient to cancel the internal conductance G_1 of the signal generator, sustained oscillations are produced without application of signal. A negative-resistance-type amplifier can be realized by operating below the oscillating condition.

PROBLEMS

7-1. Given a linear time-invariant network with transmittance function

$$H(f) = e^{-j\alpha \, \mathrm{sgn} \, f}$$

Let $r(t)$ be the response of the network when a signal $s(t)$ is applied as input. Express $r(t)$ in terms of $s(t)$ and $\hat{s}(t)$.

7-2. Show how to obtain a single-sideband wave by use of a network which produces a phase retardation of α rad at all positive frequencies. Assume that $0 < \alpha < \pi/2$ and that the amplitude of the signal input and the phase of the carrier oscillator output can be adjusted as desired.

7-3. Given (a) a signal $s(t)$ with $S(f) = 0$ except when $f_1 < |f| < f_2$, and (b) a pair of phase-shifting networks with transmittance functions defined in the range $f_1 < |f| < f_2$ by

$$H_1(f) = e^{-j2\pi f\tau} \qquad H_2(f) = -je^{-j2\pi f\tau} \operatorname{sgn} f$$

How would you generate an SSB wave without filtering the output? Why is it unnecessary to specify $H_1(f)$ and $H_2(f)$ when $|f| < f_1$ and when $|f| > f_2$? What difficulty would occur if we set $f_1 = 0$?

7-4. In Prob. 7-3, suppose $H_1(f)$ and $H_2(f)$ are defined by

$$H_1(f) = e^{-j\phi(f)} \qquad H_2(f) = -je^{-j\phi(f)} \operatorname{sgn} f$$

for $f_1 < |f| < f_2$. Would these networks produce a single-sideband output in the system forming the solution to Prob. 7-3? What demodulated signal would be obtained by multiplying the output by the carrier wave? A Fourier-integral representation of the result is appropriate.

7-5. Show how independent upper and lower sidebands on a common carrier frequency can be demodulated separately by means of phase-shifting networks.

7-6. Derive Eq. (7-37) from Eq. (7-36) directly by using the theorem of Eq. (7-33).

7-7. Derive Eq. (7-39) from Eq. (7-38) directly by using the theorem of Eq. (7-33).

7-8. In Chap. 4 it was shown that the pulse $q(t)$ with raised-cosine spectrum

$$Q(f) = \frac{A}{2f_s}\left(1 + \cos\frac{\pi f}{f_s}\right)\operatorname{rect}\frac{f}{2f_s}$$

has a number of desirable properties for data transmission, e.g., the pulse satisfies Nyquist's first and second conditions for suppression of intersymbol interference, and decays as $1/|t|^3$ for large $|t|$.

(a) Calculate the Hilbert transform $\hat{q}(t)$.

(b) Compare the merits of $\hat{q}(t)$ with those of $q(t)$ for data transmission.

(c) Explain how the defects of $\hat{q}(t)$ could be predicted from the properties of its Fourier transform.

(d) What is the envelope of the single-sideband suppressed-carrier wave generated from the signal $q(t)$?

7-9. Assume that $v(t)$ in Eq. (7-40) can be written in the form

$$v(t) = v_l(t) + v_h(t)$$

where

$$V_l(f) = 0 \qquad |f| > f_c$$

and

$$V_h(f) = 0 \qquad |f| < f_c$$

Calculate $\hat{s}_r(t) - \hat{s}_q(t)$ and $s_r(t) - \hat{s}_q(t)$ in terms of $v_l(t)$, $v_h(t)$, $\hat{v}_l(t)$, $\hat{v}_h(t)$, $\cos(\omega_c t + \theta_c)$, and $\sin(\omega_c t + \theta_c)$.

7-10. Consider a single-sideband transmitted-carrier wave represented by

$$m(t) = a_c \cos(\omega_c t + \theta) + s(t) \cos \omega_c t - \hat{s}(t) \sin \omega_c t$$

Show under what conditions an envelope detector can deliver a good approximation to the signal $s(t)$.

7-11. Assume an ideal crystal varistor in which the current-vs.-voltage relationship is given by

$$i = i_0(e^{qv/kT} - 1)$$

where

$$q = 1.59 \times 10^{-19} \text{ coulomb} = \text{charge of the electron}$$
$$k = 1.38 \times 10^{-23} \text{ joule/°K} = \text{Boltzmann's constant}$$
$$T = \text{temperature, °K}$$

Let $v = v_c \cos \omega_c t + v_1 \cos \omega_1 t$ with $0 < v_1 < v_c$.

(a) What are the amplitudes of the current components at frequencies ω_1, $m\omega_c + \omega_1$, and $m\omega_c - \omega_1$?

You may need the formula

$$\int_{-\pi}^{\pi} \exp(a \cos x) \cos mx \, dx = 2\pi I_m(a)$$

where $I_m(a) = j^{-m} J_m(ja) = $ mth-order Bessel function of imaginary argument.

(b) From your results of part (a), plot a curve of the ratio of sideband current to signal current as a function of peak carrier volts for the case of the sidebands on ω_c. Assume a temperature of 20°C. An abbreviated table of modified Bessel functions is given in Table 7-1. High precision in your curve is not demanded.

Table 7-1 Zero- and first-order Bessel functions of imaginary argument

x	$I_0(x)$	$I_1(x)$
0.0	1.000	0.0000
0.5	1.064	0.2579
1.0	1.266	0.5652
1.5	1.647	0.9817
2.0	2.280	1.591
2.5	3.290	2.517
3.0	4.881	3.953
3.5	7.378	6.206
4.0	11.302	9.759
4.5	17.48	15.39
5.0	27.24	24.34
5.5	42.69	38.59
6.0	67.23	61.34
6.5	106.3	97.73
7.0	168.6	156.0
7.5	268.2	249.6
8.0	427.6	399.9
8.5	683.2	641.6
9.0	1094.0	1031.0
9.5	1753.0	1658.0
10.0	2815.0	2672.0

(c) Repeat part (a) for a series "back-to-back" combination of identical crystals in which the cathode of one crystal is connected to the cathode of the other. It is sufficient to give the results in terms of definite integrals. For what harmonics of ω_c do the sidebands vanish?

7-12. Construct the dual of Fig. 7-6 in which the varistor is in parallel with the generators and load. How can you obtain the solution from that of Fig. 7-6?

7-13. In the circuit of Fig. 7-6, let the varistor response be defined as a symmetrical soft limiter by

$$g(v) = \begin{cases} -A & v < -v_0 \\ \dfrac{Av}{v_0} & -v_0 < v < v_0 \\ A & v_0 < v \end{cases}$$

Note that this characteristic is a piecewise straight-line approximation of the back-to-back crystal response of Prob. 7-11c.

(a) Obtain the equation which defines v_c implicitly as a function of a_c when $a_c > v_0$.

(b) Calculate g_0' and g_2' as functions of the ratio $\lambda = v_0/v_c$.

(c) Find the values of G_1 and G_u which maximize the conversion gain Γ_c.

(d) Show that the minimum value of the conversion loss $\Lambda_c = 1/\Gamma_c$ is given by

$$\Lambda_c = 2\mu^2 - 1 + 2\mu(\mu^2 - 1)^{\frac12}$$

where

$$\mu = \frac{\arcsin \lambda}{\lambda(1 - \lambda^2)^{\frac12}}$$

(e) Show that the minimum conversion loss approaches unity as $g'(v)$ approaches $\delta(v)$.

7-14. Solve the circuit of Fig. 7-6 for the case in which the upper sideband on ω_c is selected and $g(v)$ is the response of a half-wave linear rectifier defined by

$$g(v) = \begin{cases} 0 & v \le 0 \\ G_r v & v > 0 \end{cases}$$

Assume that the voltage across the varistor is

$$v_c \cos \omega_c t + v_1 \cos \omega_1 t + v_u \cos (\omega_c + \omega_1)t$$

Obtain the implicit equation for v_c. Assume that the linear approximation holds for signal and sideband components. Find the optimum values for the internal conductance of the signal generator and the load conductance of the sideband output circuit. Also find the corresponding maximum value of conversion gain.

7-15. In the varactor modulator of Fig. 7-8, assume that $\gamma(v) = g(v)$ as defined in Prob. 7-14. Evaluate the conversion gain $\Gamma_c = 4G_1G_u|v_u/s_1|^2$ using the approximation of Eq. (7-150).

7-16. Solve the circuit of Fig. 7-8 for the case in which the upper sideband on $2\omega_c$ is selected and $\gamma(v) = g(v)$ as defined in Prob. 7-13. Evaluate the conversion gain as in Prob. 7-15. What would the conversion gain be if we selected the upper sideband on ω_c?

7-17. Obtain Eq. (7-149) by solving Eqs. (7-148) for v_u.

7-18. Consider the circuit of Fig. 7-8 for the case in which the *lower* sideband on ω_c is selected and $\gamma(v) = g(v)$ as defined in Prob. 7-14.   Find the real part of the admittance facing the signal input circuit.

7-19. Assume a single-sideband transmitter has been constructed by combining the outputs of two product modulators in which 90° phase differences are specified between the two signal inputs and also between the two carrier inputs.   Suppose a measurement shows that at a particular signal frequency the phase difference between the two signal components is actually $\pi/2 - \alpha$ rad and that the amplitude of one component is $1 - \epsilon$ times the amplitude of the other.   The two carrier-frequency inputs are adjusted to be exactly equal in amplitude and 90° apart in phase.

(a) What is the ratio of amplitudes of the unwanted and wanted sideband components in the output of the transmitter?

(b) If $|\alpha|$ and $|\epsilon|$ are both small compared with unity, what percentage amplitude difference causes the same unwanted sideband leak as one degree of phase error?

7-20. From Eq. (A-30) of the appendix, it follows that

$$J_0(x) = \frac{1}{\pi} \int_{-1}^{1} \frac{e^{jxf} \, df}{(1 - f^2)^{\frac{1}{2}}}$$

Deduce a simple expression for the Hilbert transform of $J_0(2\pi t) \cos \omega_0 t$ when $\omega_0 > 2\pi$.

7-21. Write the Manley-Rowe equations for a varactor in which nonzero voltage components occur only at the signal frequency ω_1, the carrier frequency ω_c, the upper sideband frequency $\omega_c + \omega_1$, and the lower-sideband frequency $\omega_c - \omega_1$.   Solve the equations for the sideband output power when the varactor is used as a modulator and for the signal output power when the varactor is used as a demodulator.   Explain the significance of the positive and negative signs.

REFERENCES

1. Whittaker, E. T., and G. N. Watson: "A Course of Modern Analysis," 3d ed., Cambridge University Press, Cambridge, England, 1920, p. 115.
2. Bennett, W. R.: New Results in the Calculation of Modulation Products, *Bell System Tech. J.*, vol. 12, pp. 228–243, April, 1933.
3. Manley, J. M.: Some General Properties of Magnetic Amplifiers, *Proc. IRE*, vol. 39, pp. 242–251, March, 1951.
4. Manley, J. M., and H. E. Rowe: Some General Properties of Nonlinear Elements, Part I, General Energy Relations, *Proc. IRE*, vol. 44, pp. 904–913, July, 1956.
5. Bennett, W. R.: Amplification in Nonlinear Reactive Networks, *IRE Trans. Circuit Theory*, vol. CT-7, pp. 440–446, December, 1960.

8
Nonlinear Analog Modulation

8-1 MATHEMATICAL DESCRIPTION

A carrier wave can be modulated nonlinearly by impressing signal variations on either the amplitude or phase. These two processes can be related to linear modulation by a transformation from rectangular coordinates defining in-phase and quadrature sidebands to polar coordinates in which the envelope is represented by the radial coordinate and the phase by the angular coordinate. Equations (7-49) and (7-50) of the previous chapter provide a formal mathematical definition of the envelope $\rho(t)$ and the phase $\theta(t)$ of any wave $m(t)$; thus:

$$\rho(t) = [m^2(t) + \hat{m}^2(t)]^{\frac{1}{2}}$$
$$\theta(t) = \arctan \frac{\hat{m}(t)}{m(t)} \tag{8-1}$$

In the case of amplitude modulation of the carrier wave $\cos \omega_c t$ by the signal wave $s(t)$, we write

$$m(t) = [a_0 + a_1 s(t)] \cos \omega_c t \tag{8-2}$$

189

with $S(f) = 0$ for $|f| \geq f_c$ and $a_0 + a_1 s(t) \geq 0$. It follows from the theorem on the Hilbert transform of products of waves with nonoverlapping Fourier transforms, Eq. (7-33), that

$$\hat{m}(t) = [a_0 + a_1 s(t)] \sin \omega_c t \tag{8-3}$$

From (8-1),

$$\rho(t) = a_0 + a_1 s(t) \qquad \theta(t) = \omega_c t \tag{8-4}$$

The mathematical definitions thus describe pure amplitude modulation precisely when the signal is suitably restricted.

In the case of angle modulation, we write

$$\begin{aligned} m(t) &= a_c \cos [\omega_c t + k s(t)] \\ &= \frac{a_c}{2} e^{j[\omega_c t + k s(t)]} + \frac{a_c}{2} e^{-j[\omega_c t + k s(t)]} \end{aligned} \tag{8-5}$$

In the most general case, the Hilbert transform of an angle-modulated wave cannot be expressed in closed form. But in the cases of most practical interest, the Fourier transform of $e^{jks(t)}$ is negligibly small for frequencies of absolute value exceeding some finite amount less than f_c. When this is true, the first term in the complex representation of (8-5) contains negligibly small negative-frequency components, and the second term negligibly small positive-frequency components. The frequency-domain rule, Eq. (7-4), for calculating Hilbert transforms then gives the result

$$\begin{aligned} \hat{m}(t) &\approx -j \frac{a_c}{2} e^{j[\omega_c t + k s(t)]} + j \frac{a_c}{2} e^{-j[\omega_c t + k s(t)]} \\ &= a_c \sin [\omega_c t + k s(t)] \end{aligned} \tag{8-6}$$

It then follows from Eq. (8-1) that

$$\begin{aligned} \rho(t) &\approx a_c \\ \theta(t) &\approx \omega_c t + k s(t) \end{aligned} \tag{8-7}$$

The mathematical definition of Eqs. (8-1) thus describes pure angle modulation correctly under reasonable physical restrictions.

The conditions imposed on amplitude and angle modulation to validate the Hilbert-transform description are the same as those necessary to enable physical envelope and phase detectors to recover the signal from the modulated carrier. When the conditions are violated, the detectors deliver distorted versions of the signals. The amount of distortion depends upon specific detector circuits and spectral overlaps. We shall not treat the specialized problems which thereby arise, but confine ourselves to the more practical cases in which there is adequate separation of carrier and signal frequencies.

We observe that both amplitude- and angle-modulated carriers can be represented as resultants of linear in-phase and quadrature modulation by signals nonlinearly related to $s(t)$. Let

$$m(t) = r(t) \cos \omega_c t - q(t) \sin \omega_c t \qquad (8\text{-}8)$$

Then for amplitude modulation,

$$r(t) = a_0 + a_1 s(t) \qquad q(t) = 0 \qquad (8\text{-}9)$$

For angle modulation

$$r(t) = a_c \cos k s(t) \qquad q(t) = a_c \sin k s(t) \qquad (8\text{-}10)$$

8-2 PHYSICAL MODULATORS

Equations (8-9) exhibits the standard method for generating an amplitude-modulated wave, that is, multiply the signal by a sine wave and add an unmodulated carrier component.   The prescription for angle modulation presented by Eqs. (8-10) is somewhat more difficult to give a practical embodiment.   One of the important early realizations of an FM broadcast transmitter, that of Armstrong[1] in 1936, can in fact be deduced from (8-10) in the following way.   Assume that $ks(t)$ is sufficiently small to validate the approximations

$$\cos k s(t) \approx 1 \qquad \sin k s(t) \approx k s(t)$$

Then a variation of the AM procedure in which the signal is multiplied by $-a_c \sin \omega_c t$, and an unmodulated component $a_c \cos \omega_c t$ is added gives

$$
\begin{aligned}
m(t) &= a_c \cos \omega_c t - a_c k s(t) \sin \omega_c t \\
&\approx a_c \cos k s(t) \cos \omega_c t - a_c \sin k s(t) \sin \omega_c t
\end{aligned}
\qquad (8\text{-}11)
$$

This representation of angle modulation is satisfactory only when the angular variation is small.   To obtain larger amounts of angle modulation proportional to signal, Armstrong used a cascade of amplitude limiters and harmonic generators.   Writing $m(t)$ in the equivalent form

$$m(t) = a_c[1 + k^2 s^2(t)]^{\frac{1}{2}} \cos [\omega_c t + \arctan k s(t)] \qquad (8\text{-}12)$$

we note that the response of a hard limiter giving output A when $m(t)$ is positive and $-A$ when $m(t)$ is negative can be written as

$$m_h(t) = \frac{4A}{\pi} \sum_{n=0}^{\infty} \frac{(-)^n}{2n+1} \cos [(2n+1)\omega_c t + (2n+1) \arctan k s(t)]$$

$$(8\text{-}13)$$

A bandpass filter centered at the $(2n + 1)$st harmonic of ω_c selects the wave

$$m_n(t) = \frac{(-)^n 4A}{(2n + 1)\pi} \cos \left[(2n + 1)\omega_c t + (2n + 1) \arctan ks(t) \right]$$

$$\approx \frac{(-)^n 4A}{(2n + 1)\pi} \cos \left[(2n + 1)\omega_c t + (2n + 1)ks(t) \right] \qquad (8\text{-}14)$$

The approximation of Eq. (8-14) is valid if $\arctan ks(t) \approx ks(t)$. An original linear variation over the angular range $ks(t)$ thus becomes linear over the range $(2n + 1)ks(t)$, which is much larger if $2n + 1$ is a large integer. Instead of performing the desired linear magnification in one step, it is usually preferable to select the modulation on a moderately low harmonic of the carrier and repeat the process in successive stages. Note that the carrier frequency finally transmitted is not ω_c but the multiple of ω_c selected from the final stage. If the desired carrier frequency is exceeded by this process, a heterodyne stage translating the angle-modulated wave downward in frequency can be employed, and the multiplication can be continued upward from this point if the desired magnification of the modulation has not yet been attained. If a frequency-modulated wave is desired, the original signal is modified by an integrating circuit to replace $s(t)$ by its time integral before the first modulating stage.

The Armstrong FM transmitter, although based on correct analytic principles, is not the most practical way of realizing angle modulation. The VCO, or voltage-controlled oscillator, in which a tuning element is varied electronically by the signal wave, is a more common type. A varactor such as described in Sec. 7-5 can be inserted in a tuned circuit for this purpose. Other frequency modulators take advantage of the sensitivity of the oscillation frequency to the amount of phase shift in the feedback path. In a particularly successful microwave frequency modulator, the signal controls the velocity at which space-charge waves propagate in a klystron oscillator and thereby varies the oscillator output frequency.

8-3 RESPONSE OF LINEAR CIRCUITS TO NONLINEAR MODULATION

One of the most vexatious problems in nonlinear modulation theory has been the calculation of the response of a linear network to a nonlinearly modulated carrier wave. The difficulty is not an absence of rigorous computational methods, for of course the equations of linear systems are sufficiently general to yield the response to any applied excitation. Troubles have in a sense been artificially created because of a stubborn desire to derive responses to variable-amplitude, variable-frequency waves as small perturbations of the responses to constant-amplitude, constant-frequency waves. In the "adiabatic" approach, the response of a linear system to an almost-sinusoidal oscillation with slowly varying amplitude and frequency is evaluated by substituting time-varying amplitudes and frequencies for the constant amplitudes and constant frequencies which appear in the response to sinusoidal excitation. Series solutions have been constructed in which the adiabatic approximation is the first term. The convergence of such series is often subject to doubt, and the accuracy of finite terms is difficult to estimate. The method can be useful in specific cases in which the problem of accuracy can be resolved, but the general indiscriminate use of such procedures is not recommended.

The capabilities of large-scale computers should now make it unnecessary to rely on dubious approximate methods of calculating the response of a linear system. All we need do is formulate computations which the computer can perform. Naturally we should simplify the computer's task as much as possible by prescribing straightforward, orderly, and efficient procedures.

Since the amplitude- and angle-modulated waves have Fourier transforms with peak absolute values displaced from zero frequency, the usual transmission problem involves a bandpass system. It is convenient for computational purposes to deal with the system response relative to that at a suitably chosen midband frequency. Consider a linear time-invariant network with complex transmittance function $H(f)$ and real impulse response $h(t)$. Suppose the input is of form

$$m_1(t) = r_1(t) \cos \omega_c t - q_1(t) \sin \omega_c t \qquad (8\text{-}15)$$

with $R_1(f)$ and $Q_1(f)$ negligible in magnitude for $|f| \geq f_c$. The output wave can be written in similar form as

$$m_2(t) = r_2(t) \cos \omega_c t - q_2(t) \sin \omega_c t \qquad (8\text{-}16)$$

Our problem is to calculate r_2 and q_2 in terms of r_1, q_1, and h.

The following equations hold when the subscript k is either 1 or 2:

$$\hat{m}_k(t) = r_k(t) \sin \omega_c t + q_k(t) \cos \omega_c t \qquad (8\text{-}17)$$

$$z_k(t) = m_k(t) + j\hat{m}_k(t) = [r_k(t) + jq_k(t)]e^{j\omega_c t} \qquad (8\text{-}18)$$

$$z_k^*(t) = [r_k(t) - jq_k(t)]e^{-j\omega_c t} \qquad (8\text{-}19)$$

$$Z_k(f) = (1 + \operatorname{sgn} f)M_k(f) \qquad (8\text{-}20)$$

$$Z_k^\dagger(f) = (1 - \operatorname{sgn} f)M_k(f) \qquad (8\text{-}21)$$

Let us define a shifted transmittance function by

$$2H_c(f) = [1 + \operatorname{sgn}(f + f_c)]H(f + f_c) \qquad (8\text{-}22)$$

Then

$$2H_c(f - f_c) = (1 + \text{sgn } f)H(f) \tag{8-23}$$
$$2H_c(-f - f_c) = (1 - \text{sgn } f)H(-f) \tag{8-24}$$

and

$$2H_c^*(-f - f_c) = (1 - \text{sgn } f)H^*(-f) = (1 - \text{sgn } f)H(f) \tag{8-25}$$

By combining (8-23) and (8-25), we obtain

$$H(f) = H_c(f - f_c) + H_c^*(-f - f_c) \tag{8-26}$$

We observe that $H_c(f - f_c)$ vanishes for $f < 0$ and that $H_c^*(-f - f_c)$ vanishes for $f > 0$.

The frequency-domain representation of the response of the network to $m_1(t)$ is

$$M_2(f) = H(f)M_1(f) \tag{8-27}$$

We can write the right-hand side of (8-27) as the sum of expressions which hold for positive and negative frequencies separately. When $f > 0$, $H(f)$ is given by $H_c(f - f_c)$, and $M_1(f)$ is given by $Z_1(f)/2$. When $f < 0$, $H(f)$ is equal to $H_c^*(-f - f_c)$, and $M_1(f)$ is equal to $Z_1^\dagger(f)/2$. Since the products vanish when they are not applicable,

$$2M_2(f) = H_c(f - f_c)Z_1(f) + H_c^*(-f - f_c)Z_1^\dagger(f) \tag{8-28}$$

It follows from Eq. (8-20) that

$$Z_2(f) = H_c(f - f_c)Z_1(f) \tag{8-29}$$

and hence

$$Z_2(f + f_c) = H_c(f)Z_1(f + f_c) \tag{8-30}$$

Equating inverse Fourier transforms then gives

$$z_2(t)e^{-j\omega_c t} = h_c(t) * [z_1(t)e^{-j\omega_c t}] \tag{8-31}$$

From Eq. (8-18), then

$$r_2(t) + jq_2(t) = h_c(t) * [r_1(t) + jq_1(t)] \tag{8-32}$$

Since $H_c(f)$ is not compelled to have conjugate symmetry about the origin, the function $h_c(t)$ is not necessarily a real impulse response. We write

$$h_c(t) = h_r(t) + jh_q(t) \tag{8-33}$$

where h_r and h_q are real. Then equating real and imaginary parts of (8-32) separately gives

$$r_2(t) = h_r(t) * r_1(t) - h_q(t) * q_1(t)$$
$$q_2(t) = h_q(t) * r_1(t) + h_r(t) * q_1(t) \qquad (8\text{-}34)$$

This is the relationship sought. From Eq. (8-22), the complex impulse response can be written

$$h_c(t) = \int_{-f_c}^{\infty} H(f + f_c)e^{j2\pi ft}\, df = \int_0^{\infty} H(f)e^{j2\pi(f-f_c)t}\, df \qquad (8\text{-}35)$$

Since $H(f)$ has significant absolute values mainly at frequencies near f_c, the integrand is optimally free from fast oscillations.

We can, of course, express the results in the frequency domain by equating Fourier transforms of (8-34), giving

$$R_2(f) = H_r(f)R_1(f) - H_q(f)Q_1(f)$$
$$Q_2(f) = H_q(f)R_1(f) + H_r(f)Q_1(f) \qquad (8\text{-}36)$$

Convolutions are thereby replaced by products. The explicit expressions for $H_r(f)$ and $H_q(f)$ can be found by noting that

$$\begin{aligned}
2h_r(t) = 2 \operatorname{Re} h_c(t) &= h_c(t) + h_c^*(t) \\
&= \int_{-\infty}^{\infty} H_c(f)e^{j2\pi ft}\, df + \int_{-\infty}^{\infty} H_c^*(f)e^{-j2\pi ft}\, df \\
&= \int_{-\infty}^{\infty} [H_c(f) + H_c^*(-f)]e^{j2\pi ft}\, df \qquad (8\text{-}37)
\end{aligned}$$

It follows that

$$H_r(f) = \frac{1}{2}[H_c(f) + H_c^*(-f)] \qquad (8\text{-}38)$$

A similar argument applied to $h_q(t)$ shows that

$$H_q(f) = \frac{1}{2j}[H_c(f) - H_c^*(-f)] \qquad (8\text{-}39)$$

The apparent simplification may be deceptive in angle-modulation problems. Evaluations of Fourier transforms of $r_1(t)$ and $q_1(t)$ and subsequent inverse transforms of $R_2(f)$ and $Q_2(f)$ lead to more extensive computer programming than the time-domain operations of Eqs. (8-34).

The equations we have obtained serve for AM, PM, and FM. The modulation in the different cases can be expressed as follows:

Amplitude:

$$\alpha_k = (r_k{}^2 + q_k{}^2)^{1/2}$$

Phase:

$$\phi_k = \omega_c t + \arctan \frac{q_k}{r_k} \qquad (8\text{-}40)$$

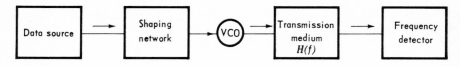

Fig. 8-1 FSK telegraph system.

Frequency:

$$\omega_k = \omega_c + \frac{r_k \dot{q}_k - q_k \dot{r}_k}{r_k{}^2 + q_k{}^2}$$

As an example consider the problem of calculating the eye pattern for the FSK (frequency-shift keying) telegraph system of Fig. 8-1. The generalized form of modulating signal can be represented by

$$s(t) = \sum_{n=0}^{N-1} b_n \, g(t - nT) \tag{8-41}$$

In the binary case, b_n can be either 0 or 1. On the assumption that the signal is generated by a causal system, we set $g(t - nT) = 0$ for $t < nT$. Let

$$\underline{s} = \int_0^t s(\tau) \, d\tau = \sum_{n=0}^{N-1} b_n \int_{nT}^t g(\tau - nT) \, d\tau = \sum_{n=0}^{N-1} b_n \int_0^{t-nT} g(\lambda) \, d\lambda \tag{8-42}$$

Then if we substitute

$$r_1(t) = \cos k\underline{s} \qquad \text{and} \qquad q_1(t) = \sin k\underline{s} \tag{8-43}$$

the value of $r_2(t)$ and $q_2(t)$ for the response of any linear time-invariant system can be calculated from Eqs. (8-34) for any choice of the b_n's. Actually there are 2^N possible sequences of b_n's, and a computer can be programmed to calculate the response for each sequence. Evaluation of the instantaneous frequency of the response from Eq. (8-40) for each sequence and translation of each sequence to a common signaling interval give the complete family of eye patterns. The end portions represent the beginning and end of a message and are not significant in a long message.

Note that if the bandwidth is finite, we cannot satisfy Nyquist's criteria for suppression of intersymbol interference because of the non-linear relation between output and input frequencies. Methods have been contrived[2-4] for satisfying the criteria at the expense of a departure from constant amplitude; this leads to a hybrid-modulated wave containing both AM and FM. In practice it is found possible to obtain reasonable margins over intersymbol interference without undue attention to the shape of the transmittance function.

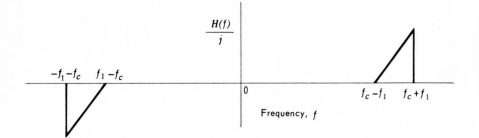

Fig. 8-2 Idealized slope-circuit response.

As a second example, consider the case of the ideal slope circuit with transmittance function $H(f)$ depicted in Fig. 8-2 and defined by

$$H(f) = j2\pi a(f - f_c + f_1)\, \text{rect}\, \frac{f - f_c}{2f_1}$$
$$+ j2\pi a(f + f_c - f_1)\, \text{rect}\, \frac{f + f_c}{2f_1} \quad (8\text{-}44)$$

We shall demonstrate that this circuit followed by an envelope detector serves as an ideal frequency detector of the purely frequency-modulated wave $m(t)$ of Eq. (8-5) if $M(f)$ vanishes for $f_c - f_1 < |f| < f_c + f_1$. If we apply the wave

$$v_1(t) = a_c e^{j[\omega_c t + ks(t)]} \quad (8\text{-}45)$$

to the transmittance function $H(f)$ given by Eq. (8-44), the response to $m(t)$ is the real part of the response $v_2(t)$ to $v_1(t)$. Under the previous assumption of band-limitedness of $m(t)$,

$$V_1(f)\, \text{rect}\, \frac{f - f_c}{2f_1} = V_1(f)$$

and $\quad (8\text{-}46)$

$$V_1(f)\, \text{rect}\, \frac{f + f_c}{2f_1} = 0$$

Then

$$V_2(f) = V_1(f)H(f) = j2\pi a(f - f_c + f_1)V_1(f) \quad (8\text{-}47)$$

and

$$v_2(t) = a\frac{d}{dt}v_1(t) - j2\pi a(f_c - f_1)v_1(t)$$
$$= aa_c j(\omega_c + k\dot{s} - \omega_c + \omega_1)e^{j(\omega_c t + ks)} \quad (8\text{-}48)$$

Finally,

$$\text{Re}\, v_2(t) = -aa_c(k\dot{s} + \omega_1)\sin(\omega_c t + ks) \quad (8\text{-}49)$$

and the envelope is seen to be proportional to $\omega_1 + k\dot{s}$. An undistorted replica of $\dot{s}$ is thus contained in the envelope if $\omega_1 + k\dot{s} \geq 0$.

The bias term ω_1 can be removed by subtracting the output of a second envelope detector preceded by the complementary slope circuit of Fig. 8-3 in which the sign of the slope is reversed. The transmittance function of the complementary slope circuit is:

$$H_-(f) = j2\pi a(f_c + f_1 - f) \operatorname{rect} \frac{f - f_c}{2f_1}$$

$$-j2\pi a(f_c + f_1 + f) \operatorname{rect} \frac{f + f_c}{2f_1} \qquad (8\text{-}50)$$

Corresponding to Eq. (8-49)

$$\operatorname{Re} v_2(t) = -aa_c(\omega_1 - k\dot{s}) \sin (\omega_c t + ks) \qquad (8\text{-}51)$$

The difference between the two envelopes is then $2aa_c\,k\dot{s}$, which is free from bias. Such a differential arrangement of slope circuits and envelope detectors is often called a "back-to-back" detector.

Note that it is not necessary for both $H(f)$ and $M(f)$ to vanish outside the range $f_c - f_1 < |f| < f_c + f_1$ to make the analysis valid. If $m(t)$ has nonzero components within the specified interval only, the values of $H(f)$ outside that interval have no effect on the response. The straight-line frequency characteristic is conveniently approximated by one side of a tuned-circuit response as indicated in Fig. 8-4. The other side shown by the dashed line does not enter into the idealized problem. An exact calculation for a physical FM wave, which cannot be truly band-limited, would have to include both sides of the tuned-circuit response.

In analyzing the slope circuit as an FM detector, we did not use the equations previously developed for referring responses to the midband

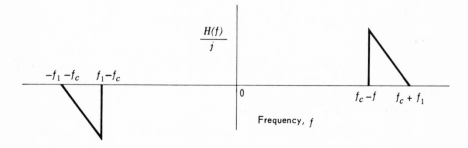

Fig. 8-3 Response of slope circuit which can be used with that of Fig. 8-2 in a back-to-back frequency detector.

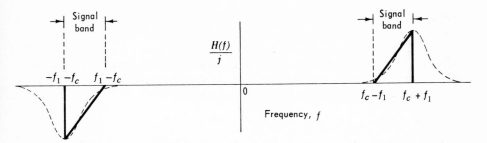

Fig. 8-4   Relation of ideal slope-circuit response to that of tuned circuit.

frequency. It so happens that because of the simple nature of the problem, the resolution with respect to f_c would in this case lead to a more complicated procedure. We now give the alternate analysis for comparison.

$$h_c(t) = \int_{f_c-f_1}^{f_c+f_1} j2\pi a(f - f_c + f_1)e^{j2\pi(f-f_c)t}\, df$$

$$= a\frac{d}{dt}\int_{f_c-f_1}^{f_c+f_1} e^{j2\pi(f-f_c)t}\, df + j2\pi a f_1 \int_{f_c-f_1}^{f_c+f_1} e^{j2\pi(f-f_c)t}\, df$$

$$= a\frac{d}{dt}\int_{-f_1}^{f_1} e^{j2\pi ft}\, df + j2\pi a f_1 \int_{-f_1}^{f_1} e^{j2\pi ft}\, df$$

$$= 2af_1\frac{d}{dt}\,\text{sinc } 2f_1 t + j4\pi a f_1{}^2\,\text{sinc } 2f_1 t \qquad (8\text{-}52)$$

Therefore,

$$h_r(t) = 2af_1\frac{d}{dt}\,\text{sinc } 2f_1 t \qquad\qquad\qquad\qquad (8\text{-}53)$$

$$h_q(t) = 4\pi a f_1{}^2\,\text{sinc } 2f_1 t$$

We note that if $x(t)$ and $y(t)$ are differentiable,

$$\frac{d}{dt}(x * y) = \frac{d}{dt}\int_{-\infty}^{\infty} x(\lambda)y(t-\lambda)\, d\lambda = \int_{-\infty}^{\infty} x(\lambda)\frac{d}{dt}y(t-\lambda)\, d\lambda$$

$$= x * \dot{y} = \frac{d}{dt}\int_{-\infty}^{\infty} x(t-\lambda)y(\lambda)\, d\lambda$$

$$= \int_{-\infty}^{\infty} y(\lambda)\frac{d}{dt}x(t-\lambda)\, d\lambda$$

$$= \dot{x} * y \qquad\qquad\qquad\qquad\qquad (8\text{-}54)$$

Therefore in the present case,

$$h_r * r_1 = 2af_1 r_1 * \frac{d}{dt}\,\text{sinc } 2f_1 t = 2af_1\dot{r}_1 * \text{sinc } 2f_1 t \qquad (8\text{-}55)$$

and

$$r_2(t) = 2af_1\dot{r}_1 * \text{sinc } 2f_1 t - 4\pi a f_1{}^2 q_1 * \text{sinc } 2f_1 t \qquad (8\text{-}56)$$

Likewise

$$q_2(t) = 4\pi a f_1{}^2 r_1 * \text{sinc } 2f_1 t + 2af_1 \dot{q}_1 * \text{sinc } 2f_1 t \tag{8-57}$$

Under the assumed condition of band-limitedness of $m(t)$, r_1 and q_1 are band-limited to the range of frequencies $-f_1$ to f_1. It follows that $\dot{r}_1$ and $\dot{q}_1$ are similarly band-limited and that the relation

$$2f_1\, x * \text{sinc } 2f_1 t = x \qquad \text{if } X = 0 \text{ for } |f| > f_1 \tag{8-58}$$

can be applied when r_1, $\dot{r}_1$, q_1, or $\dot{q}_1$ are substituted for x. Then

$$\begin{aligned} r_2(t) &= a\dot{r}_1 - 2\pi a f_1 q_1 \\ q_2(t) &= 2\pi a f_1 r_1 + a\dot{q}_1 \end{aligned} \tag{8-59}$$

Finally from (8-40) and (8-10),

$$\begin{aligned} \alpha_2{}^2 &= a^2(\dot{r}_1 - 2\pi f_1 q_1)^2 + a^2(\dot{q}_1 + 2\pi f_1 r_1)^2 \\ &= a^2 a_c{}^2(-k\dot{s} \sin ks - 2\pi f_1 \sin ks)^2 \\ &\qquad\qquad\qquad\qquad + a^2 a_c{}^2(k\dot{s} \cos ks + 2\pi f_1 \cos ks)^2 \\ &= a^2 a_c{}^2(2\pi f_1 + k\dot{s})^2 \end{aligned}$$

or

$$\alpha_2 = aa_c(\omega_1 + k\dot{s}) \tag{8-60}$$

Also

$$\begin{aligned} \phi_2 &= \omega_c t + \arctan \frac{\omega_1 r_1 + \dot{q}_1}{\dot{r}_1 - \omega_1 \dot{q}_1} \\ &= \omega_c t + \arctan \frac{\omega_1 \cos ks + k\dot{s} \cos ks}{-k\dot{s} \sin ks - \omega_1 \sin ks} \\ &= \omega_c t - \arctan (\cot ks) = \omega_c t + ks + \frac{\pi}{2} \end{aligned} \tag{8-61}$$

Equations (8-60) and (8-61) are in agreement with Eq. (8-49).

8-4 THE PHASE-LOCKED LOOP

In the previous section and also in Chap. 6, we have discussed frequency demodulators which employ linear circuits to convert angle variations to envelope variations. We consider here a different approach, which applies the general principle that the inverse of a process can be realized by inserting the original processor in a feedback loop. We have remarked that the voltage-controlled oscillator (VCO) is widely used as an angle modulator. Correspondingly, the so-called phase-locked loop, which contains a VCO in a feedback path, has important properties as an angle demodulator.

Consider the receiving circuit of Fig. 8-5 in which the incoming wave is represented by

$$v_0(t) = a_c[1 + \rho(t)] \cos [\omega_c t + \theta(t) - \pi/2] \tag{8-62}$$

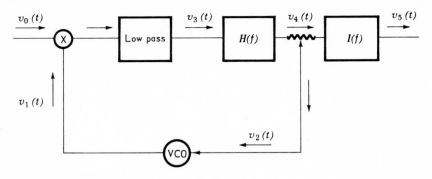

Fig. 8-5 Phase-locked loop.

In the case of most interest here, the wave $v_0(t)$ is an angle-modulated wave with additive noise. The effects of the noise on the envelope and phase are included in the functions $\rho(t)$ and $\theta(t)$. The insertion of the angle $\pi/2$, which does not affect the generality, contributes a practical convenience in the analysis. The noisy signal is multiplied by the output $v_1(t)$ of a VCO which has the control voltage $v_2(t)$; that is,

$$v_1(t) = a_1 \cos [\omega_c t + \phi(t)] \tag{8-63}$$

where

$$\dot{\phi}(t) = k_1 v_2(t) \tag{8-64}$$

A low-pass filter in the output of the multiplier suppresses the high-frequency components represented by the cosine of the sum of the two arguments. The effect of this filter on the cosine of the difference is assumed to be negligible. The input to the linear network represented by the transmittance function $H(f)$ is then

$$\begin{aligned}
v_3(t) &= k_3 a_1 a_c [1 + \rho(t)] \cos [\theta(t) - \phi(t) - \pi/2] \\
&= k_3 a_1 a_c [1 + \rho(t)] \sin [\theta(t) - \phi(t)]
\end{aligned} \tag{8-65}$$

The output of the linear network is represented by $v_4(t)$, and the loop is closed by setting

$$v_2(t) = k_2 v_4(t) \tag{8-66}$$

An interesting phenomenon occurs when $\theta(t)$ and $\phi(t)$ are sufficiently close together to make the sine of the angle in (8-65) approximately equal to the angle. When such a condition holds, we have

$$v_3(t) \approx k_3 a_1 a_c [1 + \rho(t)] u(t) \tag{8-67}$$

where

$$u(t) = \theta(t) - \phi(t) \tag{8-68}$$

If the approximation of (8-67) is assumed to be an equality, the output of the network can then be represented by its Fourier transform

$$V_4(f) = k_3 a_1 a_c H(f)[U(f) + R(f) * U(f)] \tag{8-69}$$

Equating Fourier transforms of both sides of (8-62) and combining the loop equations into one, we obtain

$$\begin{aligned} j2\pi f\Phi(f) &= k_1 V_2(f) = k_1 k_2 V_4(f) \\ &= KH(f)[U(f) + R(f) * U(f)] \end{aligned} \tag{8-70}$$

where

$$K = k_1 k_2 k_3 a_1 a_c \tag{8-71}$$

Similarly, the Fourier transforms of (8-68) must satisfy

$$\Phi(f) = \Theta(f) - U(f) \tag{8-72}$$

Substitution of (8-72) in (8-71) gives

$$j2\pi f U(f) + KH(f)[U(f) + R(f) * U(f)] = j2\pi f\Theta(f) \tag{8-73}$$

If the factor K is made very large, Eq. (8-73) is nontrivially satisfied only if

$$U(f) + R(f) * U(f) \rightarrow 0 \tag{8-74}$$

or in the time domain by

$$u(t) + \rho(t)u(t) \rightarrow 0 \tag{8-75}$$

Since $1 + \rho(t)$ represents a nonnegative envelope which does not vanish identically, we conclude that in the limit as K approaches infinity, $u(t)$ approaches zero, and

$$\phi(t) \rightarrow \theta(t) \tag{8-76}$$

This condition, in which the phase of the VCO becomes asymptotically equal to the phase of the incoming wave, is called *phase lock*.

It thus appears that the phase-locked loop can be used to recover the frequency and phase of a sinusoidal wave contaminated by noise. The effect of amplitude variations caused by noise is suppressed, and the phase variations can be reduced to retain only those falling in the band of $H(f)$. A complete study of the system, including investigation of stability, capture range, and tracking range could easily be the subject of another book.[5] Our principal interest here is in the use of the phase-locked loop as a detector of angle-modulated signals.

As K becomes large, the angle variations of the incoming wave are acquired by the phase of the local oscillator. However, a detector of phase or frequency would still be needed at this point in the loop to recover the signal carried by a PM or FM wave. A wave linearly related to $\theta(t)$ is present at the output of the low-pass filter $H(f)$ in Fig. 8-5 and can be delivered to an external load circuit through a second filter with transmittance $I(f)$ and output $v_5(t)$. In general,

$$V_5(f) = I(f)V_4(f) \tag{8-77}$$

and if the approximation $\sin(\theta - \phi) = \theta - \phi$ holds, Eqs. (8-69), (8-71), and (8-73) give

$$\begin{aligned} V_5(f) &= k_3 a_1 a_c I(f)H(f)[U(f) + R(f) * U(f)] \\ &= \frac{j2\pi f}{k_1 k_2} I(f)[\Theta(f) - U(f)] \end{aligned} \tag{8-78}$$

If $u(t)$ can be made to approach zero by increasing K,

$$V_5(f) \approx \frac{j2\pi f}{k_1 k_2} I(f)\Theta(f) \tag{8-79}$$

In particular then if $I(f) = k_1 k_2 k_4$, we obtain frequency detection with

$$v_5(t) \approx k_4 \dot{\theta}(t) \tag{8-80}$$

while if $I(f) = k_1 k_2 k_4 / (j2\pi f)$, a phase detector is realized with

$$v_5(t) \approx k_4 \theta(t) \tag{8-81}$$

A significant feature of the phase-locked loop is that the bandwidth of the incoming PM or FM wave $v_0(t)$ can be much wider than the band passed by $H(f)$. In the case of FM with a high modulation index μ, the bandwidth of $v_0(t)$ must include the complete excursion range of the instantaneous frequency and will be of the order of 2μ times the signal bandwidth. The response of $H(f)$ can and should be restricted to the signal band. The control voltage of the VCO then has the bandwidth of the signal, but the output of the VCO is a wideband frequen ·-modulated wave with instantaneous frequency tracking that of the incoming FM wave. As far as signal variations are concerned, the part of $\theta(t) - \phi(t)$ falling in the signal band is a sufficient representation if the tracking is good. Since the noise accepted by $H(f)$ is then only that arising from the r-f components differing from the instantaneous carrier frequency by no more than the signal bandwidth, the phase-locked loop gives the same improvement in signal-to-noise ratio above threshold as an ideal frequency detector.

We note, however, that in the phase-locked loop the threshold above which improvement in signal-to-noise ratio occurs is governed by the noise peaks in the narrow band accepted by $H(f)$ rather than in the wide band occupied by the high-index FM wave. It appears then that the phase-locked loop can have a lower improvement threshold than the conventional type of frequency detector if the threshold is specified in terms of ratio of average r-f noise power to average noise power in the r-f band. In fact, one might jump to the erroneous conclusion that we could increase the frequency swing indefinitely with fixed signal power in a background of white gaussian noise and thereby obtain an arbitrarily high signal-to-noise ratio in the detector output for an arbitrarily small r-f signal-to-noise ratio. The reason this cannot be done is that the instantaneous noise peaks which determine the threshold in the narrow i-f (intermediate frequency) band can cause more trouble when they disturb wideband frequency tracking than they cause by breaking the limiter in a conventional frequency detector. It is, however, possible to obtain a definite threshold reduction with the phase-locked loop. The actual amounts of improvement which have been reported vary, and there are some questions concerning the validity of the experimental comparisons.

A rigorous theoretical analysis of the phase-locked loop is difficult because of the nonlinearity of Eq. (8-65). We can avoid the linearizing approximation by inserting a conventional frequency detector in the loop as shown in Fig. 8-6. The resulting circuit, which was invented by J. G. Chaffee,[6] is called an FMFB (frequency modulation with feedback) demodulator. With $v_0(t)$ defined as before, we do not tune the VCO to the unmodulated carrier frequency ω_c but to an offset frequency $\omega_c - \omega_i$, where ω_i is the center frequency of the i-f band of the receiver. Equation (8-63) is then replaced by

$$v_1(t) = a_1 \cos\left[(\omega_c - \omega_i)t + \phi(t)\right] \tag{8-82}$$

with $\dot{\phi}(t)$ proportional to $v_2(t)$ as in (8-64). The VCO is the local or beating oscillator of a conventional superheterodyne receiver.

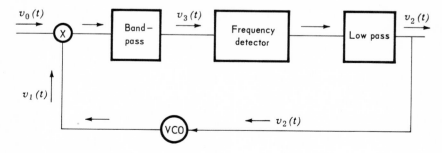

Fig. 8-6   FMFB demodulator.

The output of the multiplier or mixer contains upper and lower sidebands centered around frequencies $2\omega_c + \omega_i$ and ω_i, respectively. The bandpass filter selects the lower sideband, giving the output

$$v_3(t) = k_3 a_1 a_c [1 + \rho(t)] \cos [\omega_i t + \theta(t) - \phi(t) - \pi/2] \qquad (8\text{-}83)$$

The response of a frequency-deviation detector, i.e., a frequency detector adjusted for zero output when the input frequency is ω_i, is

$$v_2(t) = k_2[\dot{\theta}(t) - \dot{\phi}(t)] \qquad (8\text{-}84)$$

When the loop is closed,

$$\dot{\phi}(t) = k_1 k_2 [\dot{\theta}(t) - \dot{\phi}(t)]$$

or

$$\dot{\phi}(t) = \frac{k_1 k_2 \dot{\theta}(t)}{1 + k_1 k_2} \qquad (8\text{-}85)$$

and

$$\dot{\phi}(t) \rightarrow \dot{\theta}(t) \qquad \text{as } k_1 k_2 \rightarrow \infty \qquad (8\text{-}86)$$

The bandwidth of the i-f wave $v_3(t)$ is determined by $\dot{\theta}(t) - \dot{\phi}(t)$ and can be much smaller than that of the r-f wave $v_0(t)$, which has a bandwidth determined by $\dot{\phi}(t)$. A conventional FM detector would have to accept the input noise of the complete r-f band. The frequency detector of the FMFB system need accept only the noise in the reduced band accommodating the frequency swing of $\dot{\theta} - \dot{\phi}$. The conventional improvement threshold of 10 db, therefore, applies to the signal-to-noise ratio in the reduced i-f band, and the signal-to-noise ratio in the r-f band can be made lower than 10 db without losing the improvement. For the case of white noise in the r-f input, a lowered r-f signal-to-noise ratio permits a wider band, which in turn allows a greater frequency deviation, and a corresponding increase in the signal-to-noise ratio at the output of the frequency detector without increasing the received power.

As in the case of the phase-locked loop, the threshold cannot be lowered indefinitely because of the increased disturbances caused by the i-f noise peaks when the loop is exposed to an input with wider band. The FMFB detector has found an important application in satellite communication systems, in which the available bandwidth is very large and the available signal power is very small. Threshold reductions of 7 db relative to the conventional FM detector have been reported.[7]

PROBLEMS

8-1. A two-channel quadrature-carrier multiplex wave is represented by the current

$$m_1(t) = r_1(t) \cos \omega_c t - q_1(t) \sin \omega_c t$$

with $R_1(f)$ and $Q_1(f)$ equal to zero when $|f| \geq f_c$. Suppose the current $m_1(t)$ is the input to a parallel combination of inductance L, capacitance C, and resistance R tuned to give maximum response voltage at the carrier frequency ω_c. If $m_2(t)$ is the voltage across the parallel-tuned circuit, show that

$$\frac{M_2(f)}{M_1(f)} = \frac{R}{1 + jQ(f/f_c - f_c/f)}$$

where $2\pi f_c = (LC)^{-\frac{1}{2}}$ and $Q = 2\pi f_c CR$. If separation of the two signals $r_1(t)$ and $q_1(t)$ is performed by multiplying $m_2(t)$ with $\cos \omega_c t$ and $\sin \omega_c t$, respectively, and filtering the products, what is the interchannel signal-to-interference ratio when sine-wave test tones with equal amplitudes and equal frequencies are impressed on each channel?

8-2. Find the exact expression for the Hilbert transform of the frequency-modulated wave of Eq. (8-5) when $s(t) = \cos \omega t$. What is the error in the approximation of Eq. (8-6) in this case?

8-3. (a) In the lattice network of Fig. 8-7, with $H(f)$ equal to the ratio of $E_2(f)$ to $E_1(f)$, show that

$$H(f) = \frac{1 - Z(f)}{1 + Z(f)}$$

(b) Suppose the branches of the lattice are series- and shunt-tuned circuits with

$$Z(f) = 1 + jQ\left(\frac{f}{f_c} - \frac{f_c}{f}\right)$$

Find $H_c(f)$, $H_r(f)$, and $H_q(f)$.

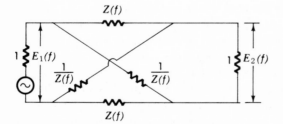

Fig. 8-7 Constant-resistance lattice network.

8-4. Figure 8-8 illustrates a widely used type of frequency detector in which variation of phase shift with frequency is utilized rather than variation of amplitude with frequency. The principles of operation are (1) the voltage across the secondary winding of a tuned transformer leads the primary voltage in phase by 90° at the frequency of resonance, (2) the curve of phase shift versus frequency is approximately a straight line throughout a range of frequencies centered at resonance, and (3) the

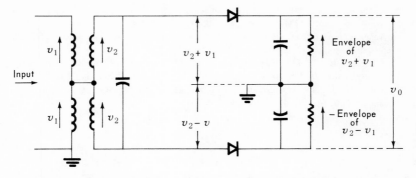

Fig. 8-8   Frequency detector based on variation of phase shift with frequency.

amplitude ratio of the secondary and primary voltages is approximately constant throughout this range.   An idealized description can be formulated as

$$\frac{V_2(f)}{V_1(f)} = j \operatorname{sgn} f\, e^{-j2\pi(f-f_c \operatorname{sgn} f)\tau} \qquad \begin{array}{l} f_1 < |f| < f_2 \\ f_1 < f_c < f_2 \end{array}$$

The voltage waves $v_2 + v_1$ and $v_2 - v_1$ are applied as inputs to envelope detectors with the diodes back to back.   The output voltage v_0 is the difference between the two envelopes as shown.

(a) Calculate v_0 for the steady-state case in which the input is a sine wave $v_1(t) = a_c \cos (\omega_c + \nu)t$, $f_1 < f_c - \nu$, $f_2 > f_c + \nu$.   Under what approximations is v_0 proportional to ν?

(b) Calculate v_0 for the angle-modulated input wave $v_1(t) = a_c \cos [\omega_c t + ks(t)]$.   Under what approximations is v_0 proportional to $\dot{s}(t)$?

8-5. In the phase-locked loop, assume $\theta(t)$ is a constant θ_0, $H(f) = 1$, and that $\phi(0) = \phi_0$. Without making any approximations show that

$$\phi(t) = \theta_0 - 2 \arctan \left(e^{-Kt} \tan \frac{\theta_0 - \phi_0}{2} \right) \qquad t > 0$$

8-6. Apply Eqs. (8-36) to the problem of interchannel interference in a two-channel DSBSC system with carriers differing in phase by 90°.   Assume a linear time-invariant transmission medium characterized by a transmittance function $H(f)$.   Should the demodulating carriers be in phase with the modulating carriers?   How would you find the demodulating carrier phases which give minimum interchannel interference?

REFERENCES

1. Armstrong, E. H.: A Method of Reducing Disturbances in Radio Signaling by a System of Frequency Modulation, *Proc. IRE*, vol. 24, pp. 689–740, May, 1936.
2. Sunde, E. D.: Ideal Binary Pulse Transmission by AM and FM, *Bell System Tech. J.*, vol. 38, pp. 1357–1426, November, 1959.
3. Bennett, W. R., and J. R. Davey: "Data Transmission," Sec. 5-8, McGraw-Hill, New York, 1965.

4. McGee, W. F.: Bandlimiting Distortionless FSK Filters, *IEEE Trans. Commun. Tech.*, vol. COM-15, pp. 721–723, October, 1967.
5. Viterbi, A. J.: "Principles of Coherent Communication," McGraw-Hill, New York, 1966.
6. Chaffee, J. G.: The Application of Negative Feedback to Frequency-modulation Systems, *Bell System Tech. J.*, vol. 18, pp. 403–437, July, 1939.
7. Enloe, L. H.: Decreasing the Threshold in FM by Frequency Feedback, *Proc. IRE*, vol. 50, pp. 23–29, January, 1962.

9

Multiplex Transmission

The name *multiplex* is applied to any system in which a transmission medium is shared by a plurality of independent signals. Means must be provided for separation of the individual signals at the output of the common path. There are two principal methods. One is based on the frequency-domain representation of signals and is called *frequency-division multiplex* or *FDM*. The other is based on the time-domain representation and is called *time-division multiplex* or *TDM*. In FDM, the signals are forced to occupy disjoint frequency ranges, while in TDM the signals are assigned disjoint time intervals.

Methods in which the transmitted signals overlap each other in both frequency and time exist but have not as yet become of comparable importance. The two-channel quadrature-carrier multiplex system is one example in which neither frequency nor time is divided, and this concept can be generalized to construct a $2N$-channel phase-discrimination system with $2N$ sets of phases assigned to N carrier frequencies. In theory any set of orthogonal functions could be made a basis for multiplexing signals confined to the interval of orthogonality, but we have seen that sinusoidal functions have definite advantages of simplicity relative to other choices which might be made. We accordingly devote most of our discussion to FDM and TDM systems.

9-1 DESCRIPTION OF AN FDM SYSTEM

A block diagram of an FDM system is shown in Fig. 9-1. Not all of the components shown are necessary in every FDM system, and we shall point out some of the different requirements of different systems as the discussion proceeds. The signals are assumed to be of the low-pass type, but their Fourier representations do not necessarily have nonzero values all the way down to zero frequency. A low-pass filter is shown following each signal input. This would not be necessary if the signal bands were already sufficiently band-limited. It is necessary if the signal sources contain high-frequency components that do not contribute significantly to satisfactory signal representation but are capable of disturbing other signals which share the common medium.

The filtered signals are impressed on modulators which shift the frequency ranges to mutually exclusive frequency intervals. The carrier supply shown provides the necessary carrier frequencies to perform the frequency translations. In many cases the carriers are harmonics of a common base frequency equal to the bandwidth allotted to each channel in the common medium. An angle modulator may, however, include a voltage-controlled oscillator and not require an external carrier supply.

The bandpass filters following the modulators restrict the band of each modulated signal to its allocated range. The resulting outputs are combined in parallel to form the input to the common medium. The bandwidth allotted to each channel depends on the type of modulation and on the filter selectivity as well as on the bandwidth of the original signal. A practical single-sideband system typically allows 25 to 35 percent increase over the signal bandwidth in order to provide a guard interval between adjacent channels. A double-sideband system would need approximately twice as great a band as SSB, and an angle-modulation system a still greater amount which increases with the peak frequency deviation.

At the receiving terminal, a bank of bandpass filters with inputs in parallel separates the signals on a frequency-occupancy basis. Individual demodulators recover the original signals. Note that the system shown in Fig. 9-1 operates in only one direction and that many multiplex systems, notably those used for voice channels, must provide for two-way transmission. This is accomplished by a complete duplication of the multiplexing facilities, with the components in reverse order and with the signal waves proceeding from right to left. Each channel has access to a

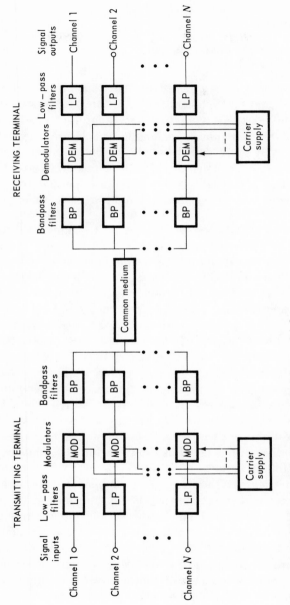

Fig. 9-1 Block diagram of a frequency-division multiplex system.

transmitting modulator and a receiving demodulator combined to form a "modem."

9-2 THE CARRIER SUPPLY PROBLEM

The carrier supply for the demodulators of Fig. 9-1 is strictly necessary only when the carrier is suppressed at the transmitter and cannot be derived from the transmitted sidebands.   In an AM system the carrier accompanies the sidebands, and the demodulator can be an envelope detector.   Similarly, a frequency demodulator measures the axis-crossing rate of the received wave and does not require a carrier supply.   An intermediate case is that of single or double sideband with partial carrier suppression, where a carrier recovery circuit is needed to extract the carrier component and to adjust its amplitude and phase for use in demodulation.

In double-sideband suppressed-carrier transmission, the carrier frequency can be recovered from the sidebands because the frequency difference between corresponding upper- and lower-sideband components is twice the carrier frequency.   For example, a device which delivers a component proportional to the product of the two sidebands can be followed by a bandpass filter and a 2:1 frequency stepdown to recover the carrier frequency.   The phase of the recovered carrier in this case has two possible values 180° apart.   In the case of speech signals, the ambiguity does not matter, but in telegraphy a polarity reversal generally produces an entirely different message.   Differential coding in which the symbols are represented by presence or absence of transitions between adjacent intervals enables telegraph signals to be read unambiguously. A negative-feedback scheme which forces a local oscillator to track the missing carrier frequency in a DSBSC wave has been described by Costas.[1]   The schematic diagram is shown in Fig. 9-2, and the theory is developed in Prob. 9-3.

The term *nonsynchronous carrier* is applied to a system such as SSBSC in which the carrier frequency is not transmitted and cannot be derived from the sidebands.   The carrier supplied at the receiver differs in both frequency and phase from that used at the transmitter by a variable amount depending on the precision and stability of the frequency standards controlling the independent carrier supplies.   The effect is to shift the components of the demodulated signal in both frequency and phase.   The distortion caused by frequency shift is called *carrier-frequency offset*.   Voice signals tolerate a frequency shift of ±20 Hz without appreciable impairment.

Most carrier telephone channels in the United States actually hold the offset to within ±2 Hz.   The resulting reproduced voice quality is

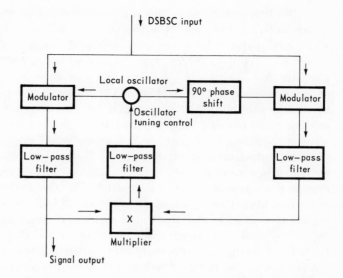

Fig. 9-2   Schematic diagram of Costas' receiver for DSBSC wave.

excellent, but other kinds of signals in which the waveform is all important may suffer.   Data transmission by frequency-shift keying would not be affected unless an extremely narrow subband were used.   VSB data signals, on the other hand, require accurate control of the waveform in order to prevent intersymbol interference.   The unshifted carrier frequency can be recovered by transmitting two pilot tones with separation related to the original carrier frequency.   A demodulating carrier derived from the pilot-tone difference has the correct frequency but not necessarily the right phase.   If waveform of the demodulated signal is important, carrier derivation should include provisions for phase correction.

9-3   EVALUATION OF PERFORMANCE

The performance of any multiplex system is evaluated in terms of two general properties: (1) intrachannel transmission and (2) interchannel interference.   In the case of FDM, transmission within a channel with all other channels inactive is principally affected by the amplitude and phase characteristics of the filters; the linearity of modulators, demodulators, and amplifiers; and the carrier offset and phase error.   Calculation of these effects is straightforward by principles we have already discussed.   The problem of interchannel interference brings in new considerations.

We first note that if the common medium of an FDM system is linear and time-invariant, the interchannel interference associated with specified signals can be completely evaluated from the filter transmittance functions. Also, time variations in the medium are not significant if they are slow relative to the signal changes since the resulting widening of signal bands is not appreciable. The principal new problem in FDM is, therefore, the effect of nonlinearity in the common medium. Since passive constituents of typical media do not contribute nonlinearity of any consequence, "one-hop" or "nonrepeatered" systems are practically immune from nonlinear interference. The greatest savings in multiplex methods, however, accrue in transmission over long distances for which intermediate repeaters must be used. The alternative to multiplexing is a plurality of single-channel systems, which are economically preferable when inexpensive transmission lines are available.

The nonlinear interference problem in FDM is thus reduced to that of linearity requirements on multichannel amplifiers. Skillful application of the highly developed theory of negative feedback has led to design and construction of wideband amplifiers with very small departure from linear response over a definite range of signal magnitudes. When such a negative feedback amplifier is driven beyond the designed linear range, a sharp break occurs making the response practically worthless as a representation of the applied signal. In the case of an applied FDM signal, an explosive disturbance called a "bat" or "crack" is received in every channel output at the receiver every time the overload condition occurs. Below overload, the interchannel interference can be described in terms of small deviations from linearity which can be conveniently expressed in terms of square- and cube-law approximations. In well-designed amplifiers these terms are small, but they can produce substantial accumulations of interference when many channels and many repeaters are included in the system.

The multichannel-amplifier problem is conveniently discussed in two parts: (1) the overload requirement as a function of the number and kind of channels, and (2) the cross-modulation requirements below overload. The most important applications so far have been to multiplex single-sideband suppressed-carrier voice transmission. The same methods of analysis are applicable to other kinds of signals, but different numerical data must be inserted. The classical treatment of the overload problem is that given by Holbrook and Dixon[2] and that of cross modulation below overload is that given by Bennett.[3]

9-4 MULTICHANNEL OVERLOAD IN FDM

The objective in establishing the load rating of a multichannel amplifier is to relate the requirement for N channels to that of one channel. The

Table 9-1   Nonsimultaneous multiplex load advantage

N	Relative overload power, db	Peak superposition requirement, db	Nonsimultaneous load advantage, db
1	0	0	0
10	6	20	14
100	9	40	31
500	13	54	41
1000	16	60	44

requirement for a single channel can be evaluated in a straightforward manner by experimental procedures and can conveniently be expressed in terms of full-load test-tone power at a specified reference point in the channel. The actual value of overload power of a particular amplifier depends on the amount of loss or gain between the reference point and the amplifier.

The general relation between N-channel load capacity and full load for one channel is not conveniently determined experimentally because of the practical difficulties of assembling large numbers of channel users under realistic conditions. Holbrook and Dixon used measured distributions of talker volumes to calculate the distribution of peaks in an N-channel SSBSC voice signal for various values of N. On the assumption of a 0.1 percent probability of overload at any instant during the period of heaviest telephone traffic, they derived curves from which the values shown in Table 9-1 were obtained. The first column shows the number of channels, and the second column shows the required decibel increment in load capacity relative to one channel. The third column is the increment which would be required if the maximum instantaneous signal values in each channel added in phase. The fourth column gives the "nonsimultaneous load advantage," which is the difference between the corresponding entries in the third and second columns.

The very impressive tabulated advantages are readily explained qualitatively. A factor of 2 arises because the amplifiers operate in one direction only and hence on the average handle only one-half of a two-way conversation. In addition to this, a speaker does not talk continuously even when the other party is listening—there must be pauses to breathe, to think, and to separate words. Also, all sounds do not produce equal peak values. The superposed multichannel signal is thus made up of individual waveforms with infrequent coincidence of large simultaneous contributions. Furthermore, the single-sideband waves do not often add in phase because of the frequency differences.

The nonsimultaneous load advantage provides a tremendous argument in favor of FDM for voice transmission. A striking illustration is provided by the fact that if a 1000-channel FDM system is designed in accordance with Table 9-1, full-load test tones impressed on only six channels bring the multichannel medium to overload and make the other 994 channels unusable.

9-5 CROSS MODULATION BELOW OVERLOAD

When the overload requirement of the multichannel amplifier has been established, there remains the problem of setting linearity requirements below overload. Since the approach to linearity must be close, the small departures should be well approximated by the first few terms of a power series. Square- and cube-law terms are usually sufficient and are also necessary because they exhibit two different types of behavior.

An effective simplification is made by replacement of the signals in the channels by sine waves. A set of relationships must be established experimentally by means of which the sine-wave results can be used to predict results with the actual signals, e.g., speech waves.

The square-law contribution can be evaluated by noting that

$$(a_1 \cos \omega_1 t + a_2 \cos \omega_2 t)^2 = \frac{a_1{}^2}{2} + \frac{a_2{}^2}{2} + \frac{a_1{}^2}{2} \cos 2\omega_1 t + \frac{a_2{}^2}{2} \cos 2\omega_2 t$$
$$+ a_1 a_2 \cos (\omega_1 + \omega_2)t + a_1 a_2 \cos (\omega_1 - \omega_2)t \quad (9\text{-}1)$$

We conclude that for every two terms, a square-law response produces (1) a d-c component equal to half the sums of the squared amplitudes, (2) second harmonics (of each term) with amplitude equal to half the square of the fundamental amplitude, and (3) components with frequencies equal to the sums and differences of the fundamental frequencies and with amplitudes equal to the products of the fundamental amplitudes.

Similarly, the contribution from a cube law can be found from

$$(a_1 \cos \omega_1 t + a_2 \cos \omega_2 t + a_3 \cos \omega_3 t)^3$$
$$= \frac{3a_1{}^3}{4} \cos \omega_1 t + \frac{3}{4} a_2{}^3 \cos \omega_2 t + \frac{3}{4} a_3{}^3 \cos \omega_3 t$$
$$= \frac{3}{4} a_1{}^2(a_1 + 2a_2 + 2a_3) \cos \omega_1 t + \frac{3}{4} a_2{}^2(a_2 + 2a_1 + 2a_3) \cos \omega_2 t$$
$$+ \frac{3}{4} a_3{}^2(a_3 + 2a_1 + 2a_2) \cos \omega_3 t + \frac{a_1{}^3}{2} \cos 3\omega_1 t + \frac{a_2{}^3}{2} \cos 3\omega_2 t$$
$$+ \frac{a_3{}^3}{2} \cos 3\omega_3 t + \frac{3}{4} a_1{}^2 a_2 [\cos (2\omega_1 + \omega_2)t + \cos (2\omega_1 - \omega_2)t]$$
$$+ \frac{3}{4} a_1{}^2 a_3 [\cos (2\omega_1 + \omega_3)t + \cos (2\omega_1 - \omega_3)t]$$

$$+ \frac{3}{4} a_1 a_2{}^2 [\cos (2\omega_2 + \omega_1)t + \cos (2\omega_2 - \omega_1)t]$$

$$+ \frac{3}{4} a_2{}^2 a_3 [\cos (2\omega_2 + \omega_3)t + \cos (2\omega_2 - \omega_3)t]$$

$$+ \frac{3}{4} a_1 a_3{}^2 [\cos (2\omega_3 + \omega_1)t + \cos (2\omega_3 - \omega_1)t]$$

$$+ \frac{3}{4} a_2 a_3{}^2 [\cos (2\omega_3 + \omega_2)t + \cos (2\omega_3 - \omega_2)t]$$

$$+ \frac{3}{2} a_1 a_2 a_3 [\cos (\omega_1 + \omega_2 + \omega_3)t + \cos (\omega_1 + \omega_2 - \omega_3)t$$
$$+ \cos (\omega_1 - \omega_2 + \omega_3)t + \cos (\omega_1 - \omega_2 - \omega_3)t] \quad (9\text{-}2)$$

For an N-channel system, we require a census of the possible modulation products showing how many fall in each channel and what their relation is to the fundamental channel-tone amplitudes. It will be noted that for a large number N of channels, the total number of square-law products becomes proportional to N^2 and the total number of cube-law products proportional to N^3. It follows that the total number of products falling in a single channel is, in effect, proportional to N for square law and to N^2 for cube law. Evaluation of the number and strengths of these products as a function of channel position is given in Bennett's paper previously referenced.

In a multirepeater system the accumulation of cross-modulation products as a function of the number of repeaters must also be evaluated. Of particular interest is the case of a repeatered medium equalized for linear phase shift but not for zero phase intercept, such as is appropriate for a broadband medium which can be used either for television or multiplex voice. The phase intercept need not be zero, because its effect can be removed by adjusting the phase of the demodulating carrier. If the delay is τ in one repeater section of such a system, the wave propagated to the second repeater is found by replacing $\omega_k t$ by $\omega_k(t - \tau) - \theta$ in every term including both fundamental and modulation products. Here τ is the slope of the phase curve of the first repeater section and θ is the phase intercept. The modulation products generated in the second repeater are found by making this replacement in the fundamental components of (9-1) and (9-2). Remodulation of products propagated from the first repeater can be neglected. Considering (9-1), we see that if $\omega_1 t$ is replaced by $\omega_1(t - \tau) - \theta$ and $\omega_2 t$ by $\omega_2(t - \tau) - \theta$ on the left, the sum-frequency product becomes proportional to $\cos [(\omega_1 + \omega_2)(t - \tau) - 2\theta]$ and the difference-frequency product to $\cos (\omega_1 - \omega_2)(t - \tau)$. The corresponding products propagated from the first repeater are $a_1 a_2 \cos [(\omega_1 + \omega_2)(t - \tau) - \theta]$ and $a_1 a_2 \cos [(\omega_1 - \omega_2)(t - \tau) - \theta]$. The two sum-frequency contributions thus have a phase difference θ, while the two difference-frequency contributions have a phase difference $-\theta$. If the value of θ is random among the repeater sections, the products from successive repeaters add as power.

Exceptions to the random phase of product contributions from different repeaters occur. Consider, for example, the cube-law product of frequency $\omega_1 + \omega_2 - \omega_3$. The product propagated from the first repeater is proportional to $\cos\left[(\omega_1 + \omega_2 - \omega_3)(t - \tau) - \theta\right]$, and the product generated in the second repeater varies as

$$\cos\left[(\omega_1 + \omega_2 - \omega_3)(t - \tau) - \theta - \theta + \theta\right]$$
$$= \cos\left[(\omega_1 + \omega_2 - \omega_3)(t - \tau) - \theta\right]$$

The two contributions add in phase. Requirements on suppression of this type of product in the individual amplifiers of a system containing many repeaters can be extraordinarily severe.

9-6 COMPOUND MODULATION METHODS

The common transmission medium can employ a modulation method within itself. An example occurs in the case of a repeatered microwave path. At these frequencies, it may not be technically feasible to construct negative-feedback amplifiers to obtain the necessary linearity. A widely and successfully used method impresses the complete wave from the FDM transmitting terminal as signal input to a frequency modulator which delivers an output in the microwave range. An example is the so-called SSB-FM system in which a group of single-sideband channels is transmitted by FM.

Since FM is insensitive to nonlinear distortion, the repeaters can be overloaded to obtain maximum power output. A linear phase curve over the microwave band becomes necessary to avoid interchannel interference, because frequency detection converts nonlinear phase versus frequency in the transmission medium to a nonlinear relationship between output and input amplitudes. The microwave medium is itself practically free from nonlinearity, and hence the main problem is in the design of the repeaters. Use of directive antennas, frequency-band shifting at adjacent repeaters, and ample guard-frequency range at the band edges reduces the difficulty of maintaining satisfactory isolation of an SSB-FM microwave signal without making the necessary phase linearity too difficult to achieve.

It is to be noted that peak-voltage requirements imposed by the SSB wave are converted to peak-frequency-deviation requirements for the SSB-FM wave. The nonsimultaneous load advantage of FDM thus becomes effective in reducing the bandwidth needed in the microwave medium.

9-7 SUMMARY OF STRENGTH AND WEAKNESS OF FDM

The principal advantages of FDM are:

1. The huge nonsimultaneous load advantage, particularly for voice transmission
2. Freedom from crosstalk in a linear common medium

The chief disadvantages are:

1. Expense and bulk of the bandpass filters
2. Vulnerability to crosstalk in a nonlinear medium

9-8 DESCRIPTION OF A TDM SYSTEM

Time-division multiplex (TDM) is actually the oldest method of transmitting and receiving independent signals over a common medium. It was first introduced to enable telegraphers to share a single line. The relatively slow signaling rates used in manual keying were readily adapted to synchronized rotating multisegment distributors. Applications to wider-band analog signals such as voice awaited the development of high-speed electronic switching and wideband transmission media.

Figure 9-3 shows a block diagram of a time-division multiplex system. Each signal channel is first restricted in bandwidth by a low-pass filter removing the frequencies which are nonessential to an adequate signal representation. As shown in Chap. 6, the signal can be reconstructed from samples taken at a rate exceeding twice the highest signal frequency. If the cutoff frequency of the low-pass filter is f_b, the sampling rate of each channel must exceed $2f_b$.

The sampling is accomplished by individual switches controlled by pulses from a timing source. For an N-channel system with sampling interval $T < 1/(2f_b)$ per channel, a train of pulses closes the switch between the filtered output of channel 1 and the line during short intervals centered at $t = t_0 + nT$, $n = 0$, ± 1, ± 2, ... The corresponding switch for channel 2 is closed at $t = t_0 + nT + T/N$, etc., with non-overlapping closure intervals for the different switches. The timing source must therefore deliver separate pulse trains to each channel switch at the rate of $1/T$ pulses/sec and with a staggering interval of T/N sec between pulses supplied to adjacent channels. Digital circuitry for realization of such a source of pulses is well known.

The samples from the channels are combined on a common bus. No channel band filters are needed, but a common sending filter or shaping network may be desirable between the common bus and the input to the common medium. The purpose of the shaping network is

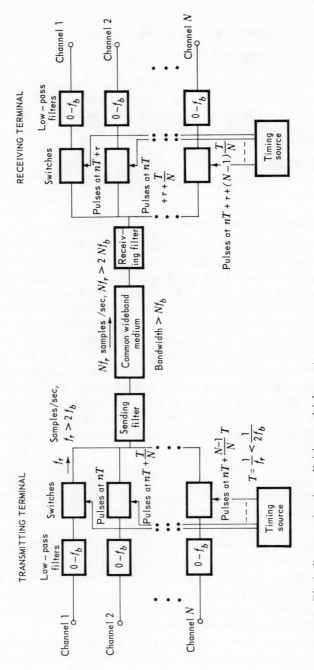

Fig. 9-3 Block diagram of a time-division multiplex system.

to control interchannel interference which can arise because of departures from amplitude constancy and phase proportionality in the frequency response of the common medium.

A receiving filter is inserted at the output of the medium. In addition to a pulse-shaping function which is shared additively with the sending filter, the receiving filter removes noise outside the band required for transmitting the samples. Distribution of the shaping between the two filters is subject to optimization with regard to signal-to-noise ratio and transmitted power.

The output of the receiving filter is applied to channel switches in parallel. Individual bandpass filters are not required. A timing source synchronous with that at the transmitter delivers the control pulses to the switches. Each switch is followed by a low-pass filter cutting off at f_b and therefore removing the lower sidebands on the sampling frequency. The low-pass filter outputs constitute the received channel signals.

The part of the TDM system between switch banks resembles the general baseband telegraph system of Fig. 4-1. There is one difference: the analog samples in the TDM system are not restricted to discrete values. Therefore, the performance cannot be described in terms of error rates, but the actual amount of intersymbol interference must be evaluated. Furthermore, the intersymbol interference in the TDM case becomes interchannel interference and is subject to a more severe requirement than intrachannel distortion. Nevertheless, the methods of reducing intersymbol interference based on Nyquist's first criterion apply, and the optimization theory given in Chap. 4 for design of the sending and receiving filters is valid. We may think of analog transmission by TDM as ∞-ary telegraphy. The lower bound on the signaling rate is $2Nf_b$, and the lower bound on the bandwidth of the common medium is Nf_b Hz.

Let us evaluate the intrachannel transmission and the interchannel interference in the frequency domain. If we assume that the sampling is instantaneous, we can represent the samples of the signal wave applied to the first channel by the product of the signal and the Dirac comb defined by Eqs. (1-57) and (1-59) with $T = 1/f_r$, $f_r > 2f_b$. Since the system is linear, we base our treatment on a single-frequency component representing the signal and write for the sampled output of the first channel,

$$
\begin{aligned}
\mu_1(t) &= s_1 \cos \omega_1 t \sum_{n=-\infty}^{\infty} \delta(t - nT) = \delta_T(t) s_1 \cos \omega_1 t \\
&= f_r s_1 \cos \omega_1 t \left[1 + 2 \sum_{m=1}^{\infty} \cos m\omega_r t \right] \\
&= f_r s_1 \left\{ \cos \omega_1 t + \sum_{m=1}^{\infty} \left[\cos (m\omega_r + \omega_1)t + \cos (m\omega_r - \omega_1)t \right] \right\}
\end{aligned}
$$

or

$$2\mu_1(t) = f_r s_1 \sum_{m=-\infty}^{\infty} [e^{j(m\omega_r+\omega_1)t} + e^{j(m\omega_r-\omega_1)t}] \tag{9-3}$$

Divergence of the series is of no consequence since we use the formula only in the calculation of the output of a system in which the response to high frequencies approaches zero.

Let $Q(f)e^{-j2\pi f\tau}$ represent the transmittance function of the combination of sending filter, transmission medium, and receiving filter. The input to the switch at the receiver is then $u_1(t)$ satisfying the equation

$$2u_1(t) = f_r s_1 \sum_{m=-\infty}^{\infty} \{Q(mf_r + f_1)e^{j(m\omega_r+\omega_1)(t-\tau)}$$
$$+ Q(mf_r - f_1)e^{j(m\omega_r-\omega_1)(t-\tau)}\} \tag{9-4}$$

We consider $v_{n+1}(t)$, the output of the switch contact assigned to the $(n + 1)$st channel. The time slot assigned to this channel lags that assigned to the first channel by nT/N. Allowing for the transmission delay τ, we equate $v_{n+1}(t)$ to the product $u_1(t)$ by $\delta_T(t - \tau - nT/N)$. Therefore,

$$2v_{n+1}(t) = u_1(t)f_r \sum_{l=-\infty}^{\infty} e^{-jl\omega_r(t-\tau-n/Nf_r)}$$
$$= f_r^2 s_1 \sum_{l=-\infty}^{\infty} \sum_{m=-\infty}^{\infty} \{Q(mf_r + f_1)e^{j(m-l)\omega_r(t-\tau)+j\omega_1(t-\tau)+j2\pi ln/N}$$
$$+ Q(mf_r - f_1)e^{j(m-l)\omega_r(t-\tau)-j\omega_1(t-\tau)+j2\pi ln/N}\} \tag{9-5}$$

Each switch contact at the receiver is assumed to be followed by an ideal low-pass filter cutting off at $f_b < f_r/2$. It follows that none of the terms in (9-5) containing a nonzero multiple of ω_r can appear in the output of this filter. Hence, the baseband wave $r_{n+1}(t)$ delivered to the $(n + 1)$st channel is obtained by setting $m = l$ in (9-5) with the result

$$2r_{n+1}(t) = f_r^2 s_1 \sum_{m=-\infty}^{\infty} \{Q(mf_r + f_1)e^{j\omega_1(t-\tau)+j2\pi mn/N}$$
$$+ Q(mf_r - f_1)e^{-j\omega_1(t-\tau)+j2\pi mn/N}\}$$
$$= f_r^2 s_1 \sum_{m=-\infty}^{\infty} \{Q(mf_r + f_1)e^{j\omega_1(t-\tau)+j2\pi mn/N}$$
$$+ Q^*(mf_r + f_1)e^{-j\omega_1(t-\tau)-j2\pi mn/N}\}$$

and hence

$$r_{n+1}(t) = f_r^2 s_1 \sum_{m=-\infty}^{\infty} \text{Re}\,\{Q(mf_r + f_1)e^{j\omega_1(t-\tau)+j2\pi mn/N}\} \tag{9-6}$$

Since $r_{n+1}(t)$ is the response of a linear system to the wave

$$s_1 \cos \omega_1 t = \text{Re}\,(s_1 e^{j\omega_1 t})$$

we can define a transmittance function $H_n(f)$ for the case of transmission from input terminals of one channel to output terminals of a channel lagging by n time slots by

$$\frac{H_n(f)e^{j2\pi f\tau}}{f_r^2} = G_n(f) = \sum_{m=-\infty}^{\infty} Q(mf_r + f)e^{j2\pi mn/N} \tag{9-7}$$

The factor $e^{j2\pi f\tau}$ represents a constant delay in the output wave and is not usually of interest. The intrachannel response can be calculated by setting $n = 0$, and the $N - 1$ different cases of interference between different channels are evaluated by setting $n = 1, 2, 3, \ldots, N - 1$.

To compare with the Nyquist I requirement for suppression of intersymbol interference, we note that the frequency of samples in the common medium is $f_s = Nf_r$. We introduce f_s into the series by setting $m = k + lN$, $k = 0, 1, 2, \ldots, N - 1$. Then

$$G_n(f) = \sum_{k=0}^{N-1} e^{j2\pi kn/N} \sum_{l=-\infty}^{\infty} Q(lf_s + kf_r + f) \tag{9-8}$$

The necessary and sufficient conditions for satisfaction of Nyquist I as given by Eq. (4-8) can be written as

$$\sum_{l=-\infty}^{\infty} Q(lf_s + f) = \frac{A}{f_s} = K \tag{9-9}$$

for all f. If (9-9) holds for f, it must also hold when f is replaced by $kf_r + f$, and we would then have

$$G_n(f) = K \sum_{k=0}^{N-1} e^{j2\pi kn/N} \tag{9-10}$$

When $n = 0$, we obtain $G_0(f) = NK$ and

$$H_0(f) = f_r A e^{-j2\pi f\tau} \tag{9-11}$$

When $n \neq 0$,

$$G_n(f) = K \frac{1 - e^{j2\pi Nn/N}}{1 - e^{j2\pi n/N}} = 0 \tag{9-12}$$

It is thus verified that the steady-state interchannel interference vanishes when Nyquist I is satisfied.

9-9 ADVANTAGES AND DISADVANTAGES OF TDM

Our previous study of FDM enables us to evaluate the relative merits of these two principal competitors in the field of multiplex analog transmission. The similar form of the two block diagrams, Figs. 9-1 and 9-3, suggests a sequential item-by-item comparison. We consider the various features in order.

1. *Low-pass filters.* These are similar in kind and identical in number for the two systems in both the sending and receiving terminals.
2. *Modulators and switches.* The modulators and demodulators in FDM and the switches in TDM perform very similar functions and are in practice virtually the same in physical structure.
3. *Carrier and timing supplies.* The carrier supply in FDM and the timing source in TDM are also very similar. The separation of harmonic carriers on a frequency basis for the different channels leads to somewhat more bulky apparatus than separation of channel switching-control pulses on a time basis, but the difference need not be great. On the other hand, synchronization of timing sources in TDM requires greater precision than synchronization of carrier supplies in FDM, because errors in the former lead to interchannel interference.
4. *Bandpass filters.* The absence of individual bandpass sending and receiving filters for each channel is an important advantage for the TDM system. A single bandpass filter shared by all channels in common is certainly less expensive than a bank of filters with different midband frequencies.
5. *The common medium.* The requirements on the medium include (*a*) linear distortion, (*b*) nonlinear distortion, and (*c*) overload. These will be discussed separately.
   (*a*) *Linear distortion.* The FDM system does not suffer crosstalk because of variations of amplitude with frequency or lack of proportionality of phase shift to frequency. The TDM system, on the other hand, is very sensitive to the presence of these linear defects in the common medium. Very accurate equalization of both amplitude and phase are necessary to prevent intolerable interchannel interference in TDM.
   (*b*) *Nonlinear distortion.* We noted previously in Sec. 9-5 that nonlinearity in the medium causes crosstalk between FDM channels. To a first approximation TDM is immune to nonlinearity as a source of crosstalk because the signals are not impressed on the medium simultaneously. The immunity would be exact only for a medium of infinite bandwidth with linear phase. Since the bandwidth must be limited in practical media and shaping filters are necessary to suppress intersymbol interference, the effect of nonlinearity cannot be ignored. It is impossible to satisfy Nyquist's first criterion by linear network design if the common medium is nonlinear.

(c) *Overload.* It was pointed out in Sec. 9-4 that the nonsimultaneous load advantage was tremendously effective in reducing the peak power required for multichannel repeaters in an FDM system for voice signals. Such considerations do not apply to TDM because the signals are not applied simultaneously. We recall that the reference used in stating load ratings for N-channel FDM systems was the case of $N = 1$, the single-channel amplifier. Before considering the overload requirement for an N-channel TDM amplifier, we establish the relation between TDM and FDM requirements for $N = 1$.

The maximum total power in the common medium determines the signal-to-noise ratio obtained in the channel outputs. Equivalent performance of FDM and TDM is obtained when the channel signal-to-noise ratios are the same for the two systems. Let the maximum total power in the FDM case be W_F and assume that the spectral density of the additive output noise is w_0. Then the maximum signal power available for one channel is W_F/L_N, where for voice signals the numbers in the second column of Table 9-1 are equal to $10 \log_{10} L_N$. We find from the tabulated values that $L_1 = 1$, $L_{10} = 4$, $L_{100} = 8$, $L_{500} = 20$, and $L_{1000} = 40$. The corresponding noise power for a single channel of an SSB system is $w_0 f_b$, where f_b is the channel bandwidth. Hence the signal-to-noise ratio for a single channel is $W_F/(L_N w_0 f_b)$.

In the case of TDM, the peak multichannel power W_T is reached while only one channel is connected to the line. The corresponding maximum power available in the output of one channel is reduced by a factor of N because no power is supplied during the time intervals allotted to the other $N - 1$ channels. Therefore, the peak power received in each channel is W_T/N. If the medium has the minimum bandwidth Nf_b, the mean total noise power is $w_0 N f_b$. Since each receiving channel is exposed to this noise $(1/N)$th of the time, the average channel noise power is $w_0 f_b$. The signal-to-noise ratio in a channel is therefore $W_T/(Nw_0 f_b)$.

To obtain the same signal-to-noise ratio per channel in the FDM and TDM cases, we equate the two values; thus

$$\frac{W_F}{L_N w_0 f_b} = \frac{W_T}{N w_0 f_b}$$

from which

$$\frac{W_T}{W_F} = \frac{N}{L_N} \tag{9-13}$$

For the voice-channel case, we thus obtain Table 9-2.

Table 9-2 Comparison of multichannel
amplifier power in FDM and TDM voice
transmission

Number of channels	$\dfrac{TDM\ load\ rating}{FDM\ load\ rating}$
N	W_T/W_F
1	1.0
10	2.5
100	12.5
500	25.0
1000	25.0

It appears that a TDM system must provide for substantially more load capacity than an FDM system with the same number of channels. However, the disadvantage is not quite so decisive as the figures of Table 9-2 indicate because of the possibility of a load reduction by companding (see Chap. 3). Compandors are particularly attractive in TDM because (1) apparatus can be shared in common by the channels, and (2) the instantaneous type can be used without increase of bandwidth. The justification of (2) is that the bandwidth required for telegraph transmission does not depend on the choice of signal levels.

Companding is also possible in an FDM system but not with the same economy of apparatus. A single compressor acting on the FDM signal would cause trouble because reduction in gain by a strong signal from one channel degrades the signal-to-noise ratio in any channel simultaneously transmitting a weak signal. Therefore individual compressors and expanders should be supplied for each channel to obtain significant companding benefit in FDM. Furthermore, if bandwidth is to be conserved, the individual units are more complicated because they must be syllabic rather than instantaneous.

9-10 PRACTICAL WEIGHTING OF FACTORS AFFECTING THE CHOICE OR REJECTION OF TDM

Our comparison of the merits of TDM and FDM has not evaluated the relative importance of the various advantages and disadvantages of each. The dominance of particular considerations is highly dependent on the state of technological art at the time of decision. The background of experience indicates, however, that the need of TDM for high precision in the amplitude- and phase-vs.-frequency characteristics of the common medium is an almost fatal defect in analog transmission systems. Exceptions may occur when relatively inefficient use of a high-quality medium is expedient, as, for example, in the case of a microwave system for emergency use over short distances.   Such exceptional cases do not have much significance in the general field of multichannel communication.

The practical prospects of TDM change radically, however, if analog-to-digital conversion of the signals is introduced.   The susceptibility to interchannel interference from linear distortion is thus greatly lessened because effects short of actual error production do no harm.   Furthermore, regenerative repeaters can be used to clean up intersymbol interference and noise before an error-causing accumulation is reached.   The principal new items required are the analog-to-digital converter at the transmitting terminal and the digital-to-analog converter at the receiving terminal.   The former, in particular, is an expensive component, but it can be shared among the TDM channels.   The basic principles of pulse-code modulation (PCM), the term commonly applied to digital transmission of analog signals, have been discussed in Chap. 6. A more intensive treatment of the whys and wherefores of this potentially superior method will be given in the next chapter.

PROBLEMS

9-1. Are channel bandpass filters necessary in a double-sideband suppressed-carrier FDM system?   Explain your answer.

9-2. Consider a four-channel phase-discrimination multiplex system in which the signals $s_1(t)$, $s_2(t)$, $s_3(t)$, and $s_4(t)$ are multiplied respectively by the carrier waves $\cos \omega_a t + \cos \omega_b t$, $\cos (\omega_a t + \alpha_1) + \cos (\omega_b t + \beta_1)$, $\cos (\omega_a t + \alpha_2) + \cos (\omega_b t + \beta_2)$, and $\cos (\omega_a t + \alpha_3) + \cos (\omega_b t + \beta_3)$, and the sum of the resulting DSBSC waves is transmitted over a common linear time-invariant medium.   Demodulation is accomplished by multiplying the sum of the DSBSC waves by the four carrier waves separately and selecting the low-frequency components by filtering.

(a) Find a set of values of α_1, α_2, α_3, β_1, β_2, β_3 such that the output of the nth demodulator is $s_n(t)$ for $n = 1, 2, 3$, and 4.

(b) What is the minimum separation of ω_a and ω_b in relation to the bandwidth of the signals?

9-3. Adapt the analysis of the phase-locked loop, Sec. 8-4, to solve Costas' DSBSC carrier recovery circuit of Fig. 9-2 under the following assumptions: (a) The DSBSC input wave is $s(t) \cos \omega_c t$.   (b) The output of the local oscillator is $\cos [(\omega_c + \nu)t + \theta(t)]$ with $\omega_c + \nu + \dot{\theta} = \omega_0 - kv(t)$, where $v(t)$ is the voltage applied to the oscillator tuning control.   (c) The low-pass filters following the two modulators pass the difference-frequency terms and suppress the sum-frequency terms.   (d) The effect of the filter following the multiplier is to replace $s^2(t)$ by its time average.   (e) The sine of $2\nu t + 2\theta(t)$ can be taken as equal to the angle.   Show that if $\theta(t) = \theta_0$ at $t = 0$,

$$\nu t + \theta(t) = \left(\theta_0 + \frac{\omega_c - \omega_0}{K} \right) e^{-Kt} + \frac{\omega_0 - \omega_c}{K}$$

where K is proportional to k times the mean square of $s(t)$.

9-4. Consider an ideal SSB wave as represented by Eq. (7-21) or (7-24). Assume the wave is demodulated by multiplication with a carrier wave $2 \cos [(\omega_c + \nu)t + \theta]$, where ν represents the frequency offset and θ the phase error.

(a) What are the expressions for the demodulated waves in the upper- and lower-sideband cases?

(b) What do these expressions become if the signal consists of a single sine wave $a_1 \cos \omega_1 t$?

(c) Assume the frequency offset is small compared with the important frequencies representing the signal. For the upper-sideband case, what is the approximate form of the demodulated wave during a time interval in which $\nu t + \theta$ is almost equal to (1) a multiple of 2π, (2) an odd multiple of π, (3) $\pi/2$ plus a multiple of 2π, and (4) $\pi/2$ plus an odd multiple of π? What would be the effect on a train of signal pulses if the variation of $\nu t + \theta$ were small during any one pulse?

9-5. Could Table 9-1 be applied to a group of SSB-FDM voice channels if the TASI system described in Sec. 3-5 is used at the terminals? Explain your answer.

9-6. A relatively inexpensive FDM system commonly used for transmission of voice channels over short distances employs amplitude modulation in each channel. Improved margin over noise is provided by individual syllabic compandors as described in Sec. 3-3. How would you expect Table 9-1 to be affected?

9-7. Assume an FDM voice system with 1000 repeater sections. A linear phase-vs.-frequency characteristic is maintained throughout the entire FDM band to provide the option of using the system for transmission of one SSB television channel instead of the FDM voice channels. The zero-frequency intercept of the linear-phase relation is allowed to be random among the repeaters. The television signal is demodulated by a transmitted carrier wave.

(a) Why is the phase intercept of no consequence?

(b) If the system is used for FDM voice channels and it is found that modulation products of frequency $\omega_1 \pm \omega_2$ govern the permissible square-law distortion while products of frequency $\omega_1 + \omega_2 - \omega_3$ govern the permissible cube-law distortion, find (1) the ratio of permissible square-law product amplitude in the complete system to that in one repeater, and (2) the corresponding ratio for cube-law products.

9-8. How many terms of the series in Eq. (9-7) must be evaluated if the common transmission medium passes no frequencies above $2Nf_b$ with $f_r = 2f_b$?

9-9. Consider a TDM system in which $Q(f)$ is the 100 percent cosine rolloff characteristic of Eq. (4-39). Suppose square-law phase distortion is introduced by replacement of $Q(f)$ with $Q(f)Y(f)$ where

$$Y(f) = e^{-j(f/f_x)^2 \operatorname{sgn} f}$$

Write the formula for the ratio of (a) the amplitude of the sine wave received in the same channel as that in which the sinusoidal signal is impressed to (b) the amplitude of the sine wave received in the channel sampled one time slot later.

REFERENCES

1. Costas, J. P.: Synchronous Communication, *Proc. IRE*, vol. 44, pp. 1713–1718, December, 1956.
2. Holbrook, B. D., and J. T. Dixon: Load Rating Theory for Multichannel Amplifiers, *Bell System Tech. J.*, vol. 18, pp. 624–644, October, 1939.
3. Bennett, W. R.: Cross-Modulation Requirements on Multichannel Amplifiers Below Overload, *Bell System Tech. J.*, vol. 19, pp. 587–610, October, 1940.

10

Digital Transmission of Analog Signals

As pointed out in the previous chapter, the almost prohibitive difficulties associated with efficient time-division multiplexing of analog signals virtually disappear when the samples of the signals are quantized and coded. The resulting system, which was described as pulse-code modulation (PCM) in Chap. 6, is immune to noise, interference, and distortion, provided that the disturbances are not large enough to cause errors in recognition of the original discrete values impressed on the line. Use of regenerative repeaters can prevent accumulation of disturbances in long systems. The many attractive features of PCM are obtained at the cost of increased bandwidth, but the bandwidth needed is not of the expensive high-precision kind.

The slow rate at which the advantages of PCM have been exploited to meet world needs in communication has often perplexed advocates of the method. In addition to describing PCM itself, the present chapter gives appropriate attention to the reasons underlying the seeming delay in perception of merits.

10-1 BASIC FACTS ABOUT PCM

PCM reduces the TDM system of Chap. 9 from ∞-ary telegraphy to n-ary telegraphy, with n representing the number of discrete values to be distinguished in the common medium. The value of n is usually made much less than M, the number of distinct levels in which the samples are quantized. The reduction is accomplished by coding the M different sample values as m-digit numbers to base n. The relations among m, M, and n can be stated in the following equivalent forms:

$$M = n^m \qquad n = M^{1/m} \qquad \text{and} \qquad m = \log_n M \qquad (10\text{-}1)$$

The actual transmission is accomplished by sending a uniquely defined sequence of m pulses to represent the particular value of the signal sample. There are n possible values for each pulse.

The recognition problem is reduced to simplest form by setting $n = 2$. Each decision is then made between only two possible values, such as $+A$ and $-A$, or A and 0, and the system is called binary PCM. The cited examples correspond, respectively, to bipolar and on-off telegraphy as described in Chap. 4. The results given in Chap. 4 for binary and multilevel telegraph systems are, in fact, directly applicable to transmission of signals by binary and general n-ary PCM.

The advantages of PCM for time-division multiplex are not obtained without cost. The outstanding penalty is the increased pulse rate. The lower bound on pulses per second in the common medium of an N-channel TDM system for signals of bandwidth f_0 was found to be $2Nf_0$. This bound applies to PCM in only the one-digit or M-ary case, which is not attractive practically because of the large number of levels to be distinguished on the line. In general, the lower bound on pulse rate for an m-digit, N-channel PCM system is $2mNf_0$, and the lower bound on the bandwidth in hertz is $mNf_0 = Nf_0 \log_n M$. It is seen that a bandwidth multiplication factor of $m = \log_n M$ applies to PCM relative to analog transmission by TDM or by FDM.

In the case of binary PCM, the bandwidth enlargement factor is given by $n = \log_2 M$. For voice transmission it has been found by subjective experiments that $M = 64$ or 128 represents the powers of two which should be considered for acceptable quality of the received message. This implies that a PCM system for voice channels requires six or seven times as much bandwidth as is needed for analog methods providing equivalent quality. In return for its bandwidth extravagance, the PCM system equates perfect performance of the transmitting medium to error-free telegraphy. If the latter can be achieved, the voice signals suffer no impairment beyond that from the original quantization. An important factor in obtaining substantially error-free telegraph reception is the use of regenerative repeaters, which remove the effects of noise, interference, and distortion in individual repeater sections. By spacing the regenerative repeaters sufficiently close together, we can prevent accumulated defects from breaking the system. If the regeneration is perfect, there is no limit on the length of the transmission path. Such procedures are not applicable in analog transmission.

Does PCM offer sufficient compensation in transmission advantages to justify the excess occupancy of bandwidth? Experience appears to show that the answer is negative if the medium can be made to meet requirements for analog transmission with a modest increment in bandwidth over the minimum called for by the baseband signals. In such cases, the preciousness of bandwidth economy, expressed in terms of total number of signal channels which can be derived, is strongly governing. In a time of rapidly expanding demands for communication facilities, the pressure is likely to be directed toward realizing the most channels which a medium can support even though the means are difficult.

Situations which have been recognized as dictating a choice of PCM include (1) the case of a wideband medium of such poor quality that satisfactory multiplexing of signals in analog form is impossible, and (2) a communication need for which the signals must be in digital form. An example of the first kind led to the development of a multichannel PCM telephone system for use on exchange-area cables, in which the high-frequency part of the band is badly contaminated by noise and crosstalk. An example of the second kind is ciphered telephony, which was in fact the first nonlaboratory application of PCM.

Before discussing these and other examples in detail, it will be helpful to review the history of PCM.

10-2 A BIT OF HISTORY

Pulse-code modulation was invented by Paul M. Rainey[1] (1880–1946) in 1926. Rainey's goal was a translation of the facsimile signal, which is continuous in form, to a binary pulse sequence which could be transmitted over telegraph channels. His disclosure in the form of a patent fully describes the principles which have been a basis of quantizing and coding ever since. Rainey's instrumentation used mechanical apparatus suitable for the low-speed signaling of that time. A. H. Reeves[2] rediscovered PCM in 1939 and proposed electronic circuitry for application to speech transmission.

Unaware of the work of Rainey and Reeves, a group of transmission research engineers at Bell Telephone Laboratories began a project in 1940 to meet a real need in secret telephony. Privacy methods used before that time applied frequency scrambling and time scrambling to

analog speech waves.   It was known that these methods provided scanty
protection against a dedicated eavesdropper.   It was also known that
the problem of constructing an unbreakable cipher had been solved for
telegraph transmission by Vernam[3] in World War I.

Vernam's method applied to binary telegraphy consisted of adding
a random key sequence to the message by the "modulo 2" rule, in which
addition is performed on the numbers 0 and 1 as in ordinary arithmetic
except that $1 + 1 = 0$.   With this rule a symbol 0 or 1 added to itself
gives zero.   If M is the message sequence and K is the key sequence, the
transmitted sequence is $M + K$, which is random if K is random.   At
the receiver the known key is added to give $M + K + K = M$, since
$K + K = 0$.   The coded sequence $M + K$ gives no information about
M if 0's and 1's are equally likely in each position of K and if successive
symbol values of K are chosen independently.   Complete realization of
these conditions requires that no key sequence ever be reused since a
repetition would impair the randomness.   When K is completely random,
the correct message M cannot be recovered from $M + K$ without knowledge of K, which must be prepared in duplicate and transported securely
to the sending and receiving terminals.   Since such complete precautions
are very unwieldy, it became a common practice to substitute synchronized long-period pseudorandom key generators for a single-use,
two-copy key.   Unauthorized decoding is not absolutely prevented by
such a procedure, but can be made very difficult, costly, and time-
consuming.

The Vernam system can obviously be applied to speech transmitted
by PCM.   If we assume as a lower bound on tolerable quality that 64
quantizing levels and a sampling rate of 6 kHz are adequate, we would
need $6 \times 6000 = 36{,}000$ binary pulses/sec for one voice channel.   More
definite acceptable quality would be obtained with 128 quantizing levels
and 8000 samples/sec, leading to $7 \times 8000 = 56{,}000$ binary pulses/sec.
These pulse rates are far too high to be accommodated by conventional
telephone channels.   It thus appears that to obtain secure voice transmission of good quality by PCM, the bandwidth available at the subscribers' premises must be increased.   Once the decision is made to
widen the band, secret telephony presents no technological difficulties.
This fact might well be given serious consideration at the present time,
because telephone customers are becoming interested in special services
such as videophone requiring a wider band of frequencies and are
becoming annoyed at the suspected activities of wiretappers.

The early PCM applications to secret telephony were aimed at an
emergency utilization of the existing telephone network.   It was realized
that a sacrifice in speech quality was inevitable, but it was demonstrated
that sufficient intelligibility could be retained by use of the vocoder as an

instrument for bandwidth reduction. As described in Chap. 3, the vocoder converts the speech information to slowly varying signals in ten spectrum channels and one pitch channel, which can be individually band-limited to frequencies below 25 Hz. Each of these channels can accordingly be represented by 50 samples/sec. The samples of the spectrum channels are adequately represented by eight levels, or 3-digit binary PCM. The pitch channel requires twice as many digits and can be regarded as the equivalent of two spectrum channels. The complete information can thus be transmitted by $12 \times 50 \times 3 = 1800$ binary pulses/sec. This is not an impossible pulse rate for a telephone channel, but more successful operation over a larger number of channels might be obtained by the equivalent information flow of 900 quaternary pulses/sec. Vernam keying, which has been described for binary signaling, can be applied equally well to the quaternary case by use of mod 4 addition. The keying can also be done on binary pulses before translation to a higher base.

The quality obtained by enciphered vocoder transmission over conventional telephone channels is not all that would be desired but is found adequate for most talkers after some practice. The advantage obtained in the form of security over the available telephone network helps to compensate for the loss of naturalness and the increased effort in sound recognition.

In the period following the end of World War II, PCM systems were investigated at many research laboratories. This work can be characterized as brilliantly successful in the laboratory but devoid of commercial applications. A representative example which illustrates why adoption of PCM methods lagged is the case of microwave radio relay systems. Here the available bandwidth was enormous compared with any of the earlier media, and it seemed likely that PCM with its powerful exploitation of excess bandwidth would play an important role. The author was of that opinion and collaborated in a publication[4] expounding cogent reasons. These arguments still make sense, but when the decision was made, stronger reasons were found for not using PCM.

A principal part of the analysis supporting the choice of PCM for microwave radio had to do with multichannel speech signals. It actually turned out that while provision of voice circuits was an important factor in making microwave radio systems economically feasible, the paramount reason for immediate development was an imminent need for television program channels between points of origin and the various telecasting stations. While telephony by PCM had been successfully tested in the laboratory, a similar demonstration for television[5] had not been accomplished at the time the decision had to be made. Furthermore, it appeared that requirements for a system of maximum length could be met by SSB-FM (see Chap. 9) for both television and multichannel voice. Since the resulting system was simpler in terms of apparatus than PCM and did not require as much extrapolation into the unknown, the decision in its favor was correct. While the situation has been described here in terms of the author's recollections of actions taken by the Bell System in the United States, the decisions made relative to microwave radio relay elsewhere in the world have proved to be substantially the same.

The first actual breakthrough to a PCM system which became viable outside the laboratory occurred in the early 50's. By that time the transistor had begun to fulfill its early promise of a small, inexpensive, stable, long-lived, low-power amplifying element. A transistorized laboratory model of a regenerative repeater was constructed[6] which could be installed in a manhole, powered from a distant station, and given no further maintenance.

Coincident with the technological capability for producing regenerative repeaters economically, there arose an expanding demand for more telephone service in the heavily populated areas. Originally the trunk lines between exchanges were provided by individual pairs of wires, which were so low in cost that multiplexing channels on one pair would be unthinkable. However, as congestion increased and the underground conduits became entirely filled by cables completely in use, the cost of more wires acquired a new order of magnitude. It was not merely a matter of buying cables, but also of digging up the streets for installation.

Multiplexing the existing cable pairs as an alternate to installing more cable became more seriously considered. The prospects for FDM and TDM were not good. The exchange-area cables were intended only for single voice-channel use on each pair of wires, and no attention was paid to properties at frequencies above the voice band. Crosstalk between pairs in the same cable increases with frequency. The pairs are exposed to high-frequency disturbances from switching transients in the central offices. The high-frequency interference picked up on one pair is transferred by parasitic coupling to other pairs in the same cable. Pairs in the same cable carry conversation in both directions, and, consequently, low-level signals from a distant point in one pair suffer from crosstalk originating from high-level signals from a nearby point. These defects are fatal to FDM and TDM but can be overcome by PCM with closely spaced regenerative repeaters.

The combination of a need for low-cost multiplexing of channels over circuits with poor high-frequency performance and the availability of a multiplex system adapted for just such an environment led to the development of the carrier system called T-1 in the Bell System nomenclature. This first appearance of PCM among the commercial communication systems has proved to be a practical success. A total of 24 voice channels are carried over a single pair of wires with regenerative repeaters spaced 6000 ft apart. The transmission system, in effect, performs baseband telegraphy at a rate of 1.5 megabits/sec. As such it has great flexibility since the pulses can be used for a wide variety of digital information other than quantized speech. For example, channels can be provided for exchange of data generated by operations with business machines and computers.

Of the many other promising applications of PCM still in the laboratory research phase, the development of wideband communication facilities for use with waveguide transmission merits special mention. It has been known since the 30's that circular waveguides have transmission modes with loss which decreases as the frequency is increased. The possibility of enormous bandwidths exists, but a high degree of accuracy is needed in the straightness and circularity of the guide. The effect of small departures from uniformity is a sequence of mode transitions. The output of the guide contains many small components which have traveled in different modes and have different transmission times. The effect is like that of a bundle of echoes accompanying the main signal. Analog transmission suffers from the resulting accumulation of distortion, but PCM with regenerative repeaters is not affected.

PCM applied to waveguide transmission would seem to be a natural way of multiplexing wideband signals such as television and groups of FDM channels. The deterrent appears to be the initial cost of the waveguide path. If the complete system were installed and fully loaded, the cost per channel would be low. In the initial phase, however, the financial outlay for construction is too great for the expected amount of immediate use. Conservation of capital expenditures has dictated the installation of coaxial cables with smaller capabilities more nearly matched to short-term needs.

Still another promising application which has been considered for PCM is in the switching field. It is perhaps not generally realized that in the design of a large-scale communication system, the means for interconnecting the users is of equal importance with the actual transmission of the signals. Simple arithmetic shows that it would not be practical in all cases to provide enough individual switches to guarantee a connection between every customer and any other customer at all times. If there were N customers, the total number of switches needed to take care of all possible traffic demands would be $N(N-1)/2$, a number which grows as N^2 when N is large.

Practical switching takes place in stages. Each customer has access to a limited number of switches, which in turn have access to trunk lines to other finite banks of switches. Under heavy traffic conditions, an attempt to set up a connection may be blocked because all switches of one bank on the route are in use.   In such a case a subsequent attempt by an alternate route may be successful.   These problems of traffic congestion must be treated statistically to reach a satisfactory balance between probability of failure and size of the switching plant.

In the case of a telephone system, most of the switches are electro-mechanical and have operating times relatively long compared with the time intervals which must be resolved in the voice waves.   The advent of high-speed electronic switches has introduced a reexamination of the switching problem in the telephone plant because of the variety of new operations which become useful if done with sufficient rapidity.   One of these is the application of time division to enable a switch to be shared between a number of simultaneous conversations.   The number of samples per second required to reproduce voice waves of commercial quality is 8000, which means that a sample is needed every 125 μsec of time.   During this interval, electronic switching is capable of handling a large number of independent samples sequentially from independent voice channels.   It is possible, therefore, to use time-division multiplex to make individual switches available to serve a plurality of subscriber connections.

Transmission of the voice samples by TDM through a common switch constitutes a pulse-amplitude-modulation system, which is subject to the exacting requirements of controlled amplitude- and phase-vs.-frequency performance over a wide band to prevent crosstalk.   Application of PCM to the voice samples brings the problem much nearer to practical solution since the intersymbol interference need only be kept small enough to prevent digital errors.   A considerable amount of laboratory research has been done on a PCM telephone exchange,[7] and feasibility of the required operations has been demonstrated.   The synchronization requirements are challenging, but can be met.   There is much to be said in favor of completely digitalized telephony.   If we were able to scrap the present plant and to build a completely new system, the advantage of PCM for both switching and transmission would have to be seriously considered.   As in the waveguide project, however, there is strong economical pressure to continue meeting current needs by extension of current methods.

The remainder of the chapter deals with the technical problems associated with a PCM multiplex system.

10-3   CODING AND DECODING

The most difficult step in the realization of a PCM terminal is the conversion of the signal samples from analog to digital form.   Conceptually all we need to do is to compare the sample with a graduated scale and pick the nearest scale number. Representation of the scale number in digital form with any desired base can be built into the comparison. The practical difficulty is that discrete decisions must be made in a very short time. The available procedures can be classified as either sequential or simultaneous.

In the sequential method the measurements answer successive questions, which in the case of binary PCM begin with whether or not the sample is in the upper or lower half of the allowed range. When the first question is answered, the next fact to be ascertained is whether or not the sample is in the upper or lower half of the subinterval in which it has been located. This process continues until the smallest subinterval containing more than one quantized value is probed. With each decision, the value of the corresponding digit (or, more properly, binit since the word "digit" indicates a base of 10) in the binary representation is determined. The binary code is thus generated while the quantizing proceeds, and the representative pulses can be transmitted to the line while the quantizing is in progress. Generalization to bases other than binary is straightforward.

A schematic diagram of a sequential 7-binit binary coder, such as used in the T-1 carrier system[8] previously mentioned, is shown in Fig. 10-1. A negative reference voltage is applied in parallel to the left contacts of seven single-pole double-throw switches. The right contacts are grounded, and the central contacts are connected through a weighting

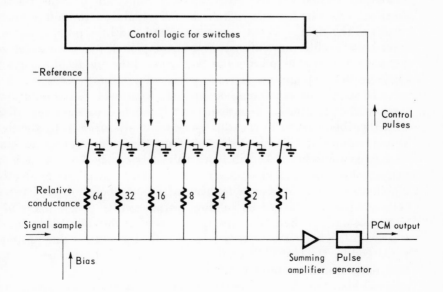

Fig. 10-1 Sequential PCM coder.

network of resistors to a common bus on which is impressed the signal sample, which must be held constant while the coding is in progress. The relative conductances of the paths between the signal and the different switches are 64, 32, 16, 8, 4, 2, and 1. A summing amplifier measures the total current through the weighting network.

At the beginning of the coding interval, all switches are in the grounded state. The first step in the coding process is to throw the first switch to the left contact. This causes a reduction of 64 units of current into the summing amplifier. If the reduction reverses the direction of the total current, the first binit of the binary code is established as zero and the first switch is returned to the ground contact. If the current does not reverse, the first binit is given the value of unity and the first switch is kept on the left contact during the remainder of the coding interval. The second switch is then thrown to the left position thereby reducing the current by 32 units. This is the total reduction if the first switch has been returned to ground, but if the first switch is still in contact with the reference voltage, the total reduction is 96 units. In either case the second binit is zero if a current reversal occurs and unity if there is no reversal. The second switch is returned to the ground position if the second binit is zero and is forced to remain on the left contact if the second binit is unity.

Continuing the process sequentially with the other switches determines the remaining binits. The direction of current flow after each switch is operated not only fixes the binit value but furnishes the information as to whether the switch should remain on the left contact or return to the right. The switches are controlled by flip-flops, which are reset by an eighth pulse after coding is completed. In the case of voice signals, it is desirable to bring the value zero to the middle of the quantizing range by adding a positive signal bias of 64 units.

In the simultaneous method, the sample is displayed as a line across a raster of code values. One realization is the flash coder of Fig. 10-2, in which a ribbon beam in a cathode-ray tube is positioned by the signal-voltage sample and illuminates a row of apertures representing the sample as a binary number. As will be explained later, the Gray code is used instead of the natural binary sequence in order to avoid large quantizing ambiguities. The binits are determined simultaneously by independent collector plates arranged as columns perpendicular to the plane of the ribbon beam. If there is an aperture in front of the collecting column at the beam height, current flows to that collector and a value of unity is registered for the binit. If there is no aperture, the beam does not reach the collector and the binit value is zero.

The bane of all quantizers is the marginal signal value equally spaced between permissible quantizing levels. In sequential binary coding, the

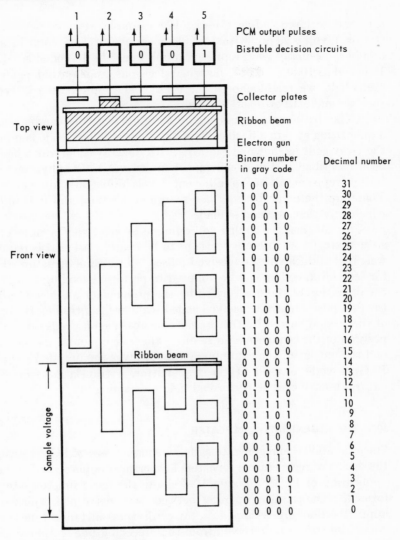

Fig. 10-2 Flash PCM coder.

important consideration is that a definite decision must be made at each step of comparison—there is no place in the system for a "maybe." The accepted strategy is to make decisions with a bistable device which goes quickly to one of its two stable states when a steady input is applied. In sequential coding it does not matter which decision is made in the marginal case, since subsequent coding is consistent with the choice. In flash coding, on the other hand, several simultaneous marginal decisions can lead to large coding errors. For example, suppose the quantizing step is 1 volt and we wish to code a sample of 15.5 volts in a 5-binit number. Equally good representations would be 15 coded as 01111 and 16 coded as 10000. But if marginal decisions are made independently on each digit, we might choose the code 11111 representing 32 volts and thereby make an error of 16.5 volts.

The size of errors produced by marginal decisions can be held to half a quantizing step in a flash coder if the natural binary code is replaced by the Gray code as shown in Fig. 10-2. In the gray code, which has already been described in the discussion of multilevel telegraphy, Sec. 4-7, the binary representations of adjacent levels differ in only one position. Therefore there can be only one marginal decision, and it is immaterial which way that decision is made.

In contrast to coding, decoding is a relatively simple operation since there are no discrete decisions to be made. All that is required is a weighted addition of the received pulses. The same structure described for sequential coding can be adapted to perform decoding by controlling the operation of the first switch by the presence or absence of a pulse in the first position of the received coded sequence, controlling the operation of the second switch by the presence or absence of a pulse in the second position of the sequence, and so on. There is, of course, no signal input, and the output of the summing amplifier gives the decoded signal value. If Gray code is used at the transmitter, a translation from Gray to natural binary code is performed before decoding.

10-4 THE REGENERATIVE REPEATER

Since the ability to regenerate signals is a major asset of PCM transmission, the design of regenerative repeaters is of critical importance for successful application of PCM. Figure 10-3 shows the basic functions to be performed. The repeater operates between sections of line, which to a first approximation are assumed linear with transmittance function $H(f)$. The pulse train $s_1(t)$ received from the preceding line section is amplified and shaped by a linear receiving filter with transmittance $Y_2(f)$. The resulting wave $s_2(t)$ should ideally satisfy Nyquist's first criterion for suppression of intersymbol interference; that is, if the interval between successive pulse values is $T = 1/f_p$, there should be a set of instants of time with spacing T such that the values of $s_2(t)$ at these instants represent the successive signal values unaffected by the other values of the sequence.

In practice, we cannot hope to attain the ideal condition of complete absence of intersymbol interference, but we should strive for the largest possible opening of the eye pattern. It is one of the advantages of PCM

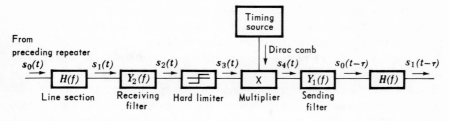

Fig. 10-3 Ideal regenerative repeater.

that a finite amount of intersymbol interference can be tolerated at the expense of a corresponding reduction in margin over noise.

Regeneration of the shaped pulse train $s_2(t)$ requires correction of both magnitude and timing. The operation can be conveniently represented by a hard limiter followed by multiplication with a timing wave. In the case of on-off binary pulses, the hard limiter is a step function of the input signal and has output

$$s_3(t) = k\,u[s_2(t)] \tag{10-2}$$

where $u[s_2]$ is the unit step function equal to zero when s_2 is negative and to unity when s_2 is positive. For bipolar binary pulses,

$$s_3(t) = k\{2u[s_2(t)] - 1\} \tag{10-3}$$

The timing wave is ideally the *Dirac comb*,

$$d(t) = \sum_{n=-\infty}^{\infty} \delta(t - nT) \tag{10-4}$$

The output of the multiplier is

$$s_4(t) = s_3(t)\,d(t) \tag{10-5}$$

and consists of a train of uniformly spaced impulses weighted by the original signal values. These impulses are shaped by a linear sending filter with transmittance function $Y_2(f)$ to produce the outgoing pulse train $s_0(t - \tau)$, which should be identical with the pulse train $s_0(t)$ impressed on the preceding line section except for the delay τ imposed by the line section and the repeater. The indicated separation of functions of the regenerative repeater may be artificial since a single unit may perform the amplitude correction, retiming, and pulse shaping. The complete response in such cases can be compared with the combination of required functions. Optimum choices for the sending- and receiving-filter transmittances $Y_1(f)$ and $Y_2(f)$ in order to minimize probability of error in a given noise environment with a constraint on average power transmitted by the repeater have been treated in Chap. 4.

It was shown in Chap. 4 that the most efficient form of binary transmission is bipolar. A bipolar regenerator is somewhat more complicated than a unipolar type, and this disadvantage might offset the 3-db improvement in signal-to-noise ratio. However, in baseband systems, it turns out that both methods suffer from zero wander unless direct coupling is used throughout. It is quite evident that on-off signaling is impaired if direct current is not transmitted since the signal wave contains a strong d-c component. A bipolar pulse train with equally likely plus and minus pulses has average value zero, but, nevertheless, suppression of zero frequency is harmful. The reason is that a long sequence of pulses of like polarity gives a response which sags toward zero and diminishes the margin over noise. The fact that at some later time an equally long run of opposite polarities will occur does not help.

The advantages of using a-c coupling, which permits transformers and blocking capacitors to aid in impedance matching and bias removal, are overwhelming in practice. Two methods which have been found effective in offsetting the resulting zero wander are quantized feedback[9] and pseudoternary coding.[10] The former method, which has a history of use dating back to submarine cable telegraphy, takes advantage of the fact that when a correct binary decision is made, the subsequent waveform impressed from the input pulse is known. A compensating wave of opposite sign can, therefore, be fed back from the output to prevent the sag associated with d-c coupling. The wave fed back is derived from a clean source free from noise and interference. The method is similar to direct-current restoration techniques used in television receivers, except that the timing feature makes the cancellation necessary only at the sampling instants. This permits a-c coupling to be used in the feedback path, since it is not necessary to insert the missing low-frequency components of the impressed signal. An a-c wave with the right values at the sampling instants is sufficient.

In pseudoternary coding of a binary sequence of 0s and 1s, the 0s are represented by sending no pulse, and the 1s are represented by sending positive and negative pulses alternately. The accumulated sag in this case can never be worse than from one isolated pulse. Since three levels must be distinguished instead of two, there is an impairment of margin over noise as well as the added complication of a bipolar regenerator. Nevertheless, the advantages of the pseudoternary method have led to its adoption in the T-1 system.

A blocking oscillator has been found effective as the nonlinear constituent of a regenerative repeater. Figure 10-4 shows the use[11] of such a circuit in a pseudoternary regenerator. Separate oscillators are used for the positive and negative pulses. A clock pulse derived from a sine wave at the signaling frequency combines with the signal pulse to

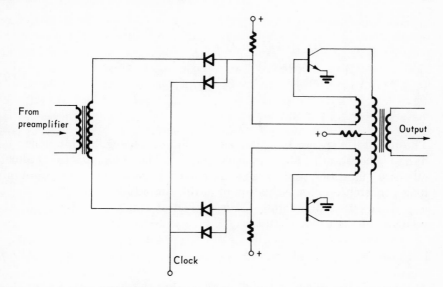

Fig. 10-4 Blocking-oscillator circuit for regeneration of pseudoternary pulses.

start the proper oscillator. One axis crossing of the sine wave generates a turn-on pulse and the other a turn-off pulse. The latter fixes the width of the outgoing signal pulse.

The timing wave could be transmitted by a separate channel, but, in practice, it is found advantageous to derive timing from the signal wave itself. The instants at which transitions occur furnish accurate timing information if the pulse train satisfies Nyquist II, which specifies that the transitions are invariant with respect to the message sequence. The information thereby available is incomplete because there are repetitions of the same symbol in a message, and therefore some signaling intervals in the received wave do not contain transitions. The deficiency can be overcome, however, by deriving a complete set of axis crossings from the response of a tuned circuit which is shock-excited by impulses applied whenever a signal transition occurs.[12] If the tuned circuit has low damping and has a natural oscillation frequency precisely matched to the signaling rate, the oscillatory response coasts between signal transitions to fill in the missing time indicators correctly.

To demonstrate the capability of an accurately tuned circuit to interpolate timing information, consider a series-tuned circuit with inductance L, capacitance C, and resistance R. The impulse response $g(t)$ is given by

$$g(t) = \begin{cases} 0 & t < 0 \\ A e^{-\alpha t} \cos{(\omega_0 t + \theta)} & t > 0 \end{cases} \qquad (10\text{-}6)$$

where

$$A = \frac{\omega_0}{2RQ^2}(4Q^2 + 1)^{1/2} \qquad Q = \frac{\omega_0 L}{R}$$

$$\omega_0 = \left(\frac{1}{LC} - \alpha^2\right)^{1/2} \qquad\qquad \alpha = \frac{R}{2L} = \frac{\omega_0}{2Q} \tag{10-7}$$

$$\tan\theta = \frac{R}{2\omega_0 L} = \frac{1}{2Q}$$

The impulse response is a damped oscillation of angular frequency ω_0, damping constant α, and amplitude $Ae^{-\alpha t}$. The quality factor Q affects all these quantities, and, in general, should have a high value to obtain long persistence of an oscillation of usable amplitude.

If impulses of weight a_n are applied at times $t = nT = n/f_p$, the response of the tuned circuit is

$$i(t) = \sum_{n=-\infty}^{\infty} a_n\, g(t - nT) \tag{10-8}$$

If t is in the interval $0 < t < T$, the fact that the responses to individual impulses do not begin before the impulses occur enables us to write:

$$i(t) = A \sum_{n=-\infty}^{0} a_n e^{-\alpha(t-nT)} \cos\left[\omega_0(t - nT) + \theta\right] \qquad 0 < t < T$$
$$\tag{10-9}$$

The desired tuning consists of making $\omega_0 = \omega_p = 2\pi f_p$. Since $f_p T = 1$, and hence $\omega_p T = 2\pi$, Eq. (10-9) becomes

$$i(t) = K_s \cos(\omega_p t + \theta) \qquad 0 < t < T \tag{10-10}$$

where

$$K_s = A \sum_{n=-\infty}^{0} a_n e^{-\alpha(t-nT)} \tag{10-11}$$

Equation (10-10) shows that no matter what message sequence is impressed, the response of a correctly tuned circuit to message impulses has the axis crossings of a sine wave at the signaling frequency. In particular, if the a_n's are positive or zero, the multiplying factor K_s is never negative and there are exactly two axis crossings in the typical interval 0 to T. These are at t_1 and t_2 defined by $\omega_p t_1 + \theta = \pi/2$ and $\omega_p t_2 + \theta = 3\pi/2$, that is, by

$$t_1 = \frac{T}{4}\left(1 - \frac{2\theta}{\pi}\right)$$

and $\tag{10-12}$

$$t_2 = \frac{3T}{4}\left(1 - \frac{2\theta}{3\pi}\right)$$

When Q is large, θ is small, and t_1 and t_2 are nearly equal to $T/4$ and $3T/4$, respectively. This is not a necessary requirement, of course, since the value of θ is a determinate quantity from which t_1 and t_2 can be precisely related to the signaling time interval. If the a_n's have both positive and negative values as in the case of pseudoternary signaling, a full-wave rectification should be performed before observing transitions. Multi-level signaling requires, in general, a succession of full-wave rectifications, or foldings about the decision levels, in order to define the transition instants uniquely.

The foregoing theory shows how timing can be extracted from the signal wave with complete accuracy. Practical timing recovery is subject to many departures from the idealized model, as will next be discussed. Sources of timing errors include the following:

1. The received wave may not satisfy Nyquist II exactly. The transition times are then influenced by the message pattern.

2. Even if the transitions occur at the proper times, their measurement can be affected by variations in amplitude of the received wave. This effect is known as amplitude-to-phase conversion and occurs in the detection of axis crossings if the threshold is not set exactly at zero.

3. The excitation of the tuned circuit may not be a satisfactory realization of a train of impulses. Although the δ function is not the only driving wave which will make the tuned circuit reproduce the correct axis crossings for any message sequence, most pulse shapes do not have this desirable property. It may be verified, for example, that if the driving pulse is rectangular, there are only two satisfactory widths: zero (corresponding to the δ function) and $T/2$.

4. The tuned circuit may not be precisely tuned to match the signaling rate.

5. The transitions may be disturbed by the presence of noise.

All the sources of timing error listed will be present in practical cases, and it becomes important to estimate tolerances. Quantitative analysis is facilitated by analyzing the frequency content of the PCM wave train. We demonstrate that a binary wave of on-off type contains a component of nonzero amplitude at the pulse frequency $f_p = 1/T$ if the Fourier transform of an individual pulse does not vanish at $f = f_p$. To show this, consider the wave

$$s(t) = \sum_{n=-\infty}^{\infty} a_n \, g(t - nT) \tag{10-13}$$

where the value of any a_n can be either 0 or 1 and $g(t)$ represents the waveform of an individual pulse. The Fourier transform of $s(t)$ can be written as

$$S(f) = \lim_{N \to \infty} S_N(f) \tag{10-14}$$

where

$$S_N(f) = \int_{-\infty}^{\infty} e^{-j2\pi ft} \sum_{n=-N}^{N} a_n\, g(t - nT)\, dt$$

$$= \sum_{n=-N}^{N} a_n\, G(f)e^{-j2\pi fnT} \qquad (10\text{-}15)$$

$G(f)$ is the Fourier transform of $g(t)$. It follows that

$$S_N(f_p) = G(f) \sum_{n=-N}^{N} a_n e^{-j2n\pi f_p T}$$

$$= G(f) \sum_{n=-N}^{N} a_n \qquad (10\text{-}16)$$

on noting that $f_p T = 1$ and $e^{-j2\pi} = 1$. Let $NT = T_0$, and assume that of the $2N + 1$ values of a_n, $k_N(2N + 1)$ are unity and $(1 - k_N)(2N + 1)$ are zero. Then

$$S_N(f_p) = k_N(2N + 1)G(f_p) = k_N\left(\frac{2T_0}{T} + 1\right)G(f_p) \qquad (10\text{-}17)$$

and

$$\lim_{N\to\infty} S_N(f_p) = \lim_{T_0\to\infty} 2kf_p T_0\, G(f_p) \qquad (10\text{-}18)$$

where

$$k = \lim_{N\to\infty} k_N \qquad (10\text{-}19)$$

Now compare (10-18) with the result obtained by calculating the Fourier transform of a single-frequency component with frequency f_p. Let

$$v(t) = a_p e^{j2\pi f_p t} \qquad (10\text{-}20)$$

We find

$$V(f) = \lim_{T_0\to\infty} \int_{-T_0}^{T_0} v(t)e^{-j2\pi ft}\, dt$$

$$= \lim_{T_0\to\infty} a_p \int_{-T_0}^{T_0} e^{j2\pi(f_p - f)t}\, dt \qquad (10\text{-}21)$$

and

$$V(f_p) = \lim_{T_0\to\infty} 2a_p T_0 \qquad (10\text{-}22)$$

In the limit, the long on-off binary PCM wave train thus produces the same Fourier-transform value at $f = f_p$ as a component $a_p e^{j2\pi f_p t}$ with

$$a_p = kf_p\, G(f_p) \qquad (10\text{-}23)$$

Observations made at the exact frequency f_p are therefore indistinguishable from the response to a pure sine wave with amplitude and phase determined by Eq. (10-23). Note that a_p vanishes if $G(f_p) = 0$. It is therefore essential to use a pulse shape for which the Fourier transform is not zero at the pulse repetition frequency.

The presence of a steady-state component of frequency f_p in the binary pulse stream can provide an adequate if not exact source of timing information even in the presence of the previously listed faults in the realization of the ideal model. In particular, even if the recovery circuit is not precisely tuned to f_p, there is a dominant steady-state component of current at this frequency. There is also a nonsinusoidal fluctuating term which is a function of the pulse pattern, but the relative effect can be reduced by sharpening the selectivity of the tuned circuit. Analytical details and calculated results are given in Ref. 12. Similar considerations govern the overriding of noise, which is distributed in frequency and hence can be discriminated against by a selective circuit passing a narrow band centered at the discrete frequency f_p of the steady-state component.

Requirements on the allowable timing error in an individual regenerative repeater must take account of the accumulation of error in the complete chain of repeaters[13,14] comprising a PCM transmission system. Each repeater not only contributes an error of its own but is affected by the errors originating in the preceding repeaters. When the errors are small, propagation of an error through a chain of repeaters can be treated as the response of a linear system. It is then advantageous to represent errors in the frequency domain; i.e., to consider the successive departures of the timing-wave axis crossings from regularly spaced instants as samples of a band-limited function of time. The effective transmittance of the chain of timing operations is typically small for high-frequency components of the error signal, and the result is that the accumulation of errors tends to result in a slow drift in timing rather than a large rapid fluctuation.

Consider an infinite train of timing markers in which the nth marker differs from nT by x_n. The values of x_n can be regarded as samples taken at the rate $f_p = 1/T$ per sec of a function $x(t)$ band-limited to the range $-f_p/2$ to $f_p/2$. Suppose the train of timing markers controls a timing recovery circuit which delivers timing markers differing from nT by y_n. Then the values of y_n can be regarded as samples of a band-limited function $y(t)$. Explicitly

$$x(t) = \sum_{n=-\infty}^{\infty} x_n \operatorname{sinc}(f_p t - n)$$

$$y(t) = \sum_{n=-\infty}^{\infty} y_n \operatorname{sinc}(f_p t - n)$$

(10-24)

For small changes, $y(t)$ is linearly related to $x(t)$, and we can define

$$H(f) = \frac{Y(f)}{X(f)} \qquad |f| < \frac{f_p}{2} \tag{10-25}$$

as the effective transmittance function of the timing-recovery circuit.

In the case of a chain of N identical regenerative repeaters with $H(f)$ as the transmittance function of timing recovery at each repeater, the timing errors resulting in the output of the last repeater from timing errors defined by x_n at the input to the first repeater are characterized by

$$Y_N(f) = H^N(f)X(f) \tag{10-26}$$

If a set of timing errors identical with x_n is added at the input to each repeater, the expression for the Fourier transform of the function whose samples give the timing error at the output of the last repeater becomes

$$Z_N(f) = \sum_{n=1}^{N} H^N(f)X(f) = \frac{1 - H^N(f)}{1 - H(f)} H(f)X(f) \tag{10-27}$$

A simple approximation of a low-pass transmittance function is furnished by an RC filter

$$H(f) = \left(1 + \frac{jf}{f_c}\right)^{-1} \tag{10-28}$$

For this case

$$Z_N(f) = \frac{f_c}{jf}\left[1 - \left(1 + \frac{jf}{f_c}\right)^{-N}\right]X(f) \tag{10-29}$$

Let

$$\left(1 + \frac{jf}{f_c}\right)^{-N} = u \tag{10-30}$$

Then

$$\ln u = -N \ln\left(1 + \frac{jf}{f_c}\right) \approx -\frac{jNf}{f_c} \qquad \text{when } f \ll f_c \tag{10-31}$$

$$u \approx e^{-jNf/f_c} \tag{10-32}$$

$$Z_N(f) \approx \frac{f_c}{jf}[1 - e^{-jNf/f_c}]X(f) \tag{10-33}$$

$$z_N(t) \approx \omega_c \int_{-\infty}^{t} x(t)\, dt - \omega_c \int_{-\infty}^{t-N/\omega_c} x(t)\, dt$$

$$\approx \omega_c \int_{t-N/\omega_c}^{t} x(t)\, dt \tag{10-34}$$

This result shows that if $x(t)$ is almost constant over a time interval of width N/ω_c, the error is proportional to N, i.e., if $x(t) \approx x_0$ in the interval $t - N/\omega_c$ to t,

$$z_N(t) \approx \omega_c x_0 \left[t - \left(t - \frac{N}{\omega_c} \right) \right] = N x_0 \tag{10-35}$$

In the case of effects of additive noise on timing, the contributions to error from the different repeaters are independent and the mean-square total error grows directly with the number of repeaters. Effects of inter-symbol interference, amplitude-to-phase conversion, improper pulse shaping, and mistuning are controlled by the pulse pattern and tend to cause coherent error contributions from the individual repeaters. Errors which add in phase cause the magnitude of the total error to have a component directly proportional to the number of repeaters. Even though such systematic errors may be small in individual repeaters, their more rapid growth in a chain makes them dominant over random sources of error. It is noteworthy that the direct addition of errors related to the pulse pattern becomes more pronounced as the repeater sections are made more nearly identical. Deliberate insertion of small random differences might in fact be helpful.

The application of PCM to wideband media with relatively poor transmission quality depends critically on the realization of inexpensive regeneration. It may, therefore, not be feasible to require extremely high precision in the timing of individual repeaters. Fortunately for the future of PCM, it is possible to clean up the errors in timing at the end of a regenerative repeater chain if the accumulation has not been too great. This is done by the use of a highly accurate clock which generates correctly spaced pulses to resample the signal wave and send out new pulses free from jitter. The precision of the timing operations possible at occasional cleanup points can be much greater than that realizable in simple unattended manhole installations.

As to the ultimate accuracy in timing which is necessary in PCM, there are two main considerations: (1) to keep the timing errors small enough to allow operation of a long system without destructive accumulation, and (2) to provide a satisfactory decoded analog signal. The second consideration, which has not previously been mentioned, arises because of the phase modulation occurring in an analog signal reconstructed from irregularly spaced samples. Both requirements are controllable by precise retiming procedures.

It appears that PCM is well provided with strategies for overcoming transmission obstacles and that when given a chance proves its merit. The analog methods have a tremendous advantage in simplicity and in background of technological experience. Offsetting this is the continuing rapid growth in the applications of digital data to computer science and related arts. The ultimate advantage of dealing with one kind of signal in a communication system may eventually be a decisive factor in favor of PCM.

PROBLEMS

10-1. Devise a method for translating from Gray to natural binary code.

10-2. How many decibels must the signal-to-noise ratio be increased if bipolar transmission is replaced by pseudoternary with the same error rate?

10-3. In Eq. (10-9), the family of curves representing $i(t)$ in the interval $0 < t < T$ for all choices of the a_n's constitutes the eye pattern of the timing recovery wave. Calculate the average trace of this eye pattern in the general case in which $\omega_0 \neq \omega_p$. Find the axis crossings of the average trace.

10-4. If the timing recovery in a regenerative repeater is performed by a single high-Q series-resonant circuit precisely tuned to oscillate at the pulse repetition frequency, what is the approximate value of f_c in Eq. (10-28)?

REFERENCES

1. Rainey, P. M.: U.S. Patent 1,608,527, November 30, 1926.
2. Reeves, A. H.: French Patent 853,183, October 23, 1939.
3. Vernam, G. S.: Cipher Printing Telegraph Systems for Secret Wire and Radio Telegraphic Communications, *AIEE Trans.*, pp. 295–301, February, 1926.
4. Feldman, C. B., and W. R. Bennett: Band Width and Transmission Performance, *Bell System Tech. J.*, vol. 28, pp. 490–595, July, 1949.
5. Goodall, W. M.: Television by Pulse Code Modulation, *Bell System Tech. J.*, vol. 30, pp. 33–49, January, 1951.
6. Wrathall, L. R.: Transistorized Binary Pulse Regenerator, *Bell System Tech. J.*, vol. 35, pp. 1059–1084, September, 1956.
7. Hartley, G. C., P. Mornet, F. Ralph, and D. J. Tarran: "Techniques of Pulse-Code Modulation in Communication Networks," Cambridge University Press, Cambridge, England, 1967.
8. Davis, C. G.: An Experimental Pulse Code Modulation System for Short-Haul Trunks, *Bell System Tech. J.*, vol. 41, pp. 1–24, January, 1962.
9. Bennett, W. R.: Synthesis of Active Networks, *Proc. Symp. Mod. Network Syn.* (Polytechnic Institute of Brooklyn), vol. 5, pp. 45–61, 1956.
10. Aaron, M. R.: PCM Transmission in the Exchange Plant, *Bell System Tech. J.*, vol. 41, pp. 99–141, January, 1962.
11. Mayo, J. S.: A Bipolar Repeater for Pulse Code Modulation Signals, *Bell System Tech. J.*, vol. 41, pp. 25–97, January, 1962.
12. Bennett, W. R.: Statistics of Regenerative Digital Transmission, *Bell System Tech. J.*, vol. 37, pp. 1501–1542, November, 1958.
13. Rowe, H. E.: Timing in a Long Chain of Regenerative Repeaters, *Bell System Tech. J.*, vol. 37, pp. 1543–1598, November, 1958.
14. Byrne, C. J., B. J. Karafin, and D. B. Robinson, Jr.: Systematic Jitter in a Chain of Digital Regenerators, *Bell System Tech. J.*, vol. 42, pp. 2679–2714, November, 1963.

appendix
Bessel Functions

Bessel functions of integer order can be defined as coefficients in the Laurent-series expansion of the function

$$f(z) = e^{(x/2)(z-1/z)} \tag{A-1}$$

which is an analytic function of z in the ring-shaped region between concentric circles centered at the origin. The function is readily expanded by direct multiplication of the absolutely convergent power series representing factors; thus

$$f(z) = e^{xz/2}e^{-x/2z} = \sum_{l=0}^{\infty} \frac{(xz/2)^l}{l!} \sum_{m=0}^{\infty} \frac{(-x/2z)^m}{m!}$$

$$= \sum_{m=0}^{\infty} \sum_{n=-m}^{\infty} \frac{(-)^m(x/2)^{2m+n_z n}}{m!(m+n)!} \tag{A-2}$$

Since $1/(m+n)! = 0$ when $n = -(m+1), -(m+2), \ldots$, we can replace the lower limit on n by $-\infty$. Then

$$f(z) = \sum_{n=-\infty}^{\infty} J_n(x)z^n \tag{A-3}$$

where

$$J_n(x) = \sum_{m=0}^{\infty} \frac{(-)^m (x/2)^{2m+n}}{m!(m+n)!} \tag{A-4}$$

Equation (A-4) defines a Bessel function of order n and argument x. The series is absolutely convergent if $|x| < \infty$. The function $f(z)$ is called the generating function of $J_n(x)$. If we substitute $z = e^{j\theta}$ in (A-1) and (A-3), we obtain

$$e^{jx \sin \theta} = \sum_{n=-\infty}^{\infty} J_n(x) e^{jn\theta} \tag{A-5}$$

Multiplication of both sides of this equation by $e^{j\omega t}$ then gives

$$e^{j\omega t + jx \sin \theta} = \sum_{n=-\infty}^{\infty} J_n(x) e^{j(\omega t + n\theta)} \tag{A-6}$$

By equating real and imaginary parts separately when ωt, x, and θ are real, we derive the useful relations

$$\begin{aligned} \cos(\omega t + x \sin \theta) &= \sum_{n=-\infty}^{\infty} J_n(x) \cos(\omega t + n\theta) \\ \sin(\omega t + x \sin \theta) &= \sum_{n=-\infty}^{\infty} J_n(x) \sin(\omega t + n\theta) \end{aligned} \tag{A-7}$$

From the series expansion of (A-4), we can show that

$$\begin{aligned} J_n(-x) &= (-)^n J_n(x) \\ J_{-n}(x) &= (-)^n J_n(x) \end{aligned} \tag{A-8}$$

If we set $\omega t = 0$ in (A-7) and make use of the second relation of (A-8), we find that

$$\begin{aligned} \cos(x \sin \theta) &= J_0(x) + 2 \sum_{n=1}^{\infty} J_{2n}(x) \cos 2n\theta \\ \sin(x \sin \theta) &= 2 \sum_{n=0}^{\infty} J_{2n+1}(x) \sin(2n+1)\theta \end{aligned} \tag{A-9}$$

Replacement of θ by $\pi/2 - \theta$ gives

$$\begin{aligned} \cos(x \cos \theta) &= J_0(x) + 2 \sum_{n=1}^{\infty} (-)^n J_{2n}(x) \cos 2n\theta \\ \sin(x \cos \theta) &= 2 \sum_{n=1}^{\infty} (-)^n J_{2n+1}(x) \cos(2n+1)\theta \end{aligned} \tag{A-10}$$

The fact that many of the expressions we have exhibited are Fourier series enables an evaluation of the corresponding integrals which determine the Fourier coefficients. From (A-5), for example, we deduce that

$$\frac{1}{2\pi} \int_{-\pi}^{\pi} e^{jx \sin \theta} e^{-jn\theta} \, d\theta = J_n(x) \tag{A-11}$$

Replacing the integrand by its equal

$$e^{jx \sin \theta - n\theta} = \cos (x \sin \theta - n\theta) + j \sin (x \sin \theta - n\theta)$$

and noting that the second term is an odd function of θ, we obtain

$$\frac{1}{2\pi} \int_{-\pi}^{\pi} \cos (n\theta - x \sin \theta) \, d\theta = J_n(x) = \frac{1}{\pi} \int_0^{\pi} \cos (n\theta - x \sin \theta) \, d\theta \tag{A-12}$$

If we replace θ by $\pi/2 - \theta$ in (A-5), we have

$$e^{jx \cos \theta} = \sum_{n = -\infty}^{\infty} j^n J_n(x) e^{-jn\theta} \tag{A-13}$$

from which

$$\frac{1}{2\pi} \int_{-\pi}^{\pi} e^{jx \cos \theta} e^{jn\theta} \, d\theta = j^n J_n(x) \tag{A-14}$$

or

$$\frac{1}{\pi} \int_0^{\pi} e^{jx \cos \theta} \cos n\theta \, d\theta = j^n J_n(x) \tag{A-15}$$

Other useful integrals obtainable by similar methods are

$$\frac{1}{\pi} \int_0^{\pi} \sin (2n + 1)\theta \sin (x \sin \theta) \, d\theta$$
$$= \frac{2}{\pi} \int_0^{\pi/2} \sin (2n + 1)\theta \sin (x \sin \theta) \, d\theta = J_{2n+1}(x) \tag{A-16}$$

$$\frac{1}{\pi} \int_0^{\pi} \cos 2n\theta \cos (x \sin \theta) \, d\theta$$
$$= \frac{2}{\pi} \int_0^{\pi/2} \cos 2n\theta \cos (x \sin \theta) \, d\theta = J_{2n}(x) \tag{A-17}$$

$$\frac{2}{\pi} \int_0^{\pi/2} \cos (2n + 1)\theta \sin (x \cos \theta) \, d\theta = (-)^n J_{2n+1}(x) \tag{A-18}$$

$$\frac{2}{\pi} \int_0^{\pi/2} \cos 2n\theta \cos (x \cos \theta) \, d\theta = (-)^n J_{2n}(x) \tag{A-19}$$

The modified Bessel function $I_n(x)$ is defined by

$$I_n(x) = j^{-n} J_n(jx) = \sum_{m=0}^{\infty} \frac{(x/2)^{2m+n}}{m!(m + n)!} \tag{A-20}$$

The series expansion differs from that for $J_n(x)$ in that there is no alternating sign. This means that as x increases through real values from zero to infinity, the value of $I_n(x)$ increases monotonically to infinity. This is in contrast to the behavior of $J_n(x)$, which oscillates with monotonically decreasing amplitude as x increases. When x is large, the limiting forms for both are shown by the asymptotic expansions:

$$
\begin{aligned}
J_n(x) \sim \left(\frac{2}{\pi x}\right)^{\frac{1}{2}} \Bigg\{ &\Bigg[1 - \frac{(4n^2 - 1^2)(4n^2 - 3^2)}{2!(8x)^2} \\
&+ \frac{(4n^2 - 1^2)(4n^2 - 3^2)(4n^2 - 5^2)(4n^2 - 7^2)}{4!(8x)^4} - \cdots \Bigg] \\
&\hspace{5cm} \cos\left(x - \frac{2n+1}{4}\pi \right) \\
&- \frac{4n^2 - 1^2}{8x}\Bigg[1 - \frac{(4n^2 - 3^2)(4n^2 - 5^2)}{3!(8x)^3} + \cdots \Bigg] \\
&\hspace{5cm} \sin\left(x - \frac{2n+1}{4}\pi \right) \Bigg\}
\end{aligned}
\tag{A-21}
$$

$$
I_n(x) \sim \frac{e^x}{(2\pi x)^{\frac{1}{2}}}\left[1 - \frac{4n^2 - 1^2}{8x} + \frac{(4n^2 - 1^2)(4n^2 - 3^2)}{2!(8x)^2} - \cdots \right]
\tag{A-22}
$$

These series are divergent but can be used for computation, because it can be shown that the remainders are of the same order of magnitude as the first terms neglected.

The various formulas given for series and integrals involving $J_n(x)$ can be modified to give corresponding results for $I_n(x)$. The equations corresponding to (A-8) become

$$
\begin{aligned}
I_n(-x) &= (-)^n I_n(x) \\
I_{-n}(x) &= I_n(x)
\end{aligned}
\tag{A-23}
$$

If we replace x by x/j, θ by $\pi/2 - \theta$, and n by $-n'$ in (A-5), we obtain

$$
\begin{aligned}
e^{x \cos \theta} &= \sum_{n=-\infty}^{\infty} I_n(x) e^{jn\theta} \\
&= I_0(x) + 2 \sum_{n=1}^{\infty} I_n(x) \cos n\theta
\end{aligned}
\tag{A-24}
$$

It follows that

$$
\int_{-\pi}^{\pi} e^{x \cos \theta} \cos n\theta \, d\theta = 2\pi I_n(x)
\tag{A-25}
$$

Because of the periodicity of the integrand, the limits of integration can be replaced by any pair of values in which the upper limit exceeds the lower by 2π.

Bessel functions satisfy the following recurrence relations

$$J_{n-1}(x) + J_{n+1}(x) = \frac{2nJ_n(x)}{x}$$

$$I_{n-1}(x) - I_{n+1}(x) = \frac{2nI_n(x)}{x}$$

$$\text{(A-26)}$$

The derivatives with respect to argument are given by

$$\frac{d}{dx} J_n(x) = \frac{1}{2} J_{n-1}(x) - \frac{1}{2} J_{n+1}(x)$$

$$\frac{d}{dx} I_n(x) = \frac{1}{2} I_{n-1}(x) + \frac{1}{2} I_{n+1}(x)$$

$$\text{(A-27)}$$

We can verify from these formulas that

$$\frac{d}{dx} [x^{n+1} J_{n+1}(x)] = x^{n+1} J_n(x)$$

$$\frac{d}{dx} [x^{1-n} J_{n-1}(x)] = -x^{1-n} J_n(x)$$

$$\frac{d}{dx} [x^{n+1} I_{n+1}(x)] = x^{n+1} I_n(x)$$

$$\frac{d}{dx} [x^{1-n} I_{n-1}(x)] = x^{1-n} I_n(x)$$

$$\text{(A-28)}$$

The definition of Bessel functions for integer-order n can be extended to noninteger-order ν by replacing $(m + n)!$ in (A-4) and (A-20) by $\Gamma(\nu + m + 1)$. The Fourier-series relations do not have any significance for noninteger orders, and the integrals based on Fourier-series expansions are not valid. The following integral holds for both integer and non-integer values of ν provided that the real part of ν exceeds $-\frac{1}{2}$:

$$J_\nu(z) = \frac{(z/2)^\nu}{\Gamma(\nu + \frac{1}{2})\Gamma(\frac{1}{2})} \int_0^\pi \cos{(z \cos \theta)} \sin^{2\nu} \theta \, d\theta \qquad \text{(A-29)}$$

By the substitution $x = \cos \theta$, the integral can also be written as

$$J_\nu(z) = \frac{(z/2)^\nu}{\Gamma(\nu + \frac{1}{2})\Gamma(\frac{1}{2})} \int_{-1}^1 (1 - x^2)^{\nu - \frac{1}{2}} \cos zx \, dx \qquad \text{(A-30)}$$

For general values of ν, $y = J_\nu(x)$ and $y = J_{-\nu}(x)$ are two independent solutions of the linear second-order differential equation

$$x^2 \frac{d^2y}{dx^2} + x \frac{dy}{dx} + (x^2 - \nu^2)y = 0 \qquad \text{(A-31)}$$

When ν is an integer, the two solutions become dependent, as shown by (A-8), and an independent second solution must be found if the differential equation is to be satisfied for the most general boundary conditions.

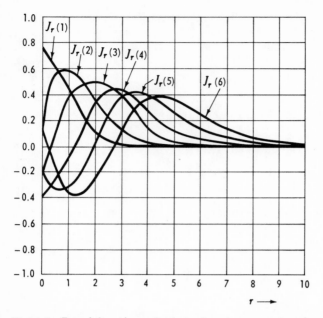

Fig. A-1 Bessel functions of constant real argument and ascending order.

The recurrence formulas and the formulas for the derivative hold for all values of ν.

It is clear from the series definitions that both $J_\nu(x)$ and $I_\nu(x)$ with x real and fixed must approach zero as ν goes to infinity. By plotting the curves of $J_\nu(x)$ versus ν for different values of x as in Fig. A-1, we see that the approach to zero becomes rapid above $\nu = x$. This behavior is significant in the problem of estimating the bandwidth of an angle-modulated wave.

For further information concerning the properties of Bessel functions, the classic reference is G. N. Watson, "Theory of Bessel Functions," Macmillan, New York, 1944. The integral in Prob. 5-5 is evaluated on page 394 of this reference.

Name Index

Subject Index